A-Level
Physics

Exam Board: OCR B (Advancing Physics)

Revising for Physics exams is stressful, that's for sure — even just getting your notes sorted out can leave you needing a lie down. But help is at hand...

This brilliant CGP book explains **everything you'll need to learn** (and nothing you won't), all in a straightforward style that's easy to get your head around. We've also included **exam questions** to test how ready you are for the real thing.

There's even a free Online Edition you can read on your computer or tablet!

A-Level revision? It has to be CGP!

Published by CGP

Editors:
Emily Garrett, David Maliphant, Rachael Marshall, Sam Pilgrim, Frances Rooney, Charlotte Whiteley,
Sarah Williams and Jonathan Wray.

Contributors:
Tony Alldridge, Stuart Barker, Jane Cartwright, Peter Cecil, Peter Clarke, Mark A. Edwards, Barbara Mascetti, John Myers,
Zoe Nye, Moira Steven, Andy Williams and Tony Winzor.

ISBN: 978 1 78294 307 5

With thanks to Ian Francis for the proofreading.
With thanks to Jan Greenway for the copyright research.

NASA's Earth Observatory image on page 22 using Landsat data from the U.S. Geological Survey Courtesy of USGS/NASA

Clipart from Corel®
Printed by Elanders Ltd, Newcastle upon Tyne.

Based on the classic CGP style created by Richard Parsons.

Contents

If you're revising for the **AS exams**, you'll need Modules 1-4.
If you're revising for the **A-level exams**, you'll need the whole book.

Module 6: Section 2 — Charge and Field

Module 6: Section 3 — Probing Deep into Matter

Module 6: Section 4 — Ionising Radiation and Risk

Do Well In Your Exams

The Scientific Process

'How Science Works' is all about the scientific process — how we develop and test scientific ideas. It's what scientists do all day, every day (well, except at coffee time — never come between a scientist and their coffee).

Scientists Come Up with **Theories** — Then **Test Them**...

Science tries to explain **how** and **why** things happen — it **answers questions**. It's all about seeking and gaining **knowledge** about the world around us. Scientists do this by **asking** questions, **suggesting** answers and then **testing** their suggestions to see if they're correct — this is the **scientific process**.

1) **Ask** a question about **why** something happens or **how** something works. E.g. what is the nature of light?

2) **Suggest** an answer, or part of an answer, by forming a **theory** (a possible **explanation** of the observations) — e.g. light is a wave. (Scientists also sometimes form a **model** too — a **simplified picture** of what's physically going on.)

3) Make a **prediction** or **hypothesis** — a **specific testable statement**, based on the theory, about what will happen in a test situation. For example, if light is a wave, it will interfere and diffract when it travels through a small enough gap.

4) Carry out a **test** — to provide **evidence** that will support the prediction (or help to disprove it). E.g. Young's double-slit experiment (p.58-59).

The evidence supported Quentin's Theory of Flammable Burps.

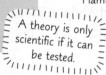

A theory is only scientific if it can be tested.

...Then They **Tell** Everyone About Their **Results**...

The results are **published** — scientists need to let others know about their work. Scientists publish their results in **scientific journals**. These are just like normal magazines, only they contain **scientific reports** (called papers) instead of the latest celebrity gossip.

1) Scientific reports are similar to the **lab write-ups** you do in school. And just as a lab write-up is **reviewed** (marked) by your teacher, reports in scientific journals undergo **peer review** before they're published.

2) The report is sent out to **peers** — other scientists that are experts in the **same area**. They examine the data and results, and if they think that the conclusion is reasonable it's **published**. This makes sure that work published in scientific journals is of a **good standard**.

3) But peer review **can't guarantee** the science is **correct** — other scientists still need to **reproduce** it.

4) Sometimes **mistakes** are made and bad work is published. Peer review **isn't perfect** but it's probably the best way for scientists to self-regulate their work and to publish **quality reports**.

...Then **Other Scientists** Will **Test** the Theory Too

Other scientists read the published theories and results, and try to **test the theory** themselves. This involves:
- Repeating the **exact same experiments**.
- Using the theory to make **new predictions** and then testing them with **new experiments**.

If the **Evidence** Supports a Theory, It's **Accepted** — for Now

1) If all the experiments in all the world provide good evidence to back it up, the theory is thought of as **scientific 'fact'** (for now).

2) But it will never become **totally indisputable** fact. Scientific **breakthroughs or advances** could provide new ways to question and test the theory, which could lead to **new evidence** that **conflicts** with the current evidence. Then the testing starts all over again...

And this, my friend, is the **tentative nature of scientific knowledge** — it's always **changing** and **evolving**.

The Scientific Process

So scientists need evidence to back up their theories. They get it by carrying out experiments, and when that's not possible they carry out studies. But why bother with science at all? We want to know as much as possible so we can use it to try and improve our lives (and because we're nosy).

Evidence *Comes From* Controlled Lab Experiments...

1) Results from **controlled experiments** in **laboratories** are **great**.
2) A lab is the easiest place to **control variables** so that they're all **kept constant** (except for the one you're investigating).

Module 1 (pages 4-9) is all about designing and carrying out experiments.

...*That You can Draw* Meaningful Conclusions *From*

1) You always need to make your experiments as **controlled** as possible so you can be confident that any effects you see are linked to the variable you're changing.
2) If you do find a relationship, you need to be careful what you conclude. You need to decide whether the effect you're seeing is **caused** by changing a variable (this is known as a **causal relationship**), or whether the two are just **correlated**. There's more about drawing conclusions on page 9.

"Right Geoff, you can start the experiment now... I've stopped time..."

Society *Makes Decisions* Based on *Scientific Evidence*

1) Lots of scientific work eventually leads to **important discoveries** or breakthroughs that could **benefit humankind**.
2) These results are **used by society** (that's you, me and everyone else) to **make decisions** — about the way we live, what we eat, what we drive, etc.
3) All sections of society use scientific evidence to make decisions, e.g. politicians use it to devise policies and individuals use science to make decisions about their own lives.

Other factors can **influence** decisions about science or the way science is used:

Economic factors

Society has to consider the **cost** of implementing changes based on scientific conclusions — e.g. the cost of reducing the UK's carbon emissions to limit the human contribution to **global warming**.
Scientific research is often **expensive**. E.g. in areas such as astronomy, the Government has to **justify** spending money on a new telescope rather than pumping money into, say, the **NHS** or **schools**.

Social factors

Decisions affect **people's lives** — e.g. when looking for a site to build a **nuclear power station**, you need to consider how it would affect the lives of the people in the **surrounding area**.

Environmental factors

Many scientists suggest that building **wind farms** would be a **cheap** and **environmentally friendly** way to generate electricity in the future. But some people think that because **wind turbines** can **harm wildlife** such as birds and bats, other methods of generating electricity should be used.

So there you have it — how science works...

Hopefully these pages have given you a nice intro to how science works, e.g. what scientists do to provide you with 'facts'. You need to understand this, as you're expected to know how science works yourself — for the exam and for life.

Planning and Implementing

Science is all about getting good evidence to support (or disprove) your theories, so scientists need to be able to spot a badly designed experiment, interpret the results of an experiment or study, and design their own experiments too...

You Might have to **Design an Experiment** to Answer a **Question**

1) You might be asked to design a physics experiment to **investigate** something or answer a question.

2) It could be a **lab experiment** that you've seen before, or something **applied**, like deciding which building material is best for a particular job.

3) Either way, you'll be able to use the physics you know and the skills in this topic to figure out the best way to investigate the problem.

A **Variable** is Anything that has the Potential to **Change** in an Experiment

1) First, you need to identify your **independent** and **dependent variables**:

> The **independent** variable is the thing you **change**.
> The **dependent** variable is the thing you **measure**.

> **Example 1:** If you're investigating how changing the potential difference across a component affects the current through it, the **independent variable** is the **potential difference**, and the **dependent variable** is the **current**.

2) Apart from the independent and dependent variables, **all other variables** should stay the same during your experiment. If not, you can't tell whether or not the independent variable is responsible for any changes in your dependent variable, so your results won't be **valid** (p.8). This is known as **controlling variables**. It might be worth **measuring control variables** that are likely to change during your experiment to check that they really are under control.

> **Example 1 (continued):** In the example above, you need to use the same **circuit components**, and keep the **temperature** of the apparatus **constant** — e.g. by letting the circuit cool down between readings.

> **Example 2:** If you're investigating the value of **acceleration due to gravity** by dropping an object and timing its fall, **draughts** in the room could really mess up your results. Picking an object that is more **resistant** to being blown about (like a ball-bearing) will help make your results more **precise** and therefore more **valid** (p.8).

Select Appropriate **Apparatus** and **Techniques**

1) You need to think about what **units** your measurements of the independent and dependent variables are likely to be in before you begin (e.g. millimetres or metres, milliseconds or hours).

2) Think about the **range** you plan on taking measurements over too — e.g. if you're measuring the effect of increasing the force on a spring, you need to know whether you should increase the force in steps of 1 newton, 10 newtons or 100 newtons. Sometimes, you'll be able to **estimate** what effect changing your independent variable will have, or sometimes a **pilot** ('trial') **experiment** might help.

3) Considering your measurements before you start will also help you choose the most appropriate **apparatus** and **techniques** for the experiment:

> *There's a whole range of apparatus and techniques that could come up in your exam. Make sure you know how to use all the ones you've come across in class.*

> **Examples:**
> - If you're measuring the length of a **spring** that you're applying a force to, you might need a **ruler**. If you're measuring the diameter of a **wire**, you'd be better off with a set of **callipers**.
> - If you're measuring the extension of a wire, and the extension may be small, you'll need to use a long piece of wire. If it's **too long** to suspend vertically from a clamp, you'll need to use a pulley like on p.44.
> - If you're measuring a **time interval**, you could use a **stopwatch**. If the time is **really short** (for example if you're investigating acceleration due to gravity), you might need to use something more sensitive and responsive (see next page), like **light gates**.

4) Whatever apparatus and techniques you use, make sure you use them **correctly**. E.g. if you're measuring a length with a ruler, make sure your eye is level with the point where you're taking the measurement.

5) While you're planning, you should also think about the **risks** involved in your experiment and how to manage them — e.g. if you're investigating a material that might snap, wear safety goggles to protect your eyes.

Planning and Implementing

Be Aware of *Sensitivity* and *Response Time*

1) An instrument's **sensitivity** is a measure of how much the quantity it's measuring needs to change by for the change to be detected.

2) You can calculate sensitivity using the equation on the right. It's the ratio of **change in output** (the change shown on your measuring device) to **change in input** (the change in the quantity the device is measuring).

$$\text{sensitivity} = \frac{\text{change in output}}{\text{change in input}}$$

3) The **response time** of an instrument is how long it takes for the output to change after a change in input.

4) The **quality** of your data will be **poor** if the response time is **too long** or the sensitivity **too low**. You need to make sure that the sensitivity and response time of your equipment are **appropriate** for what you're measuring.

Figure Out how to *Record* your Data Before you *Start*

Before you get going, you'll need a **data table** to record your results in.

1) It should include space for the **independent** and **dependent variables**. Specify the **units** in the headers, not within the table itself.

2) Your table needs room for repeated measurements. You should aim to **repeat** each measurement at least **three times**. Repeated measurements can reduce the effect of random errors in your results (see p.12) and makes spotting **anomalous** results, like this one, much easier.

| P.d. / V | Current / A | | | |
	Trial 1	Trial 2	Trial 3	Average
1.00	0.052	0.047	0.050	0.050
1.50	0.790	0.075	0.079	0.077
...	...	...	...	...

3) Include space in your table for any data processing you need to do, e.g. calculating an **average** from repeated measurements, or speed from measurements of distance and time.

4) Usually, your data will be **quantitative** (i.e. you'll be recording numerical values). Occasionally, you may have to deal with **qualitative** data (data that can be observed but not measured with a numerical value). It's still best to record this kind of data in a table to keep your results **organised**, but the layout may be a little **different**.

You Could be Asked to *Evaluate* An *Experimental Design*

If you need to evaluate an experimental design, whether it's your own or someone else's, you need to think about the same sorts of things that you would if you were designing the experiment yourself:

- Does it **actually test** what it sets out to test?
- Is the method **clear** enough for someone else to follow?
- Apart from the **independent** and **dependent variables**, is everything else **properly controlled**?
- Are the **apparatus** and **techniques appropriate** for what's being measured? Will they be used correctly?
- Have enough **repeated measurements** been planned?
- Is the experiment going to be conducted **safely**?

Practice Questions

Q1 Why should you control all the variables (other than the dependent and independent variables) in an experiment?
Q2 What do you need to consider when selecting your apparatus?
Q3 What is meant by sensitivity and response time? How is sensitivity calculated?
Q4 Why should you take repeated measurements in an experiment?

Exam Question

Q1 A student is investigating the effect of light level on the resistance of an LDR (light-dependent resistor). The student connects the LDR to a power supply, and measures the resistance of the LDR at various distances from a light source using a multimeter.
a) State the independent and dependent variables for this experiment. [1 mark]
b) State two variables that the student needs to control in order to ensure his results are valid. [2 marks]

The best-planned experiments of mice and men...

...often get top marks. The details of planning and carrying out an experiment will vary a lot depending on what you're investigating, but if all this stuff is wedged in your brain you shouldn't go far wrong, so make sure you've got it learned.

Analysing Results

You've planned an experiment, and you've got some results (or you've been given some in your exam).
Now it's time to look into them a bit more closely...

Check for **Anomalous Results** and do any **Calculations** You Need to **First**

1) Before you calculate anything, check for any **anomalous results**. If there's something in the results that's **clearly wrong**, then don't include it in your calculations — it'll just **muck everything up**. Be careful though, you should only exclude an anomalous result if you have **good reason** to think it's wrong, e.g. it looks like a decimal point is in the **wrong place**, or you suspect that one of the control variables **changed**. And you should talk about any anomalous results when you're evaluating the experiment (pages 8-9).

2) For most experiments, you'll at least need to calculate the mean (average) of some **repeated measurements**:

$$\text{mean (average) of a measurement} = \frac{\text{sum of your repeated measurements}}{\text{number of repeats taken}}$$

In class, you could use a spreadsheet to process your data (and plot graphs), but it's important that you know how to do it by hand for the exam.

3) Calculate any quantities that you're interested in that you haven't **directly measured**.

You should try to give any values you calculate to the same number of significant figures as the data value with the **fewest significant figures** in your calculation, **or one more** where it's sensible. If you give your result to too many significant figures, you're saying your final result is more **precise** than it actually is (see p.8).

Present Your Results as a **Scatter Graph**

Make sure you know how to plot a graph of your results:

If you need to use your graph to measure something, select axes that will let you do this easily (e.g. by measuring the gradient or the intercept, see the next page).

1) Usually, the **independent variable** goes on the *x*-axis and the **dependent variable** goes on the *y*-axis. Both axes should be **labelled** clearly, with the quantity and **units**. The **scales** used should be sensible (i.e. they should go up in sensible steps, and should spread the data out over the full graph rather than bunching it up in a corner).

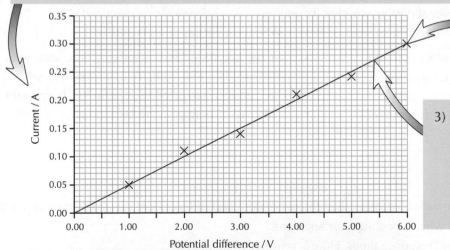

2) Plot your points using a **sharp pencil**, to make sure they're as **accurate** as possible.

3) Draw a **line of best fit** for your results. Around **half** the data points should be above the line, and half should be below it (you should ignore anomalous results). Depending on the data, the line might be **straight**, or **curved**.

Graphs can Show Different Kinds of **Correlation**

Remember, correlation does not necessarily mean cause — p.3.

The **correlation** describes the relationship between the variables. Data can show:

Positive correlation:
As one variable increases the other increases.

Negative correlation:
As one variable increases the other decreases.

No correlation:
No relationship between the variables.

Analysing Results

You Might Need to Find a Gradient or Intercept

If the line of best fit is **straight**, then the graph is **linear**. This means if one variable changes by a given amount, the other variable will always change by the **same multiple** of that amount. The **line of best fit** for a linear graph has the **equation:**

$$y = mx + c$$

Where *m* is the **gradient** of the line and *c* is the **y-intercept**.

If the line of best fit goes through the origin (*c* is 0), you can say the variables are **directly proportional** to each other:

$$y \propto x$$

∝ just means 'is directly proportional to'.

Example: This graph shows displacement against time for a motorbike travelling west. Find the bike's velocity.

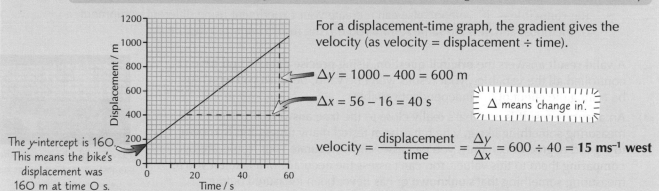

For a displacement-time graph, the gradient gives the velocity (as velocity = displacement ÷ time).

$\Delta y = 1000 - 400 = 600$ m

$\Delta x = 56 - 16 = 40$ s

Δ means 'change in'.

The *y*-intercept is 160. This means the bike's displacement was 160 m at time 0 s.

$$\text{velocity} = \frac{\text{displacement}}{\text{time}} = \frac{\Delta y}{\Delta x} = 600 \div 40 = \textbf{15 ms}^{-1} \textbf{ west}$$

If a graph has a **curved** line of best fit, you can find the gradient at a given point on the line by drawing a **tangent** to the curve (see page 83). It's sometimes helpful to choose axes that turn a curved graph into a straight one instead:

Example:

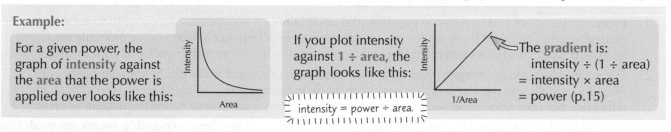

For a given power, the graph of **intensity** against the **area** that the power is applied over looks like this:

intensity = power ÷ area.

If you plot intensity against **1 ÷ area**, the graph looks like this:

The **gradient** is:
intensity ÷ (1 ÷ area)
= intensity × area
= power (p.15)

Practice Questions

Q1 Describe what you should do with anomalous results when processing data.

Q2 How do you calculate an average of repeated results?

Q3 Sketch a graph showing a negative correlation.

Exam Question

Q1 An engineer is investigating the performance of a prototype car with a new kind of environmentally-friendly engine. The data below shows the speed of the car, going from stationary to over 70 kilometres per hour.
(In this question, you may use the formula: acceleration = change in speed ÷ time taken to change speed.)

Time / s	0	2	4	6	8	10	12	14	16
Speed / km per hour	0	3	8	24	36	52	66	69	71

a) Draw a graph showing speed against time for this data. [4 marks]

b) State the times between which the graph is linear. [1 mark]

c) Using the graph, calculate the maximum acceleration of the car. [4 marks]

My level of boredom is proportional to the time I've spent on this page...

This stuff can get a bit fiddly, especially measuring the gradient of a curved line, but for the most part it's not too bad, and you should have seen a lot of it before. So dust off your pencil sharpener, and get to work...

Evaluating and Concluding

Once you've drawn your graphs and analysed your results, you need to think about your conclusions.

Evaluate the Quality of Your Results

Before you draw any conclusions, you should think about the quality of the results — if the quality's not great you won't be able to have much confidence in your conclusion. Good results are **precise**, **valid** and **accurate**.

1) The smaller the **range** that the repeats for each measurement are spread over, the more **precise** your data. A **precise** result is one that is **repeatable** and **reproducible**.

Precision is sometimes called reliability.

- **Repeatable** — **you** can **repeat** an experiment multiple times and get the **same results**. For experiments, doing more repeats enables you to assess how precise your data is — the **more repeats** you do, and the more **similar** the results of each repeat are, the more **precise** your data.

- **Reproducible** — if **someone else** can recreate your experiment using different equipment or methods, and gets the **same results** you do, the results are reproducible.

2) A **valid result** answers the **original question**, using **precise data**. If you haven't controlled all the variables, your results won't be valid, because you won't just be testing the effect of the independent variable.

3) An **accurate result** is one that's really close to the **true answer**. If you're measuring something like *g*, which has been tested many times, and is known to a good degree of certainty, you can assess how accurate your results are by **comparing** them to this value. You can't assess the accuracy of a result if you're measuring something that's **unknown** or has never been measured before.

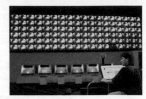

David might have taken the suggestion that he repeat his experiment a bit far...

All Results have Some Uncertainty

1) **Every** measurement you take has an **experimental uncertainty**. If you measured a piece of string with a ruler marked in cm, you might think you've measured its length as 30 cm, but at **best** you've probably measured it to be 30 ± **0.5** cm. And that's without taking into account any other errors that might be in your measurement.

2) The ± sign gives you the **range** in which the **true** length (the one you'd really like to know) probably lies. 30 ± 0.5 cm tells you the true length is very likely to lie in the range of 29.5 to 30.5 cm. The maximum difference between your value and the true value (here 0.5 cm) is sometimes called the **margin of error**.

3) The smaller the uncertainty in a result or measurement, the smaller the range of possible values the result could have and the more precise your data can be. There are two measures of uncertainty you need to know about:

> **Absolute uncertainty** — the **total uncertainty** for a measurement.
>
> **Percentage error** — the uncertainty given as a **percentage** of the measurement.

If you measure a length of something with a ruler, you actually take two measurements, one at each end of the object you're measuring. There is an uncertainty in each of these measurements. E.g. a length of 17.0 cm measured using a mm ruler will have an uncertainty of 0.05 + 0.05 = ± 0.1 cm (see page 12).

Example: The resistance of a filament lamp is given as 5.0 ± 0.4 Ω. Give the absolute uncertainty and the percentage error for this measurement.

The **absolute uncertainty** is **0.4 Ω**.

To get the percentage error, just convert this to a percentage of the lamp's resistance: (0.4 ÷ 5.0) × 100 = **8%**

Significant Figures give Uncertainties

If no uncertainty is given for a value, the **assumed uncertainty** is **half of one increment** of the **last significant figure** that the value is **given** to. For example, 2.0 is given to 2 **significant figures**, and the last significant figure has an increment of 0.1, so you would assume an uncertainty of 0.05.

You should always assume the **largest** amount of uncertainty when doing an experiment, so keep an eye on the uncertainty when taking measurements and doing calculations (see p.12-13 for more on evaluating uncertainties).

Evaluating and Concluding

Draw **Conclusions** that Your Results **Support**

1) A conclusion **explains** what the data shows. You can only draw a conclusion if your data **supports** it.

2) Your conclusion should be limited to the **circumstances you've tested** it under — if you've been investigating how the current flowing through a resistor changes with the potential difference across it, and have only used potential differences between 0 and 6 V, you can't claim to know what would happen if you used a potential difference of 100 V, or if you used a different resistor.

3) You also need to think about how much you can **believe** your conclusion, by evaluating the quality of your results (see previous page). If you doubt the quality of your results, you can't form a **strong conclusion**.

Think About how the Experiment Could be **Improved**

Having collected the data, is there anything you think should have been done **differently**?
Were there any **limitations** to your method?

1) If the results aren't **valid**, could you change the experiment to fix this, e.g. by changing the data you're collecting?

2) If the results aren't **accurate**, what could have caused this?
Systematic errors (p.12) can affect accuracy — are there any that you could prevent?

3) Are there any changes you could make to the **apparatus** or **procedure** that would make the results more **precise**?

- The **less random error** (p.12) there is in the measurement, the more **precise** your results.
  Increasing the number of **repeats** could help to reduce the **effect** of random errors in your results.

- By using the most **appropriate** equipment — e.g. swapping a millimetre ruler for a micrometer to measure the diameter of a wire — you can instantly cut down the **random error** in your experiment.

- You can also use a **computer** to collect data — e.g. using light gates to measure a time interval rather than a stopwatch. This makes results more **precise** by reducing **human error**.

4) Are there any other ways you could have **reduced the errors** in the measurements?

Practice Questions

Q1 What is a valid result?

Q2 What is the difference between saying the results of an experiment are precise and saying that they are accurate?

Q3 What should you think about when you are trying to improve an experimental design?

Exam Questions

Q1 The resistance of a fixed resistor is given as 50.00 Ω.
According to the manufacturer, there is a 0.02% uncertainty in this value.
What is the minimum possible resistance of the resistor in Ω, to 2 decimal places?

A: 49.00 Ω   B: 49.99 Ω   C: 49.90 Ω   D: 49.09 Ω   [1 mark]

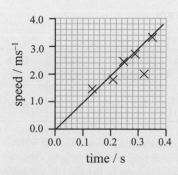

Q2 A student is investigating how the speed of a falling object is affected by how long it has been falling for. He drops an object from heights between 10 cm and 60 cm and measures its speed at the end of its fall, and the time the fall takes, using light gates. He plots a graph of the final speed of the object against the time it took to fall, as shown on the left.

a) Identify the anomalous result.   [1 mark]

b) The student concludes that the speed of any falling object is always proportional to the time it has been falling for.
Explain whether or not the results support this conclusion.   [2 marks]

In conclusion, Physics causes headaches...

Valid, precise, and accurate... you'd think they all mean the same thing, but they really don't.
Make sure you know the difference, and are careful about which one you use, or you'll be throwing marks away.

Quantities, Units and Graphs

Learning physics is a lot like building a house — both involve drinking a lot of tea. Also, both have important foundations — if you skip this stuff everything else is likely to go a bit wrong. So, here goes brick-laying 101...

A **Physical Quantity** has both a **Numerical Value** and a **Unit**

1) Every time you measure something or calculate a quantity you need to give the **units**.

2) The **Système International** (S.I.) includes a set of **base units** for physical quantities from which lots of other units are derived. Here are the S.I. base units that you need to know:

Quantity	S.I. base unit
mass	kilogram, kg
length	metre, m
time	second, s
current	ampere, A
temperature	kelvin, K
amount of a substance	mole, mol

Kilograms are a bit odd — they're the only S.I. unit with a scaling prefix (see below).

You're more likely to see temperatures given in °C. To convert from °C to K, add 273.15.

Remembering how S.I. derived units are defined will help you make sure the other quantities in your equations are in the right units.

3) Many more units can be derived from these base units — e.g. newtons, N, for force are defined by $kg\,m\,s^{-2}$. The newton is an **S.I. derived unit**.

4) The S.I. derived units you'll need will be covered throughout the book and you need to remember them.

5) You also need to have a rough idea of the size of each S.I. base unit and S.I. derived unit in this book, so that you can **estimate quantities** using them.

Example: Pressure is measured in pascals (Pa). Use the formula pressure = force ÷ area to show that 1 Pa is equal to $1\ kg\,m^{-1}s^{-2}$.

Pressure = force ÷ area, so the units $Pa = \dfrac{N}{m^2}$

Force = mass × acceleration, so the units $N = kg \times ms^{-2} = kg \times m \times s^{-2}$

So the units of pressure can be written as $Pa = \dfrac{kg \times m \times s^{-2}}{m^2} = kg \times m^{-1} \times s^{-2} = \mathbf{kg\,m^{-1}s^{-2}}$

6) You might also have to **convert** between units using a **conversion factor**. For example, to convert an angle from **degrees** to **radians**, multiply by $\dfrac{\pi}{180}$. To get **back to degrees**, multiply by $\dfrac{180}{\pi}$. Radians are an S.I. derived unit, but you're **more likely** to see angles given in degrees in some areas of physics.

You'll be given 1 radian = 57.3° in your formula book, so if you get stuck you can use that.

Prefixes Let You Scale Units

Physical quantities come in a **huge range** of sizes. Prefixes are scaling factors that let you write numbers across this range without having to put everything in standard form.

These are the prefixes you need to know:

prefix	pico (p)	nano (n)	micro (μ)	milli (m)	centi (c)	deci (d)	kilo (k)	mega (M)	giga (G)	tera (T)
multiple of unit	1×10^{-12}	1×10^{-9}	1×10^{-6}	0.001 (1×10^{-3})	0.01 (1×10^{-2})	0.1 (1×10^{-1})	1000 (1×10^{3})	1×10^{6}	1×10^{9}	1×10^{12}

Example: Convert 0.247 megawatts into kilowatts.

$1\ MW = 1 \times 10^6\ W$ and $1\ kW = 1 \times 10^3\ W$

So the scaling factor to move between MW and kW is:

$(1 \times 10^6) \div (1 \times 10^3) = 1 \times 10^3$.

So $0.247\ MW = 0.247 \times 1 \times 10^3 = \mathbf{247\ kW}$

It's really easy to get muddled up when you're converting between prefixes. The rule is, if you're moving to the right in the table above, your number should get smaller, and if you're moving to the left the number should get larger. If your answer doesn't match the rule, you've made a mistake.

Quantities, Units and Graphs

You can find the *Mean*, *Median* and *Spread* from a *Frequency Plot*

After you've done an experiment and recorded data, you usually draw a **scatter graph** of the results (see page 6). But if you draw a **frequency plot** that shows the **distribution of data** by plotting the **frequency** (the number of times a value occurs within a given interval) of each data value **against** the **data values**, you can use it to find:

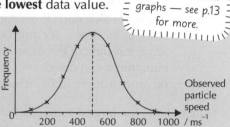

1) The **mean** — this is a type of average. For data with a **roughly symmetrical** distribution, you can estimate the mean by finding the value of the **peak** of the **best fit curve**.

2) The **median** — this is the **middle value** of your data. For a symmetrical distribution, this is the **same** as the mean.

3) The **spread** — this is how **wide** the distribution curve is and shows how spread out your data is. The easiest way to calculate the spread is by finding the **range**. But be careful to exclude any **anomalous** values that look **too high** or **too low** — these will give you an **incorrect range**.

4) The **range** — This is the **difference** between the **highest** data value and the **lowest** data value.

You can also find uncertainties from graphs — see p.13 for more.

Example: The graph shows a distribution of particle speeds. Estimate the mean, median and spread of the data.

The best fit curve is roughly symmetrical, so the value of the peak is the mean and the median, and is **500 ms^{-1}**.

The spread can be estimated from the range: 980 − 20 = **960 ms^{-1}**.

All of these values can be **affected** by **anomalies** in your data. Page 6 shows you how to deal with anomalous results.

Log Graphs Can be used for Exponentials and Power Laws

You could take the log of your data values and plot these values on normal axes instead.

1) **Logarithm (log) graphs** allow you to plot **exponential** and **power law** relationships on smaller graphs. It's often **not practical** to plot exponential relationships on normal graphs — you'd need a **huge** sheet of paper, or you'd only see a **tiny part** of the relationship.

2) Log graphs are easily recognised because each **increment** on an axis represents an **equal factor** (e.g. **every grid line** could represent a **×10** increase). This factor is known as the **base** of the log.

3) You need to be **careful** when reading data points that are **between grid lines** — because the scale is **logarithmic**, the middle of a grid square is **not** the midpoint between the values of the adjacent grid lines.

Not all axes start at O. Sometimes an axis will start with a little zig-zag if it doesn't start at O, but we won't use those here.

Practice Questions

Q1 What are the S.I. units of mass, current and temperature?

Q2 What is meant by an S.I. base unit and an S.I. derived unit?

Q3 Which quantity best represents the magnitude of room temperature: 1×10^1 K, 1×10^2 K or 1×10^3 K?

Q4 What is π radians in degrees?

Q5 What is: a) 20 000 W in kilowatts, b) 2×10^{-6} W in milliwatts, c) 1.23×10^7 W in gigawatts?

Q6 How would you find the mean, median and spread from a frequency scatter graph with a symmetrical best fit line?

Exam Questions

Q1 Work done is measured in joules. Use the formula work done = force × distance to show that 1 joule is equal to 1 kg m^{2}s^{-2}. [2 marks]

Q2 The graph on the right shows the threshold of hearing (the minimum intensity of sound a person can hear) for a range of frequencies.

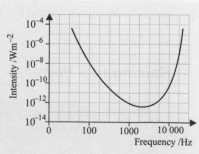

a) Explain how you can tell that the axes of the graph are logarithmic. [2 marks]

b) Estimate the minimum intensity (to the nearest power of 10) of a 100 Hz sound which could be heard by a human. [1 mark]

What's the S.I. base unit for boring...

Not the most exciting pair of pages these, I'll admit, but it's important that you have the basics down, or else you're leaving yourself open to simple little mistakes that'll cost you marks. So get cracking learning those S.I. units.

Measurements and Uncertainties

There are errors and uncertainties in every measurement. You need to know how to deal with them...

Uncertainty *is Caused by* Random *and* Systematic Errors

Every measurement you take has an experimental uncertainty (p.8) caused by two types of error:

1) **Systematic errors** (including **zero errors**) are the same every time you repeat the experiment (they shift all the values by the same amount). They may be caused by the **equipment** you're using or how it's **set-up**, e.g. not lining up a ruler correctly when measuring the extension of a spring. Systematic errors are really **hard to spot**, and they affect the **accuracy** of your results. It's always worth **checking your apparatus** at the start of an experiment, e.g. measure a few known masses to check that a mass meter is **calibrated** properly.

2) **Random errors** vary — they're what make the results a bit different each time you repeat an experiment. If you measured the length of a wire 20 times, the chances are you'd get a slightly different value each time, e.g. due to your head being in a slightly different position when reading the scale. It could be that you just can't keep controlled variables (p.4) exactly the same throughout the experiment. Using equipment with a **higher resolution** means that the equipment can detect smaller changes. This can reduce random error and so your results can be more **precise** (p.8). **Repeating measurements** can also reduce the effect of random errors.

Identifying the **largest sources** of uncertainty as far as possible is important when trying to design an experiment which minimises uncertainties. Sometimes all other smaller uncertainties are **dwarfed** by the largest one.

Sometimes You Need to Combine Uncertainties

You have to combine the uncertainties of different measured values to find the uncertainty of a calculated result:

Adding *or* Subtracting *Data —* ADD *the* Absolute Uncertainties

Example: A wire is stretched from 0.3 ± 0.1 cm to 0.5 ± 0.1 cm. Calculate the extension of the wire.

1) First subtract the lengths without the uncertainty values: 0.5 – 0.3 = 0.2 cm
2) Then find the total uncertainty by adding the individual absolute uncertainties: 0.1 + 0.1 = 0.2 cm
So, the extension of the wire is **0.2 ± 0.2 cm**.

Multiplying *or* Dividing *Data —* ADD *the* Percentage Uncertainties

Example: A force of 15 N ± 3% is applied to a stationary object which has a mass of 6.0 ± 0.3 kg. Calculate the acceleration of the object and state the percentage uncertainty in this value.

1) First calculate the acceleration without uncertainty: $a = F \div m = 15 \div 6.0 = 2.5$ ms^{-2}
2) Next, calculate the percentage uncertainty in the mass: % uncertainty in $m = \frac{0.3}{6.0} \times 100 = 5\%$
3) Add the percentage uncertainties in the force and mass values to find the total uncertainty in the acceleration: Total uncertainty = 3% + 5% = 8%
So, the acceleration = **2.5 ms^{-2} ± 8%**

Raising *to a* Power *—* MULTIPLY *the* Percentage Uncertainty *by the* Power

Example: The radius of a circle is $r = 40$ cm ± 2.5%. What will the percentage uncertainty be in the area of this circle (πr^2)?

The radius will be raised to the power of **2** to calculate the area.
So, the percentage uncertainty will be 2.5% × 2 = **5%**

Percentage uncertainty (or percentage error) is covered on page 8.

Measurements and Uncertainties

Uncertainty Bars *Show the* Uncertainty *of Individual Points*

1) Most of the time, you work out the **uncertainty** in your **final** result using the uncertainty in **each measurement** you make.

2) When you're plotting a **graph**, you can show the uncertainty in **each measurement** by using **uncertainty** (error) **bars** to show the **range** the point is likely to lie in. E.g. the uncertainty bars on the graph on the right show the error in each measurement of the extension of an object when a force is applied.

3) You can have uncertainty bars for both the dependent and the independent variable.

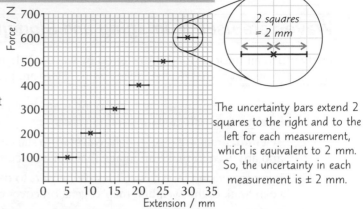

The uncertainty bars extend 2 squares to the right and to the left for each measurement, which is equivalent to 2 mm. So, the uncertainty in each measurement is ± 2 mm.

You Can Calculate *the* Uncertainty *of Final Results from* Lines of Worst Fit

Normally when you draw a graph you'll want to find the **gradient** or **intercept** (p.7). For example, you can calculate *k*, the **force constant** of the object being stretched, from the **gradient** of the graph on the right — here it's about 20 000 Nm⁻¹. You can find the **uncertainty** in that value by using **worst lines**:

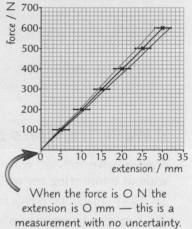

1) Draw lines of best fit which have the **maximum** and **minimum** possible slopes for the data and which should go through all of the **uncertainty bars** (see the pink and blue lines on the right). These are the **worst lines** for your data.

2) Calculate the **worst gradient** — the gradient of the slope that is **furthest** from the gradient of the line of best fit. The blue line's gradient is about 21 000 Nm⁻¹ and the pink line's gradient is about 19 000 Nm⁻¹, so you can use either here.

When the force is O N the extension is O mm — this is a measurement with no uncertainty.

3) The **uncertainty** in the gradient is given by the **difference** between the **best gradient** (of the line of best fit) and the **worst gradient** — here it's 1000 Nm⁻¹. So this is the uncertainty in the value of the spring constant. For this object, the spring constant is 20 000 ± 1000 Nm⁻¹ (or 20 000 Nm⁻¹ ± 5%).

4) Similarly, the uncertainty in the *y*-intercept is just the **difference** between the **best** and **worst** intercepts (although there's no uncertainty here since the best and worst lines both go through the origin).

Practice Questions

Q1 Give two examples of possible sources of random error and one example of a possible source of systematic error in an experiment. Which kind of error is least likely to affect the precision of the results?

Q2 Describe what uncertainty bars on data points on a graph show.

Q3 What are worst lines? How could you use them to find the uncertainty in the intercept of a graph?

Exam Question

Q1 A student is investigating the acceleration of a remote controlled car. The car has an initial velocity of 0.52 ± 0.02 ms⁻¹ and accelerates to 0.94 ± 0.02 ms⁻¹ over an interval of 2.5 ± 0.5 s.

 a) Calculate the percentage uncertainty in the car's initial speed. [1 mark]

 b) Calculate the percentage uncertainty in the car's final speed. [1 mark]

 c) Calculate the car's average acceleration over this interval. Include the absolute uncertainty of the result in your answer. (acceleration = change in velocity ÷ time taken). [4 marks]

Physics is the meaning of life — of that, I'm 42% certain...

Uncertainties are a bit of a pain, but they're really important. Learn the rules for combining uncertainties, and how to read uncertainties from graphs using uncertainty bars and worst lines. Random and systematic errors are an exam favourite too, so make sure you know the difference, and how to minimise both in your experiments.

The Nature of Waves

This section's all about what happens when you take a picture with your mobile and send it to your mate Dave... with a few other minor details... it's all waves waves waves.

Waves are used in Imaging and Signalling

Pretty much all information is transferred by waves. Whenever you create an image or send a signal, it'll be waves that do the lackey work. Here are just a few examples of where they're used:

1) **Medical scanning** — e.g. ultrasound scans build up an image of a fetus by detecting reflected **ultrasound waves**.

2) **Scientific imaging** — e.g. light waves from stars and galaxies take billions of years to reach the Earth, and are used to make an image that can be recorded electronically.

3) **Remote sensing** — e.g. satellites use sensors to detect waves from distant objects to do things like keep track of the weather, map vegetation cover or even make very accurate elevation maps.

4) **Seeing** — anything you see, from stars to the cat being sick on your nicest pair of jeans, is thanks to millions of light waves hitting your retinas and forming an image.

5) **Heat cameras** sense infrared waves being emitted by the hot thing you're looking at. Infrared radiation is also the type of electromagnetic wave that carries the signal from your TV remote control to your telly to switch over to your favourite soap...

6) **Communications** — e.g. your mobile phone sends and receives **microwaves** that carry the signal containing that all-important text message.

7) **Data streaming** — e.g. when you stream music or videos over the internet, the data normally travels part of the way from a server to your home as a light wave through fibre optic cables.

A Wave Transfers Energy Away from its Source

A **progressive** (moving) wave carries **energy** and usually information from one place to another **without transferring any material**. Here are some ways you can tell waves carry energy:

1) Electromagnetic waves can cause things to **heat up**.

2) **X-rays** and **gamma rays** knock electrons out of their orbits, causing **ionisation**.

3) Loud **sounds** make things **vibrate**.

4) **Wave power** can be used to **generate electricity**.

5) Since waves carry energy away, the **source** of the wave **loses energy**.

Smile, wave and transfer energy away from its source...

Here are all the bits of a Wave you Need to Know

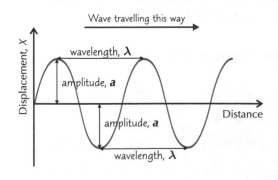

1) **Displacement, X**, metres — how far a **point** on the wave has **moved** from its **undisturbed position**.

2) **Amplitude, a**, metres — **maximum displacement**.

3) **Wavelength, λ**, metres — the **length of one whole wave**, e.g. from **crest** to **crest** or **trough** to **trough**.

4) **Period, T**, seconds — the **time taken** for a **whole vibration**.

5) **Frequency, f**, hertz — the **number of vibrations per second** passing a given **point**.

6) **Phase difference** — the amount by which **one wave lags behind another** wave. **Measured** in degrees or radians. See page 10.

The Frequency is the Inverse of the Period

$$\text{Frequency} = \frac{1}{\text{Period}}$$

$$f = \frac{1}{T}$$

It's that simple.
Get the **units** straight: **1 Hz = 1 s⁻¹**.

The Nature of Waves

The *Wave Equation* Links *Wave Speed, Frequency* and *Wavelength*

1) **Wave speed** can be measured just like the speed of anything else:

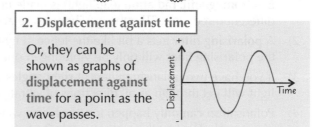

$$\text{Wave speed } (v) = \frac{\text{Distance } (d)}{\text{Time } (t)}$$

2) You can use this equation to derive the **wave equation** (but thankfully you don't have to do that, you just need to be able to use it).

| **Speed of wave** (v) = frequency (f) × wavelength (λ) | $v = f\lambda$ |

Remember, you're not measuring how fast a physical point (like one molecule of rope) moves. You're measuring how fast a point on the wave form moves.

All *Electromagnetic Waves* are *Transverse* Waves

1) **A transverse wave** is a wave where the **vibration** is at **right angles** to the wave's **direction** of travel.

2) All **electromagnetic waves** are **transverse**. Other examples of transverse waves are **ripples** on water and waves on **ropes**.

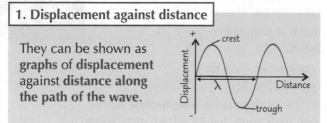

Vibrations from side to side — Wave travelling this way

3) There are **two** main ways of **drawing** transverse waves:

1. Displacement against distance

They can be shown as **graphs** of displacement against **distance** along the path of the wave.

Graph with + and − Displacement axis, crest, trough, λ, Distance axis

2. Displacement against time

Or, they can be shown as graphs of **displacement against time** for a point as the wave passes.

Graph with + and − Displacement axis, Time axis

Both sorts of graph often give the **same shape**, so make sure you check out the label on the **horizontal axis**. Displacements **upwards** from the centre line are given a **+ sign**. Displacements downwards are given a **− sign**.

4) Not all waves are transverse, **sound** for example is a **longitudinal** wave — the vibrations are along the wave's direction of travel.

Intensity is a Measure of How Much *Energy* a Wave is *Carrying*

1) Intensity is the **rate of flow** of **energy** per **unit area** at **right angles** to the **direction of travel** of the wave — for example the amount of light energy that hits your retina per second.

2) It's measured in **watts per square metre** (Wm^{-2}).

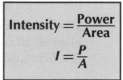

$$\text{Intensity} = \frac{\text{Power}}{\text{Area}}$$
$$I = \frac{P}{A}$$

Practice Questions

Q1 Give four examples of how waves can be used to generate images.

Q2 Write the equation that links the frequency and period of a wave.

Q3 Give one example of a transverse wave.

Q4 Describe the direction of vibrations in a transverse wave.

Exam Questions

Q1 A buoy floating on the sea takes 6.0 seconds to rise and fall once and complete a full period of oscillation. The difference in height between the buoy at its lowest and highest points is 1.2 m. Waves pass it at a speed of 3.0 ms^{-1}.

    a) Calculate the wavelength of the waves.   [2 marks]

    b) State the amplitude of the waves.   [1 mark]

Q2 A 10.0 W light beam is shone onto a screen. The beam covers an area of 0.002 m^2 on the screen. Calculate the intensity of the light beam on the screen.   [1 mark]

ARRRGH... waves are everywhere — there's no escape...

Even just reading this sentence is one instance of using waves in signalling and imaging. A bunch of light waves are being reflected off the page and carrying the 'signal' to your eyes, which pass it on to the brain so you can see. Clever.

Polarisation

Polarisation is all about making a wave move up and down in only one direction. No, not that one direction.

A **Polarised Wave** Only **Oscillates** in One Direction

1) If you **shake a rope** to make a **wave**, you can move your hand **up and down** or **side to side** or in a **mixture** of directions — it still makes a **transverse wave**.

2) But if you try to pass **waves in a rope** through a **vertical fence**, the wave will only get through if the **vibrations** are **vertical**. The fence filters out vibration in other directions. This is called **polarising** the wave.

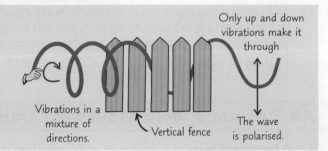

Only up and down vibrations make it through

Vibrations in a mixture of directions.

Vertical fence

The wave is polarised.

Electromagnetic Radiation can be Polarised

1) **Electromagnetic radiation** (e.g. light) is made up of two transverse waves vibrating in different directions. (The things vibrating are actually electric and magnetic fields.)

2) A **polarising filter** acts a bit like the fence. Light that has passed through the polarising filter will only be vibrating in one direction.

3) If you have two polarising filters at **right angles** to each other, then **no** light will get through as all directions of vibration will be blocked.

4) Polarisation **can only happen** for **transverse** waves. You **can't** polarise **longitudinal waves** like sound. The fact that you can polarise light is one **indication** that it's a transverse wave.

Liz was starting to think her polarising filter might be slightly too effective.

Investigate **Polarisation** of **Light** Using Two **Polarising Filters**

You can observe polarisation by shining unpolarised white light through two polarising filters.

1) Align the transmission axes of two **polarising filters** so they are both **vertical**. Shine unpolarised light on the first filter. Keep the position of the **first filter fixed** and **rotate** the second one.

2) Light that passes through the first filter will always be **vertically polarised**.

3) When the transmission axes of the two filters are **aligned**, **all** of the light that passes through the first filter also passes through the second.

4) As you rotate the second filter, the amount of light that passes through the second filter **varies**.

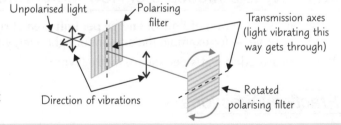

Unpolarised light

Polarising filter

Transmission axes (light vibrating this way gets through)

Direction of vibrations

Rotated polarising filter

Just like vectors, you can think of the transmission axis of the rotating filter as having a **vertical** and **horizontal** **component**. The **larger** the **vertical component**, the **more** vertically polarised light will pass through the filter.

5) As the second filter is rotated, **less** light will get through it as the **vertical** component of the second filter's transmission axis **decreases**. This means the **intensity** of the light getting through the second filter will gradually **decrease**.

6) When the two transmission axes are at **45°** to each other, the intensity will be **half** that getting through the first filter. When they're at **right angles** to each other **no** light will pass through — the **intensity** is **0**.

7) As you continue turning, the intensity should then begin to **increase** once again.

8) When the two axes **realign** (after a 180° rotation), **all** the light will be able to pass through the second filter again.

Maximum

Light intensity, Wm⁻²

0

0   90   180   270   360

Angle of rotation of filter from the plane of polarisation, °

You come across polarising filters more often than you'd think. For example, **3D films** use polarised light to create depth — the filters in each lens are at right angles to each other so each eye gets a slightly different picture. **Polaroid sunglasses** also use polarising filters — reflected light is partially polarised so the sunglasses block this out to help prevent glare.

Polarisation

You Can *Polarise Microwaves* Using a *Metal Grille*

Polarising filters don't work on **microwaves** — their **wavelength** is too long. Instead, **metal grilles** (squares full of metal wires which are all aligned) are used to polarise them. You can investigate the polarisation of microwaves using a **microwave transmitter** and a **microwave receiver** linked to a **voltmeter**.

A metal grille

1) Place a metal **grille** between the microwave **transmitter** and **receiver** as shown below. (Handily, microwave transmitters transmit **polarised** microwaves, so you only need one metal grille.)

2) The intensity of microwaves passing through the grille is at a **maximum** when the direction of the vibration of the microwaves and the wires on the grille are at **right angles** to each other.

3) As you rotate the grille, the **intensity** of polarised microwaves able to pass through the grille **decreases**, so the reading on the voltmeter **decreases**.

4) When the wires of the metal grille are **aligned** with the direction of the polarised waves, **no signal** will be shown on the voltmeter.

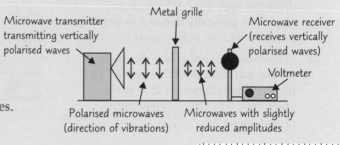

Microwave transmitter transmitting vertically polarised waves

Metal grille

Microwave receiver (receives vertically polarised waves)

Voltmeter

Polarised microwaves (direction of vibrations)

Microwaves with slightly reduced amplitudes

The **intensity** drops to **zero** when the wires are **aligned** with the **direction of polarisation** of the microwaves, because the grille is **absorbing their energy** (see below).

Be careful here — this is the **opposite effect** to polarising filters on the previous page, where aligning the polarising filter with the direction of vibrations gave the maximum intensity of waves passing through the filter.

Make sure all of your electrical equipment is safely connected before you turn it on — microwave transmitters operate at very high voltages.

1) The vibrating electric field of the microwave **excites** electrons in the metal grille.

2) The energy of the incoming microwaves is **absorbed** by the grille and **re-emitted** in **all directions**.

3) Only a few of those re-emitted waves are vibrating in the **direction** of the microwave receiver.

4) The microwave **receiver** only receives microwaves in **one plane**, so even if the **re-emitted** wave travels towards the receiver, it might not be picked up.

5) When the wires and vibrations of the waves are **aligned**, **more** electrons are excited than when they're at right angles to each other — all the energy is absorbed and the **intensity** reading drops to **zero**.

6) When the wires and vibrations are at **right angles** to each other, some electrons in the grille are still excited and so there is still a **small drop** in **intensity**.

Practice Questions

Q1 What is meant by a polarised wave? Why can't you polarise sound waves?

Q2 Describe an experiment that shows visible light can be polarised.

Q3 Explain why the intensity of vertically polarised microwaves passing through a metal grille will drop to zero when the grille is aligned with the direction of polarisation.

Exam Question

Q1 Two polarising filters are placed on top of each other and held in front of a source of white unpolarised light.

a) No light can be seen through the filters.
State the angle between the transmission axes of the two filters. [1 mark]

b) The filters are rotated so that the angle between their transmission axes is 45°.
Describe the difference in the intensity of the light once it has passed through both filters compared to the light once it has only passed through the first filter. [1 mark]

c) Give one use of polarising filters. [1 mark]

Forget polarisation, I need a mental filter...

...to stop me talking rubbish all the time. Polarisation isn't too bad once you get your head around it. It's just a case of filtering out different directions of wave vibrations. Make sure you really know it though as you'll have to be able to explain how both the experiments for polarising light and microwaves work. Doesn't that sound like a barrel of laughs.

Forming Images with Lenses

Astronomers use focal lengths, opticians use powers. Either way, you need to know how to deal with lens powers...

Refraction Happens when a Wave Changes Speed at a Boundary

1) When a ray of light meets a boundary between one medium and another, some of its energy is **reflected** back into the first medium and the rest of it is **transmitted** through into the second medium.

2) If the light meets the boundary at an angle to the normal, the transmitted ray is bent or "**refracted**" as it travels at a **different speed** in each medium. The more **optically dense** a material is, the more slowly light travels in it.

3) The **amount** of refraction depends on the **wavelength** of the light — so the **focal length** (see below) for a given lens will change depending on wavelength.

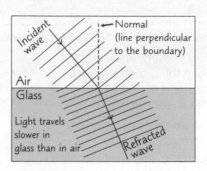

Steph wasn't quite sure this was what her teacher had meant when he asked her to demonstrate that rays bend in water.

Converging Lenses Change the Curvature of Wavefronts

1) **Lenses** change the curvature of wavefronts by **refraction**.

2) A lens **adds curvature** to waves as they pass through it. If waves are uncurved before passing through the lens, and parallel to the lens axis, they will be given spherical curvature, centred on the **focus** (or **focal point**) of the lens.

3) A converging lens curves the wavefronts by **slowing down** the light travelling through the middle of the lens more than light at the lens edges. All points on a wavefront take the **same amount of time** to get to the focus point.

4) The **focal length**, *f*, is the distance between the **lens axis** and the **focus**.

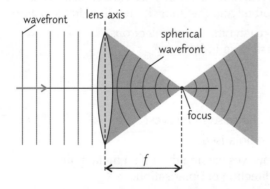

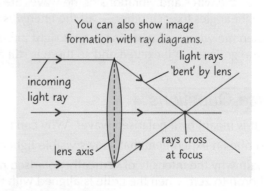

5) The **more powerful** (thicker) the lens, the more it will **curve** the wavefronts that travel through it — so the **shorter** its **focal length**.

6) The **power, P,** of a lens with focal length *f* metres is:

$$P = \frac{1}{f}$$

where lens power is measured in **dioptres**, D.

7) The **curvature** of a wave is defined as:

$$curvature = \frac{1}{radius\ of\ curvature}$$

So the **amount of curvature** a lens adds to a wave passing through it is $\frac{1}{f}$ — which is just the **power** of the lens.

The thicker the lens, the more curved its sides, so the more curvature it adds to a wave.

Forming Images with Lenses

You can use the **Lens Equation** to Find **Where** an **Image** Will be **Formed**

1) The distances between a lens, the image and the source are related to each other by **the lens equation**:

$$\frac{1}{v} = \frac{1}{u} + \frac{1}{f}$$

u = distance between object and lens axis,
v = distance between image and lens axis,
f = focal length.

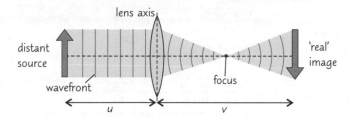

This equation assumes that the lens is thin. Thin converging lenses are used in glasses and contact lenses, magnifying glasses and microscopes.

2) You always measure the **distances** from the **lens axis**, and count distances to the **right** as **positive**, and distances to the **left** as **negative** — just like when you're drawing graphs.

3) The lens equation also tells you about **curvature**.

curvature after = curvature before + curvature added by lens
$$\frac{1}{v} \quad = \quad \frac{1}{u} \quad + \quad \frac{1}{f}$$

4) If you've got a **distant light source**, the wavefronts approaching a converging lens will be **flat** ($1/u = 0$). The converging lens will then give them a curvature of $1/f$. Easy.

5) If the source is at the **focus** of the lens, the wavefronts will start off **curved** with a **negative curvature** (because u is measured as a negative distance). This negative curvature is then cancelled out by the positive curvature added by the converging lens — so the wavefronts will be made **flat**.

6) For sources in between, the wavefronts before and after will be curved, and have a difference in curvature of $1/f$.

7) Don't forget that you can also draw all this in the form of **light rays** being 'bent' by the lens. It's just a different way of thinking about it — you still use the lens equation in exactly the same way.

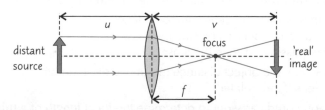

Example: An image of Mabel the cow is being projected onto a screen 80 cm from a 3.25 D lens. How far must the picture slide of Mabel be from the lens?

$P = \frac{1}{f} = 3.25$ D, $v = 80$ cm $= 0.8$ m.

Rearrange the lens equation: $\frac{1}{u} = \frac{1}{v} - \frac{1}{f} = \frac{1}{0.8} - 3.25$

$= 1.25 - 3.25 = -2$

$u = \frac{1}{-2} = -0.5$ m,

so the slide must be **0.5 m** from the lens.

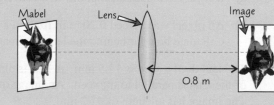

A Lens Can Produce a **Magnified Image**

There are a couple of ways of measuring the magnification of a lens. You just need to know about the **linear magnification**.

The **linear magnification** of a lens is $m = \dfrac{\text{image height}}{\text{object height}}$, which is equal to $m = \dfrac{v}{u}$.

MODULE 3: SECTION 1 — IMAGING AND SIGNALLING

Forming Images with Lenses

Focus an *Image* on a *Screen* to Find the *Power* of a Converging Lens

You can determine the **focal length** of a thin converging
lens by doing an experiment like this one...

1) Set up the equipment as shown, connecting
the bulb to a low-voltage power supply.

2) Place the bulb exactly **0.200 m** away from the lens
(i.e. $u = 0.200$ m) and turn on the power supply.
Move the screen until you can see a clear picture
of the filament on the screen.

3) Measure the **distance** between the **lens** and
the **screen**. This is your value for v. Record
u and v in a table, as shown below.

4) Repeat the experiment 5 or more times, for a range
of different values of u. (Don't increase u so much that
you can no longer see the image of the filament though.)

5) **Work out** $\frac{1}{u}$ and $\frac{1}{v}$ for each of your
readings. **Add** them together to get $\frac{1}{f}$,
which is the **power** of the lens.

6) Find the **average** of your values for $\frac{1}{f}$
and **divide** 1 by your answer to
find the **focal length** f of your lens.

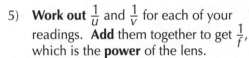

Distance from lamp to lens, u (metres)	Distance from lens to screen, v (metres)	$\frac{1}{u}$	$\frac{1}{v}$	Power, $\frac{1}{f} \left(= \frac{1}{u} + \frac{1}{v}\right)$
0.203	0.629	4.926...	1.589...	6.515...
...	...	...	...	...

Practice Questions

Q1 Define the focal length and power of a converging lens.

Q2 Describe what happens to wavefronts as they pass through a thin converging lens.

Q3 A wave passes through a thin converging lens with focal length f.
If the wavefronts have no curvature before entering the lens,
what is their curvature after passing through the lens?

Q4 Write an equation to show how the object distance (u), image distance (v)
and focal length of a thin lens (f) are related.

Q5 Describe an experiment you could carry out to determine the focal length of a thin converging lens.

Exam Questions

Q1 a) Define the focus (focal point) of a converging lens. [1 mark]

   b) An object was placed 0.20 m in front of a converging lens of focal length 0.15 m.
       Calculate how far behind the lens the image was formed. [2 marks]

Q2 The length of a seed is 12.5 mm. A lens is placed in front of the seed, so that the axis
    of the lens is parallel to the seed. An image of the seed is projected onto a screen.
    The image has a length of 47.2 mm.

   a) Calculate the linear magnification of the lens. [1 mark]

   b) If the seed is 4.0 mm from the lens, calculate how far the screen is from the lens. [2 marks]

   c) Calculate the power of the lens in dioptres. [2 marks]

By the power of Grayskull... I HAVE THE POWER...

*This is all fairly straightforward — just a few formulas, a handful of diagrams and the odd practical to learn. But don't
drop your guard — this topic is a great one for experiment-based questions in exams, so make sure you know how to
deal with uncertainties and margins of error. See page 12 for what you need to know on error analysis.*

Information in Images

Don't panic if waves are getting a bit too much for you — it's time for something completely different.

A *Single Binary Digit* is Called a *Bit*

Decimal	Binary
0	0
1	1
2	10
3	11
4	100

1) The **binary number system**, like the **decimal** system, is a way of writing numbers.

2) The difference is that the **decimal** system uses **ten digits** (0-9) while the **binary** system only uses **two** (**0 and 1**). The table shows the first few values in each system.

3) The **zeros** and **ones** that make up binary numbers are called **binary digits** — a **single binary digit** is called a **bit**. A group of **eight bits** is called a **byte**.

4) So to get from **bits to bytes**, **divide** by **8**. To go from **bytes to bits**, multiply by **8**.

In binary, 1 kilobyte is 1024 bytes, 1 megabyte is 1024 KB, and 1 gigabyte is 1024 MB.

$$\text{bits} = 8 \times \text{bytes} \quad \text{and} \quad \text{bytes} = \frac{\text{bits}}{8}$$

one byte

| 1 | 0 | 0 | 1 | 0 | 1 | 1 | 0 |

one bit

10010110 = 150

The *Binary System* is used to Store *Data* in *Computer Memory*

1) When you **save** a file on your computer, the computer stores the data as a **string of bits**.

2) The **number of bits** in a string (**b**) determines how many **alternatives** that string can represent. For example, a **single** bit has only **two** alternatives (0 and 1), while one **byte** (eight bits) has **256** alternatives. The number of alternatives **doubles** with each additional bit, which means:

$$\text{Number of alternatives} = 2^{\text{Number of bits}} \quad \text{or} \quad N = 2^b$$

If you're calculator doesn't let you calculate $\log_2 N$ directly, you can do $(\log_{10} N \div \log_{10} 2)$, which gives you the same thing.

3) The **number of bits** you need depends on how many **alternatives** you want:

$$\text{Number of bits} = \log_2(\text{Number of alternatives}) \quad \text{or} \quad b = \log_2 N$$

4) For example, if you wanted to represent any letter of the **alphabet**, you'd need a string with **26 alternatives** — one for every letter. Substituting 26 into the **equation** gives $b = \log_2 26 \approx 4.7$ — so you'd need **five bits**.

Images Are Stored as *Arrays* of *Binary Numbers*

1) If you **zoom** in on part of a **digital photograph**, you'll see the individual **pixels** (single points that make up the image) — check out the example on the right.

2) When an **image** is stored in a digital camera (e.g. on a **memory card**) or on a **computer**, each pixel is represented by a **binary number**.

3) The **binary numbers** are stored in an **array**. This is a grid of numbers arranged so that the **location of** each **number** in the grid **matches** the location of the **pixel** in the photo.

4) The **value** of the binary number maps to (it gives) the **colour** of the corresponding **pixel**.

5) In **coloured images**, each pixel can be described by **three** binary numbers — one for each of the **primary colours** of light (**red**, **green** and **blue**). The **length** of the binary numbers used depends on **how many** colours are needed. On a typical PC display, each of the numbers for red, green and blue are 8-bits long, giving 256^3 = 16.8 million possible colours.

Image Resolution can mean *Different Things*

1) Usually **image resolution** refers to the **length** represented by **each pixel**. If an object of width 1.0 m is represented by 200 pixels in an image, then the resolution is 1.0 ÷ 200 = 0.005 metres per pixel.

2) The resolution of an image can also mean the **number of pixels** in the format **width × height** — for example the resolution of a **full HD telly** screen is 1920 × 1080.

3) Sometimes you might see resolution given in terms of **megapixels** — the **total number of pixels** in an image. For example, a **digital camera** that produces images of width 3790 pixels and height 2130 pixels has a resolution of 3790 × 2130 = 8 072 700 pixels or 8 megapixels in total.

Information in Images

The *Amount of Information* in an Image Depends on the *Bits per Pixel*

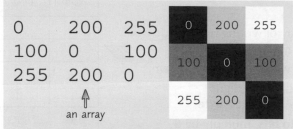

an array

The **image** shown above can be made up of **256 shades** of grey, from 0 (black) to 255 (white).

The shade of each pixel (in the array on the left) is represented by a number between 0 and 255.

Each of these shade numbers is stored in memory as an **8-bit binary number**.

red (R)   green (G)   blue (B)

255,   255,   255

0,0,0	255,0,0	0,255,0
0,0,255	255,255,0	0,255,255
255,0,255	255,255,255	0,0,0

The colours in the image shown are made up of 3 numbers, each providing **256 possible shades** of red, green or blue.

This means there are 256 × 256 × 256 = **16.8 million** possible different RGB combinations in the image.

Each pixel needs **three different 8-bit binary numbers** in the array on the left — so each pixel requires 3 × 8 = **24 bits**.

The more **bits per pixel**, the **more information** is held by each pixel — and the **more pixels** there are in an image, the **more information** is held by the image. So the **total** amount of information in an image is given by:

total amount of information = number of pixels × bits per pixel

Multiplying by a Fixed Value *Improves Contrast*

The **values** of the binary numbers that make up an **image** determine how it looks — if you **change** the **values**, you **change** the **image**. Take a look at the example below to see what happens.

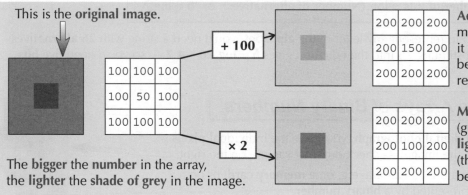

This is the **original image**.

100	100	100
100	50	100
100	100	100

+ 100

× 2

The **bigger** the **number** in the array, the **lighter** the **shade of grey** in the image.

200	200	200
200	150	200
200	200	200

Adding a fixed positive value makes the image **lighter**, but it **doesn't change** the **difference** between the **dark** and **light** regions (**contrast**).

200	200	200
200	100	200
200	200	200

Multiplying by a fixed value (greater than 1) makes the image **lighter**, and **increases** the **contrast** (there's a bigger difference between colour values).

Adding *False Colour* can *Highlight Features*

1) In the example above, a value of '**50**' in the array mapped to a **dark shade of grey** in the image, while a value of '**100**' mapped to a slightly **brighter shade**. But you could map '**2**' to a **dark shade of pink** and '**4**' to a **brighter shade** — or '**2**' to **orange** and '**4**' to **green**.

2) This process is called adding **false colour**. You can use **any** colours you like, but they're usually picked to **highlight certain features** — e.g. the **important features** could be made a really **bright** colour.

3) False colour images are often used in **remote sensing** of data. For example, a **thermal imaging camera** shows **heat** in colour instead of visible light. Satellites can be used to map **different parts** of the **electromagnetic spectrum** to red, green and blue to show features that **can't be seen** in **true colour** images.

You can transform an image by changing the colours that the values in its array map to — not the array itself.

A false colour satellite image of a river delta.

Information in Images

Replacing Pixels *With the **Median** of their Neighbours **Reduces Noise***

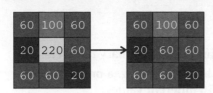

This array shows a bright spot in a uniform darker region — the spot is probably noise. Replacing the central value with the median of its value and the surrounding values reduces the brightness of the region.

1) **Noise** is **unwanted interference** affecting a signal. In images this is usually **bright** or **dark** spots on the picture.

2) One way you can get rid of **noise** is to **replace** each pixel with the **median** (see p.11) of itself and the eight pixels surrounding it.

3) The result is that any '**odd**' (i.e. very **high** or very **low**) values are **removed** and the image is made **smoother**.

*Edge Detection Tells You if there is **Something** in your Image*

1) If you're trying to work out if there is **something** in your **image** (rather than just a load of **noise**), using **edge detection** to find any **edges** can be a really **useful** first step.

2) The **Laplace rule** is a method of **finding edges**. To apply the rule, you **multiply** the value of a pixel by **four**, then **subtract** the value of the pixels immediately **above**, **below**, to the **left** and to the **right** of it. If the answer is negative, the pixel is treated as if its value is 0 (ie. it maps to the colour black).

3) Edge-detected images are usually then **inverted** so that **white becomes black** and vice versa.

4) The result is that any pixel **not** on an **edge** goes **white** — so you're left with **just** the **edges**.

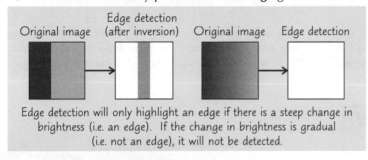

Edge detection will only highlight an edge if there is a steep change in brightness (i.e. an edge). If the change in brightness is gradual (i.e. not an edge), it will not be detected.

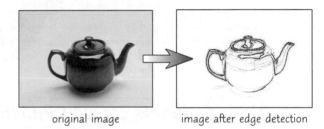

original image   image after edge detection

Practice Questions

Q1 What's the difference between a bit and a byte? Find the number of bits in 1024 bytes.

Q2 A string contains 3 500 000 different alternatives. What is the minimum number of bits required?

Q3 How can the brightness and contrast of an image be changed?

Q4 What is the Laplace rule used for? How do you apply it?

Exam Questions

Q1 A TV can display 65 536 different colours. It displays a still image of width 1920 pixels and height 1080 pixels.

a) Calculate the number of bytes required to store the colour of each pixel. [2 marks]

b) Calculate the total amount of information contained in the image in bits. [1 mark]

c) An image contains a 1.5 m² square that spans exactly a quarter of the available width. What is the resolution of the screen? [2 marks]

Q2 The diagram shows part of an array that describes an image. The image is made up of 256 shades of grey — 0 represents black and 255 represents white.

100	99	100
97	185	98
101	101	98

a) Sketch the image that this part of the array describes. [1 mark]

b) Describe how noise can be removed from digital images by finding a median value. [1 mark]

c) Apply this technique to the central value of the array shown. [1 mark]

All this talk of bytes is making me a megabit hungry — mmm, tasty bites...

It doesn't matter how many attempts you take, or how many filters you apply — all your selfies are really just a long list of ones and zeroes (unless you actually print them out on paper). Now — everybody say cheeeese...

Digital and Analogue Signals

You've just seen how information can be stored digitally, but what if you want to send that information?
And what if the information isn't digital to start with? So many questions — read on to find out the answers.

Analogue *Signals* Vary Continuously

1) **Digital signals**, like the images on the previous three pages, are represented by **binary numbers**.

2) The **values** that a **digital signal** can take depend on the **number of bits** used — e.g. a **one bit** signal can only take the values **0 and 1**, but a **one byte** signal can take **256 different values**.

3) **Analogue signals** are **not limited** in the values they can take — they **vary continuously**. For example, **speech** is an **analogue signal** — the **sound waves** produced **vary continuously** over a range of **loudness** and **frequency**.

Digital Signals *Are* Resistant *to the Effects of* Noise

When you **transmit** an electronic signal it will pick up **noise** (interference) from **electrical disturbances** or other **signals**. The receiver needs to be able to **reconstruct** the **original signal** from the **noisy signal** if they're to get an **accurate representation** of what was sent. This is **much easier** with **digital** than analogue signals because the **number of values** a digital signal can take is **limited**.

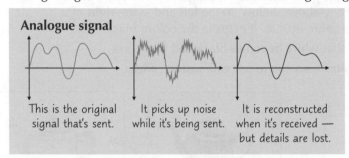

Analogue signal

This is the original signal that's sent. | It picks up noise while it's being sent. | It is reconstructed when it's received — but details are lost.

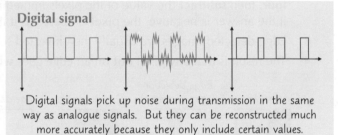

Digital signal

Digital signals pick up noise during transmission in the same way as analogue signals. But they can be reconstructed much more accurately because they only include certain values.

Analogue Signals *can be* Digitised

1) It's possible to turn an **analogue signal** into a **digital signal** — this is called **digitising** the signal.

2) To digitise a signal, you take the **value** of the signal at **regular time intervals**, then find the **nearest digital value**.

3) Each **digital value** is represented by a **binary number**, so you can **convert** the **analogue** values to **binary** numbers.

4) The **digital signal** you end up with won't be **exactly** the same as the **analogue signal**, but it's usually quite **close**.

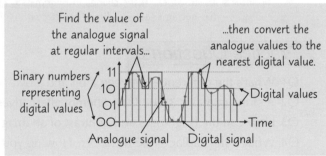

Find the value of the analogue signal at regular intervals...

...then convert the analogue values to the nearest digital value.

Binary numbers representing digital values: 11, 10, 01, 00

Digital values

Time

Analogue signal   Digital signal

The Quality *of a* Digitised Signal *Depends on its* Resolution

1) How well a **digitised** signal matches the original depends on **two** factors — the **difference** between the possible **digital values** (**resolution**) and the **time** from one **sample** to the next (**sampling rate**, see p.26).

2) If a signal is digitised using only a **few**, **widely spaced** digital values, it's likely that a lot of the analogue values sampled will be **far** from the **nearest digital value**. But, if a **large** number of **closely spaced** digital values are used, most of the analogue values will be **very close** to a digital value, so will only change **slightly**.

3) This means that the **higher the resolution** (i.e. the **more possible digital values** there are), the **more closely** the digitised signal will **match** the original.

4) **Resolution** is determined by the **number of bits** in the **binary numbers** representing the digital values — the **greater** the number of **bits**, the **greater** the **resolution**.

5) When **music** is digitised to make **CDs**, a resolution of **16 bits** is used. This gives a total of **65 536 digital values** and means the recorded music is **very similar** to the **original**.

6) **Low resolution** digital signals are often used in **telephone lines**, and other systems where top-quality audio isn't essential. Telephone conversations have to be **audible**, but you **don't need** an **accurate reproduction** of the callers' voices — even if this does mean the music sounds **distorted** when you're put on hold. Using a lower resolution and sampling rate means a **lower rate of transmission** (p.27) can be used to send information.

Digital and Analogue Signals

Digital Signals Have Several Advantages Over Analogue Signals

1) Digital signals can often be **sent**, **received** and **reproduced** more easily than analogue signals because they can only take a limited number of values.

2) Digital files can be **compressed** to reduce their size, and **manipulated** easily for artistic effect.

3) **Noise** is more of a problem for analogue signals than digital signals (see previous page).

4) A digital signal can be used to represent **different** kinds of **information** in the **same way** — for example, **images** and **sounds** can both be represented as a string of bits.

5) **Computers** can be used to **easily process** digital signals, since computers are **digital devices** too.

But they have some Disadvantages too

1) Digital signals can **never** reproduce analogue signals **exactly** — some **information** will always be **lost**.

2) Because digital signals can be copied more easily, digital information like films and music can be **reproduced illegally unlimited times**.

3) **Confidential information**, such as **personal data** and **photographs**, may be **stolen** and **copied** without the owners' knowledge or consent more easily, for example by **hackers**, **infected networks** or **malicious websites**.

> The UK Government wants to switch all radio broadcasts over to **digital (DAB) signals** as these can (in theory) have better audio quality and more stations can fit in less space. But **analogue** radio devices remain **very popular** among the public, and the **bit rate** used for DAB radio broadcasts is often **low**, producing a **lower quality sound** than FM radio.

Signals are Made Up of Lots of Different Frequencies

1) The wave on page 14 is the **simplest** kind of **signal** because it contains just **one frequency**. In practice, most **signals** are made up of **several** waves, all with **different frequencies**, added together.

2) When these waves are added together, the **amplitude** of the final signal is the **sum** of the **amplitudes** of the individual waves at each point in time.

3) For example, if you play a **musical note**, the sound you hear contains the **frequency** (pitch) of the **main note** and a load of **other frequencies**. It's these '**other frequencies**' that make instruments **sound different**, even though they're playing the **same note**.

4) The **fundamental frequency** is the **lowest frequency** wave that makes up a sound wave. You can spot it by finding the **shortest repeating part** of the sound wave and calculating the inverse of its period.

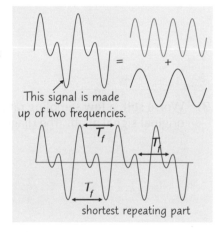

This signal is made up of two frequencies.

shortest repeating part

Practice Questions

Q1 Explain how a digital signal is different from an analogue one.

Q2 What is meant by resolution in the context of digitising analogue signals?

Q3 Give three advantages of digital signals over analogue signals.

Exam Question

Q1 The diagram shows the waveform of a musical note played on an instrument.

a) Calculate the fundamental frequency of the note. [1 mark]

b) The wave is sampled every 0.001 s.
The first sample occurs at 0.0 ms.
Sketch the waveform of the reconstructed signal. [2 marks]

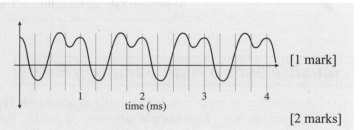

How do finger puppets communicate? With digital signals...

Digital signals are everywhere these days — CDs, MP3s, DVDs, TV, DAB radio — there's just no escape. Analogue signals are still around, though — lots of radio stations broadcast FM or AM analogue signals (for now at least...). Some people prefer analogue signals for listening to music and use vinyl (ask your dad) instead of MP3s or CDs.

Sampling and Transmitting Signals

Noise Limits the Number of Bits used for Sampling

1) You've just seen that the **higher the resolution**, the **better** a digitised signal **matches** the original.

2) But, if the original signal contains **noise** (as most real signals do), then a really **fine resolution** will reproduce all the little wiggles caused by the **noise** — **not useful**.

3) In practice, the **resolution** is **limited** by the **ratio** of the total **variation** in the **signal** to the **variation** caused by **noise**:

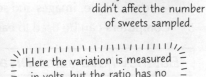

Lesley made sure noise didn't affect the number of sweets sampled.

$$\text{Maximum number of bits} = \log_2\left(\frac{\text{total variation}}{\text{noise variation}}\right) \quad \text{or} \quad b = \log_2\left(\frac{V_{\text{total}}}{V_{\text{noise}}}\right)$$

Here the variation is measured in volts, but the ratio has no units because they cancel.

Minimum Sampling Rate is Twice the Maximum Frequency

1) When you **digitise** a signal, you **record the value** of (**sample**) the original signal at **regular intervals**. The **rate** at which you **sample** the signal is called the **sampling rate** — imaginative name, I know.

2) The **sampling rate** has to be **high** enough to record all the **high frequency** detail of the signal. The diagram below shows how **detail** can be **lost** if the sampling rate is too **low**.

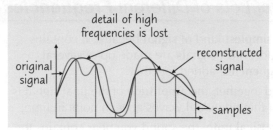

3) Worse still, a **low** sampling rate can **create** low frequency signals — called **aliases** — that **weren't** in the original signal at all. The diagram **below** shows how **aliases** can be **created** by a **low sampling rate**.

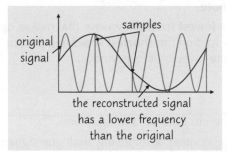

4) To avoid these problems, the **sampling rate** must be at least **twice** the **highest frequency** in the original signal.

Minimum rate of sampling > 2 × maximum frequency of signal

Music Needs a High Sampling Rate

1) A recording of music needs to be able to **accurately reproduce** the **original sounds**. This means that a **high sample rate** must be used to make sure **high frequency details** aren't **lost**, and to avoid the creation of **aliases** in the recording.

2) **CD** and **MP3-quality** audio uses a sampling rate of **44 100 Hz**. The maximum frequency sound that can be recorded at this sampling rate is about **20 000 Hz**, which is roughly the highest-frequency sound audible to the human ear.

3) The audio on **video DVDs** and in **digital TV broadcasts** uses a slightly higher sampling rate of **48 000 Hz**, while **Blu-ray Discs**™ can use a sampling rate of up to **192 000 Hz**.

Sampling and Transmitting Signals

Rate of Transmission = Samples per Second × Bits per Sample

By now you should know **how** signals are **transmitted** — what's also important is the **rate** at which they're transmitted. The **rate of transmission** of a digital signal depends on **two** factors:

1) The number of **samples per second** — this must be at least **twice** the **highest frequency** in the signal to ensure that all the frequencies within its spectrum are transmitted accurately.

2) The number of **bits per sample** — this must be **high enough** that the transmitted signal **closely** matches the original, but not so high that it is negatively affected by **noise**.

> Rate of transmission of a digital information (bits per second) = samples per second × bits per sample

Time Taken to Transmit a Signal = Bits ÷ Rate of Transmission

To find the **time** it will take to **transmit** a signal, you need to know the **number of bits** that need to be transmitted, and the **rate of transmission** (in bits per second):

> Time taken to transmit a signal = number of bits to transmit ÷ rate of transmission

The speed of your Internet connection is usually measured in **bits**, or more likely megabits (Mb), **per second**. Note the lower case b — **Mb** means mega**bits**, whereas **MB** means mega**bytes**.

Don't get them confused — if you've got an Internet upload connection of 2 megabits per second and want to upload a 2 megabyte image to a social network, it won't take 1 second — it will take at least 8 seconds.

To **speed up** the process, and **use less storage space**, you could **compress** your image to **reduce** the file size.

Practice Questions

Q1 Why is there a maximum number of bits used for sampling?
Q2 Describe two problems that can be caused by an insufficient sampling rate.
Q3 The minimum rate of sampling for a signal is 72 kHz. What is the maximum frequency of the signal?
Q4 Why is music often sampled a rate of 40-50 kHz?

Exam Questions

Q1 A digital signal has a total variation of 160 mV and a noise variation of 10 mV.
Find the maximum number of bits that should be used when sampling this signal. [2 marks]

Q2 The telephone system samples your voice 8000 times a second and converts this into an eight bit digital signal.

a) Find the rate of transmission for bits in this telephone system. [1 mark]

b) Calculate how many bytes are sent each second. [1 mark]

Q3 An Internet radio station streams a single channel of digital audio at a rate of 128 kbit s^{-1}.

a) The audio the station broadcasts contains 16 bits per sample. Calculate the sampling rate. [1 mark]

b) A listener wants to stream the radio station using her mobile phone.
She tests her mobile data connection and finds that she can download a 2.0 MB file in 110 seconds.
State whether her connection is sufficient to stream the radio station. [3 marks]

Music needs a high sampling rate — just don't tell the copyright lawyers...

Aaaand that's the end of that section. I don't know about you, but I've enjoyed this little foray into the physics behind tech that most of us use every day. Once you've got every last bit learned, you can feel OK about taking a byte out of your revision time to stream a celebratory self array of binary numbers to your favourite social network...

Charge, Current and Potential Difference

This section isn't about the sixth sense, common sense or extrasensory perception. It's about proper, sensible physics...

Many **Sensors** are **Powered** using **Electricity**

Your body is pretty amazing at sensing things, within limits.
E.g. skin is a good temperature sensor — you know about it when you spill
hot tea on your lap — but you won't know that the temperature of the tea is 62.3 °C.

Make sure you learn all the circuit symbols that come up in this section, and know how to design and use circuits including them.

1) **Electronic sensors** are designed to sense things we can't (or are too lazy to) sense.
   Any change in whatever the sensor's detecting will change the current in
   the connected circuit. The **current** is processed to give you a reading.

2) There are loads of different types of sensor out there. From everyday things like
   temperature sensors that use **thermistors** (p.31), to **electron microscopes** which can
   be used to 'see' individual atoms (see p.49). Excited yet? I know I am...

Current — the **Flow** of **Charged Particles**

1) **Current** is measured as the **rate of flow** of
   charged particles (usually electrons). You
   can calculate current using the equation:

   $$I = \frac{\Delta Q}{\Delta t}$$

   Where I is the current in amperes (A), ΔQ is
   the charge in coulombs (C) that flows during
   Δt, and Δt is the time taken in seconds (s).

   If it helps, think of the **current** in a **wire** like the flow rate of **water** in a **pipe**. Just as the flow rate
   is a measure of how much water goes through the pipe in a given time interval, the current is a
   measure of the number of charged particles that move past a point in a wire in a given time.

2) The **coulomb** is the unit of charge. One coulomb (C) is defined as the amount of charge
   that passes a point in 1 second when the current is 1 ampere.

3) You can measure the current flowing through part of a circuit
   using an **ammeter**. This is the circuit symbol for an ammeter: —(A)—

   Attach an ammeter in series with the component you're investigating.

4) **Conventional current** flows from positive to negative terminal of a power supply.
   This direction was picked before scientists discovered current is usually caused by the
   flow of electrons. Electrons are negatively charged and flow from negative to positive
   terminals — so conventional current is in the **opposite direction** to electron flow.

Potential Difference is the **Energy** per **Unit Charge**

1) To make electric charge flow through a conductor, you need to do **work** on it.

2) **Potential difference** (p.d.), **V**, is
   defined as the **energy converted
   per unit charge moved**:

   $$V = \frac{W}{Q}$$

   W is the energy in joules. It's the
   work you do moving the charge.

   Potential difference is sometimes called voltage.

   The **potential difference** across a component is **1 volt** (V) when you convert **1 joule**
   of energy moving **1 coulomb** of charge through the component. This **defines** the volt.

   $$1\,V = 1\,JC^{-1}$$

   Back to the 'water analogy'
   again. The p.d. is like the
   pressure that's forcing water
   along the pipe.

   Resistor
   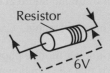
   6V

   Here you do 6 J of work moving
   each coulomb of charge through the
   resistor, so the p.d. across it is 6 V.
   The energy gets converted to heat.

3) You can measure the potential difference across a component
   using a **voltmeter**. This is the circuit symbol for a voltmeter: —(V)—

4) The potential difference across components in parallel is **the same**, so the **voltmeter**
   should be connected in **parallel** with the component you're investigating.

Charge, Current and Potential Difference

Power is the Rate of Transfer of Energy

Power (P) is **defined** as the **rate** of **transfer** of **energy** (the rate of work done). It's measured in **watts (W)**, where **1 watt** is equivalent to **1 joule per second**.

in symbols: $P = \dfrac{W}{t}$

There's a really simple formula for **power** in **electrical circuits**:

$P = IV$

This makes sense, since:

1) **Potential difference (V)** is defined as the **energy transferred** per **coulomb**.
2) **Current (I)** is defined as the **number** of **coulombs** transferred per **second**.
3) So **p.d.** × **current** is **energy transferred per second**, i.e. **power**.

By rearranging $P = IV$ and substituting in the potential equations for difference and current, you can see that:

$V = \dfrac{P}{I} = \dfrac{W}{Q}$

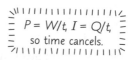
$P = W/t, I = Q/t,$ so time cancels.

Energy is Easy to Calculate if you Know the Power

Sometimes it's the **total energy** transferred **(the total work done)** that you're interested in. In this case you simply need to **multiply** the **power** by the **time**.

$W = Pt$, so $W = VIt$

Example: A prancing electro-monkey is powered by a 6.0 V battery and draws a current of 0.80 A. How much energy would the electro-monkey transfer if switched on and left to prance for exactly 2 minutes?

$V = 6.0$ V, $I = 0.80$ A, $t = 120$ seconds. So, $W = VIt = 6.0 \times 0.80 \times 120 = 576 = $ **580 J (to 2 s.f.)**

Practice Questions

Q1 Describe in words how current and charge are related.
Q2 Define a) the coulomb and b) potential difference.
Q3 How does conventional current relate to the flow of electrons in a typical circuit?
Q4 Power is measured in watts. What is 1 watt equivalent to?
Q5 Calculate the current in a 12 W light bulb when it is connected to a 230 V electrical supply.

Exam Questions

Q1 A current of 0.18 A flows through a motor for 6.0 seconds. The motor does 75 J of work in this time.

a) Calculate the power of the motor. [1 mark]

b) Calculate the potential difference across the motor. [1 mark]

Q2 A kettle runs off the mains supply (230 V). Only 88% of the electrical energy that is input is transferred usefully to the water. Calculate how much electric charge will pass through the kettle if it transfers 308 J of energy to the water it contains. [2 marks]

[THIS JOKE HAS BEEN CENSORED]... it was a good one as well...

Talking of jokes, I saw this bottle of wine the other day called 'raisin d'être' — 'raison d'être' meaning 'reason for living', but spelled slightly differently to make 'raisin', meaning 'grape'. Ho ho. Chuckled all the way home.

Resistance and Conductance

Resistance is what causes components to heat up. It's how your toaster works, and why computers need cooling fans...

Everything has Resistance

1) If you put a **potential difference** (p.d.) across an **electrical component**, a **current** will flow.

2) **How much** current you get for a particular **p.d.** depends on the **resistance** of the component.

3) You can think of a component's **resistance** as a **measure** of how **difficult** it is to get a **current** to **flow** through it.

4) **Resistance** is measured in **ohms** (Ω). A component has a resistance of 1 Ω if a potential difference of 1 V makes a current of 1 A flow through it.

Mathematically, **resistance** is: $R = \dfrac{V}{I}$
This equation **defines** resistance.

Learn the equations for resistance and conductance — you won't be given them in the exam.

You also need to know the formula for the **inverse** of resistance — conductance, G. $\Rightarrow$ $\boxed{G = \dfrac{I}{V}}$
This is a measure of how good an electrical conductor a component is. It's measured in Ω^{-1} or siemens, S.

5) The resistance equation gives you a whole new way of calculating electrical power if you substitute it into $P = IV$. $\Rightarrow$ $V = IR$, so $P = IV = I^2R$

6) This power is the rate at which a component converts electrical energy into other types of energy, e.g. heat. This is known as **power dissipation**. This can be useful, e.g. the dissipation of power as light from a bulb. In other situations, power dissipation causes problems we need to work round. E.g. computers have cooling fans to get rid of some of the heat that builds up in their circuits, and mains electricity is transmitted at a high voltage (so low current) to minimise the power dissipated during transmission.

I-V Graphs Show How Resistance Varies

1) The term '**I-V characteristic**' refers to a **graph** which shows how the **current** (I) flowing through a **component changes** as the **potential difference** (V) across it is increased.

2) The **shallower** the **gradient** of a characteristic **I-V** graph, the **greater** the **resistance** of the component.

3) A **curved line** shows that the resistance of the component **changes** with the potential difference across it.

You can investigate the *I-V* characteristic of a component using a **test circuit** like this one:

1) Use the **variable resistor** to alter the **potential difference** across the component and the **current** flowing through it, and record V and I.

2) **Repeat** your measurements and take **averages** to reduce the effect of random errors (see p.12) on your results.

3) **Plot a graph** of current against potential difference from your results. This graph is the *I-V* **characteristic** of the component and you can use it to see how the **resistance** changes.

If you have access to a computer, you could enter your data into a spreadsheet and use this to plot the graph.

This is the circuit symbol for a variable resistor.

For an Ohmic Conductor, R is a Constant

Metal wires and resistors are ohmic conductors

Conductors that **obey** Ohm's law (mostly metals) are called **ohmic conductors**. Ohm's law states that:

Provided external factors such as **temperature** are **constant**, the **current** through an ohmic conductor is **directly proportional** to the **potential difference** across it (that's $V = IR$).

1) As you can see from the graph, **doubling** the p.d. **doubles** the **current**.

2) The gradient is **constant**, which means that **resistance** is **constant**.

3) Remember, Ohm's law is **only** true for **ohmic conductors** where external factors like **temperature** are **constant**.

4) **Non-ohmic conductors** don't have this relation between current and p.d. There are **examples** of non-ohmic conductors on the next page.

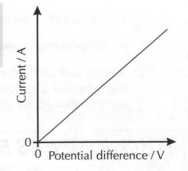

Resistance and Conductance

The *I-V Characteristic* for a *Filament Lamp* is *Curved*

Filament lamp circuit symbol:

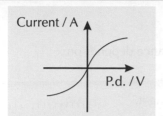
Current / A
P.d. / V

1) The characteristic graph for a **filament lamp** is a **curve**, which starts **steep** but gets **shallower** as the **potential difference rises**.
2) The **filament** in a lamp is just a **coiled up** length of **metal wire**, so you might think it should have the **same characteristic graph** as a **metallic conductor**.
3) However, **current** flowing through the lamp **increases** its **temperature**, so its **resistance increases** (see below).

The *Resistance* of a *Thermistor* Depends on *Temperature*

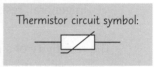
Thermistor circuit symbol:

A **thermistor** is a **resistor** with a **resistance** that depends on its **temperature**, so you can use them as **temperature sensors**.

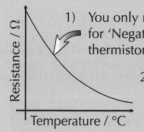
Resistance / Ω
Temperature / °C

1) You only need to know about **NTC thermistors** — NTC stands for 'Negative Temperature Coefficient'. The resistance of an NTC thermistor **decreases** with **temperature** (so its conductance increases).

2) Increasing the **current** through the thermistor increases its **temperature**. The **increasing gradient** of this graph tells you that the **resistance is decreasing** as the thermistor heats up.

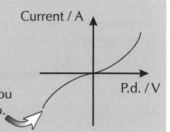
Current / A
P.d. / V

An **LDR** (**light dependent resistor**), is similar to a thermistor, but is sensitive to **light**, not heat — the more light falls on it, the lower its resistance.

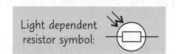
Light dependent resistor symbol:

Filament lamps, thermistors, LDRs and diodes are all examples of non-ohmic conductors. You can tell by looking at their *I-V* graphs.

Diodes Only Let *Current Flow* in *One Direction*

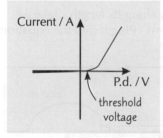
Current / A
P.d. / V
threshold voltage

Diodes (including light emitting diodes (LEDs)) are designed to let **current flow** in **one direction** only. You don't need to be able to explain how they work, just what they do.

1) **Forward bias** is the **direction** in which the **current** is **allowed to flow** — it's the direction the triangles point in the circuit symbols on the right.
2) **Most** diodes require a **threshold voltage** of about **0.6 V** in the **forward direction** before they will conduct.
3) In **reverse bias**, the **resistance** of the diode is **very high** and the current that flows is **very tiny**.

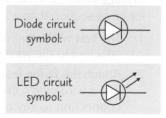
Diode circuit symbol:

LED circuit symbol:

Practice Questions

Q1 State the formulas for resistance and conductance.
Q2 Sketch the test circuit used to investigate the *I-V* characteristic of a component, and explain how it is used.
Q3 State Ohm's law. Give an example of an ohmic conductor.
Q4 Draw an *I-V* characteristic graph for a diode. Label the areas of forward bias and reverse bias.

Exam Question

Q1 a) A current of 2.8 A is passed through a wire from a 1.5 V power supply. Find the resistance of the wire. [1 mark]
b) When the same power supply is connected to a different wire, the current is 0.15 A.
Calculate the conductance of the wire. [1 mark]
c) Explain why the wires become warm after a period of operation. [2 marks]

You light up my world like an LED — with One-Directional current...

The examiners like testing this kind of stuff as if you've really done the experiment, so your results aren't perfect and you have fun errors to deal with. If errors aren't your thing, have a quick flick to page 12 to calm your nerves.

Electrical Properties of Solids

From a remote-controlled car to a supercomputer... if what you're building involves electricity, you're going to want to know about resistivity and conductivity...

Three Things Determine Resistance

If you think about a nice, **simple electrical component**, like a **length of wire**, its **resistance** depends on:

1) **Length (L).** The **longer** the wire, the **more difficult** it is to make a **current flow**.

2) **Area (A).** The **wider** the wire, the **easier** it will be for the electrons to pass along it.

3) **Resistivity (ρ).** This **depends** on the **material** the wire's made from, as the **structure** of the material may make it easy or difficult for charge to flow. In general, resistivity depends on **external factors** as well, like **temperature**.

ρ is the Greek letter rho, the symbol for resistivity.

The **resistivity** of a material is defined as the **resistance** of a **1 m length** with a **1 m²** **cross-sectional area** — it's given by $\rho = \dfrac{RA}{L}$. Resistivity is measured in **ohm metres** (Ωm).

In your exams, you'll be given this equation in the form:

$$R = \frac{\rho L}{A}$$

where R = resistance in Ω, A = cross-sectional area in m², and L = length in m

Typical values for the resistivity of conductors are really small. E.g. for copper (at 25 °C) $\rho = 1.72 \times 10^{-8}$ Ωm.

As we all know by now, conductance is the inverse of resistance (p.30). And surprise surprise... the inverse of resistivity is **conductivity**, σ.

The **conductivity**, σ, of a material is defined as the **conductance** of a **1 m length** with a **1 m²** **cross-sectional area** — it's given by $\sigma = \dfrac{GL}{A}$. It's measured in **siemens per metre** (S m⁻¹).

$$G = \frac{\sigma A}{L}$$

To Find the Resistivity of a Wire you Need to Find its Resistance

You'll need to **measure** the test wire's cross-sectional area before you start. Assume that the wire is **cylindrical**, and so its cross-section is **circular**. Then you can find the cross-sectional area using: **area of a circle = πr^2**

Using a **micrometer**, measure the **diameter** of the wire in at least **three** different points along its length. Take an **average** value of the diameter and divide by **two** to get the **radius** (make sure this is in m). Plug it into the equation for cross-sectional area and... **ta da**. Now you can get your teeth into the electricity bit...

1) The **test wire** should be **clamped** to a ruler with the circuit attached to the wire where the ruler reads zero.

2) Attach the **flying lead** to the test wire — the lead is just a wire with a crocodile clip at the end to allow connection to any point along the test wire.

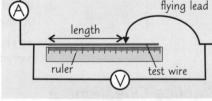

3) Record the **length** of the test wire **connected** in the circuit, the **voltmeter reading** and the **ammeter reading**.

4) Use your readings to calculate the **resistance** of the length of wire, using:

$$R = \frac{V}{I}$$

5) Repeat this measurement and calculate an average resistance for the length.

6) Repeat for several **different** lengths, for example between 0.10 and 1.00 m.

7) Plot your results on a graph of ***R*** against ***L***, and draw a **line of best fit**.

The **gradient** of the line of best fit is equal to $\dfrac{R}{L} = \dfrac{\rho}{A}$. So **multiply** the **gradient** of the line of best fit by the **cross-sectional area** of the wire to find the resistivity of the wire material.

You could find ρ for a single length using the resistivity formula, but this will give you an overestimate as it'll include the resistance of the ammeter and all the wires and connections.

8) The other components of the circuit also have a resistance, but the gradient of the line of best fit isn't affected by the resistance within the rest of the circuit.

9) The **resistivity** of a material depends on its **temperature**, so you can only find the resistivity of a material **at a certain temperature**. Current flowing in the test wire can cause its temperature to increase, so you need to try to keep the temperature of the test wire **constant**, e.g. by only having small currents flow through the wire.

10) To find the conductivity of a wire instead, do the same experiment. As $\sigma = 1/\rho$, you can use your final result to calculate the metal's conductivity if that's what you need.

Electrical Properties of Solids

Different Materials have Different Numbers of Charge Carriers

How conductive a material is depends on its **number density of mobile charge carriers** — the number of free electrons (or ions that are free to move) there are per cubic metre of the material. The more **mobile charge carriers** a material has per unit volume, the **better** a **conductor** it will be.

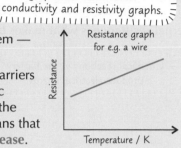

Conductance and resistance graphs are often called conductivity and resistivity graphs.

Metals

In a **metal**, the **charge carriers** are **free electrons** (see p.48). Metals are **good conductors** because they have absolutely shedloads of them — the **number density of mobile charge carriers** is **high**.

If you **increase** the **temperature** of a metal, the **number** of mobile charge carriers **stays about the same**. As the electrons move, they scatter from the metallic lattice. As the temperature increases, the lattice **vibrates** more, increasing the electron scattering, so the electrons are slightly less free to move. This means that as the **temperature increases**, the **conductivity** of a metal will slightly **decrease**.

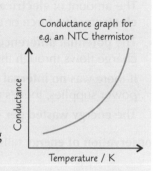

Resistance graph for e.g. a wire

Resistance

Temperature / K

Semiconductors

Just as in metals, the mobile charge carriers in **semiconductors** are free electrons. Semiconductors have a much **lower** charge carrier number density (fewer free electrons) than metals, so they have a **lower conductivity**.

As you **increase** the **temperature** of a semiconductor, more electrons are freed to conduct. This means that as the temperature **increases**, the **conductivity** of a semiconductor **rapidly increases**.

Just as in metals, the semiconductor atom lattice will also vibrate more, scattering the free electrons as they move — but its effect is much smaller than the effect of the huge increase in charge carriers.

Conductance graph for e.g. an NTC thermistor

Conductance

Temperature / K

Thermistors are made up of semiconductors whose conductivity changes with **temperature**, as described above. **Light dependent resistors** (LDRs) are made up of semiconductors whose conductivity is mostly controlled by **light** rather than heat — their conductivity **increases** with increasing light levels.

Insulators

A **perfect insulator** wouldn't have **any mobile charge carriers**, so it wouldn't be able to conduct at all. (What can I say... it's short and sweet...)

Practice Questions

Q1 What three factors does the resistance of a length of wire depend on?

Q2 Write down the units of resistivity and conductivity.

Q3 Describe how a metal's conductance varies with temperature.

Q4 Why are semiconductors poorer conductors than metals at lower temperatures?

Q5 Explain why insulators do not conduct electricity.

Exam Question

Q1 This question is about an experiment to measure the resistivity of copper.

a) Describe the equipment and method you would use to measure the resistivity of copper using a copper wire. You should include a labelled circuit diagram as part of your answer. [6 marks]

b) Sketch graphs to show how conductance and resistance vary with temperature for a copper wire. Describe and explain why these graphs differ from those for a NTC thermistor. [5 marks]

Insulator Airlines — the no-charge carriers...

That resistivity experiment's a popular one to come up in exams — so make sure you learn it. Try to think about where errors are creeping into your measurements too, and how you might be able to reduce them... see p.9 for ideas...

E.m.f. and Internal Resistance

There's resistance everywhere — inside batteries, in all the wires (although it's very small) and in the components themselves. I'm assuming the resistance of the wires is zero on the next two pages, but you can't always do this.

Batteries have Resistance

Resistance comes from **electrons colliding** with **atoms** and **losing energy** to other forms.

In a **battery**, **chemical energy** is used to make **electrons move**. As they move, they collide with **atoms** inside the battery — so batteries **must** have resistance. This is called **internal resistance**.

Internal resistance is what makes **batteries** and **cells warm up** when they're used.

Resistor circuit symbol:

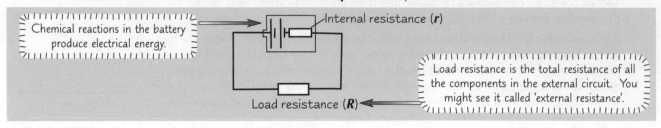

Chemical reactions in the battery produce electrical energy.

Internal resistance (**r**)

Load resistance is the total resistance of all the components in the external circuit. You might see it called 'external resistance'.

Load resistance (**R**)

1) The amount of **electrical energy** the battery produces for each **coulomb** of charge is called its **electromotive force** or **e.m.f.** (ε). Be careful — e.m.f. **isn't** actually a force. It's measured in **volts**.

2) The **potential difference** across the **load resistance** (**R**) is the **energy transferred** when **one coulomb** of charge flows through the **load resistance**. This potential difference is called the **terminal p.d.** (**V**).

3) If there was **no internal resistance**, the **terminal p.d.** would be the **same** as the **e.m.f.** However, in **real** power supplies, there's **always some energy lost** (as heat energy) overcoming the internal resistance.

4) The **energy wasted per coulomb** overcoming the internal resistance is called the **lost volts** (**v**).

Conservation of energy tells us:

energy per coulomb supplied by the source	=	energy per coulomb transferred in load resistance	+	energy per coulomb wasted in internal resistance

There are Loads of Calculations with E.m.f. and Internal Resistance

Examiners can ask you to do **calculations** with **e.m.f.** and **internal resistance** in loads of **different** ways. You've got to be ready for whatever they throw at you.

$$\varepsilon = V + v \qquad \varepsilon = I(R + r)$$
$$V = \varepsilon - v \qquad V = \varepsilon - Ir$$

Learn these equations for the exam. Only this one will be on your formula sheet.

These are all basically the **same equation**, just written differently. If you're given enough information you can calculate the e.m.f. (ε), terminal p.d. (**V**), lost volts (**v**), current (**I**), load resistance (**R**) or internal resistance (**r**). Which equation you should use depends on what information you've got, and what you need to calculate.

You Can Work Out the E.m.f. of Multiple Cells in Series or Parallel

For cells **in series** in a circuit, you can calculate the **total e.m.f.** of the cells by **adding** their individual e.m.f.s.

$$\varepsilon_{total} = \varepsilon_1 + \varepsilon_2 + \varepsilon_3 + ...$$

This makes sense if you think about it, because each charge goes through each of the cells and so gains e.m.f. (electrical energy) from each one.

This requires all your cells to be connected in the **same direction** — if one is connected in the opposite direction, you should **subtract** its e.m.f. rather than adding it.

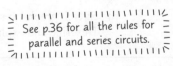

See p.36 for all the rules for parallel and series circuits.

For identical cells **in parallel** in a circuit, the **total e.m.f.** of the combination of cells is the **same size** as the e.m.f. of each of the individual cells.

$$\varepsilon_{total} = \varepsilon_1 = \varepsilon_2 = \varepsilon_3 + ...$$

This is because the current will split equally between identical cells. The charge only gains e.m.f. from the cells it travels through — so the overall e.m.f. in the circuit doesn't increase.

E.m.f. and Internal Resistance

Investigate **Internal Resistance** and **E.m.f.** With This **Circuit**

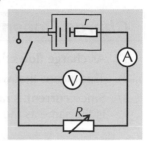

1) **Vary** the **current** in the circuit by changing the value of the **load resistance** (**R**) using the variable resistor. **Measure** the **p.d.** (**V**) for several different values of **current** (**I**). Include a **switch** in your circuit to **turn off** the current whenever possible to **reduce** the effect of **heating** in the wires on the **resistance** of the circuit.

2) Record your data for V and I in a table, and **plot the results** in a graph of V against I.

To find the **e.m.f.** and **internal resistance** of the cell, start with the equation:

$$V = \varepsilon - Ir$$

1) Rearrange to give $V = -rI + \varepsilon$

2) Since ε and **r** are constants, that's just the equation of a **straight line**:

Equation of a straight line
gradient $y = \mathbf{m}x + \mathbf{c}$ — y-intercept

3) So the intercept on the vertical axis is ε.

4) And the gradient is $-\mathbf{r}$.

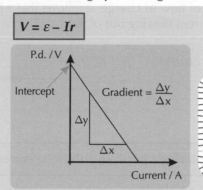

P.d. /V

Intercept

Gradient $= \dfrac{\Delta y}{\Delta x}$

Δy

Δx

Current / A

Think about how you'd reduce errors in this experiment. E.g. make sure the circuit doesn't change temperature so the resistance of the components doesn't change.

3) Choosing values for the **load resistance** is a **balancing act** — a **low load resistance** will give a **large current**, which will **reduce** the **percentage uncertainty** (see page 8) in the ammeter reading of the current. But **large currents** will cause significant **heating in the wires**, which will invalidate your results. So you need to **compromise**.

4) For this experiment (as for any experiment using voltmeters and ammeters), you can assume that the **voltmeter** has a very **high resistance**, and the resistance of the **ammeter** is very **low**.

5) Voltmeters have a **very high internal resistance**, so the **current** through them is so **low** you can usually assume it is **negligible** (zero). This means including the voltmeter in the circuit doesn't affect the **current** through the **variable resistor**.

6) The **ammeter** has a resistance that's so low it's negligible, and so the voltage across it is also negligible. This means including the ammeter in the circuit doesn't affect the **potential difference** across the **variable resistor**.

7) An **easier** way to **measure** the **e.m.f.** of a **power source** is by connecting a **voltmeter** across its **terminals**. As above, the **current** through the voltmeter is assumed to be **negligible** and so any **difference** between your measurements and the **e.m.f.** will be so small that the difference isn't usually significant.

Practice Questions

Q1 What is the effect of internal resistance on the potential difference supplied by a battery?

Q2 What is e.m.f.?

Q3 Write the equation to calculate the terminal p.d. of a power supply from e.m.f., current and internal resistance.

Q4 Describe an experiment you could carry out to determine the internal resistance of a battery.

Exam Questions

Q1 A battery with an internal resistance of 0.80 Ω and an e.m.f. of 24 V powers a dentist's drill with resistance 4.0 Ω.

   a) Calculate the current in the circuit when the drill is connected to the power supply. [2 marks]

   b) Calculate the potential difference wasted overcoming the internal resistance. [1 mark]

Q2 A bulb of resistance R is powered by two cells connected in series each with internal resistance r and e.m.f. ε. Which expression represents the current flowing through each cell? [1 mark]

  A $\dfrac{\varepsilon}{R+r}$ B $\dfrac{\varepsilon}{2(R+2r)}$ C $\dfrac{2\varepsilon}{R+2r}$ D $\dfrac{\varepsilon}{R+2r}$

Overcome your internal resistance for revision...

Make sure you know all your e.m.f. and internal resistance equations, they're an exam fave. A good way to get them learnt is to keep trying to get from one equation to another... pretty dull, but it definitely helps.

Conservation of Energy & Charge in Circuits

There are some things in Physics that are so fundamental that you just have to accept them. Like the fact that there's loads of Maths in it. And that energy is conserved. And that Physicists get more homework than everyone else.

Charge Doesn't 'Leak Away' Anywhere — it's Conserved

1) As **charge flows** through a circuit, it **doesn't** get **used up** or **lost**.

2) This means that whatever **charge flows into** a junction will **flow out** again.

3) Since **current** is **rate of flow of charge**, it follows that whatever **current flows into** a junction is the same as the current **flowing out** of it.

Example: *CHARGE FLOWING IN 1 SECOND*

$$Q_1 = 6\,C \Rightarrow I_1 = 6\,A$$

$$Q_2 = 2\,C \Rightarrow I_2 = 2\,A$$
$$Q_3 = 4\,C \Rightarrow I_3 = 4\,A$$

$$I_1 = I_2 + I_3$$

Kirchhoff's first law says:

> The total **current entering a junction** = the total **current leaving it**.

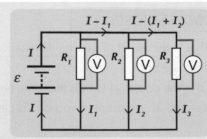

Energy conservation is vital.

Energy is Conserved too

1) **Energy is conserved**. You already know that. In **electrical circuits**, **energy** is **transferred round** the circuit. Energy **transferred to** a charge is **e.m.f.**, and energy **transferred from** a charge is **potential difference**.

2) In a **closed loop**, these two quantities must be **equal** if energy is conserved (which it is).

Kirchhoff's second law says:

> The **total e.m.f.** around a **series circuit** = the **sum** of the **p.d.s** across each component.   (or $\varepsilon = \Sigma IR$ in symbols)

Exam Questions might get you to Combine Resistors in Series and Parallel

A **typical exam question** could give you a **circuit** with bits of information missing, leaving you to fill in the gaps. Not the most fun... but on the plus side you get to ignore any internal resistance stuff (unless the question tells you otherwise)... hurrah. You need to remember the **following rules**:

Series Circuits:

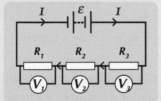

1) **same current** at **all points** of the circuit (since there are no junctions)

2) **e.m.f. split** between **components** (by Kirchhoff's 2nd law), so:
$$\varepsilon = V_1 + V_2 + V_3$$

3) $V = IR$, so if I is constant:
$$IR_{total} = IR_1 + IR_2 + IR_3$$

4) cancelling the Is gives:

$$R_{total} = R_1 + R_2 + R_3$$

5) As $R = \frac{1}{G}$, you can write this in terms of conductance:
$$\frac{1}{G_{total}} = \frac{1}{G_1} + \frac{1}{G_2} + \frac{1}{G_3}$$

Parallel Circuits:

1) **current** is **split** at each **junction**, so: $I = I_1 + I_2 + I_3$

2) **same p.d.** across **all components** (three separate loops — within each loop the e.m.f. equals sum of individual p.d.s)

3) so, $V/R_{total} = V/R_1 + V/R_2 + V/R_3$

4) cancelling the Vs gives:

$$\frac{1}{R_{total}} = \frac{1}{R_1} + \frac{1}{R_2} + \frac{1}{R_3}$$

$\varepsilon = V$ in this case, as we're ignoring internal resistance.

5) As $R = \frac{1}{G}$, you can write this in terms of conductance:

$$G_{total} = G_1 + G_2 + G_3$$

Conservation of Energy & Charge in Circuits

Worked Exam Question

Example:

A battery of e.m.f. 16 V and negligible internal resistance is connected in a circuit as shown on the right.

a) Show that the group of resistors between X and Y could be replaced by a single resistor of resistance 15 Ω.

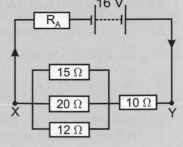

You can find the combined resistance of the 15 Ω, 20 Ω and 12 Ω resistors using:

$1/R = 1/R_1 + 1/R_2 + 1/R_3 = 1/15 + 1/20 + 1/12 = 1/5 \Rightarrow R = 5\ \Omega$

So overall resistance between X and Y can be found by $R = R_1 + R_2 = 5 + 10 = \mathbf{15\ \Omega}$

b) If $R_A = 20\ \Omega$:

   i) calculate the potential difference across R_A,

Careful — there are a few steps here. You need the p.d. across R_A, but you don't know the current through it. So start there: total resistance in circuit = 20 + 15 = 35 Ω, so current through R_A can be found using $I = V_{total}/R_{total}$: $I = 16/35$ A

then you can use $V = IR_A$ to find the p.d. across R_A: $V = 16/35 \times 20 = \mathbf{9\ V\ (to\ 1\ s.f.)}$

   ii) calculate the current in the 15 Ω resistor.

You know the current flowing into the group of three resistors and out of it, but not through the individual branches. But you know that their combined resistance is 5 Ω (from part a) so you can work out the p.d. across the group:

$V = IR = 16/35 \times 5 = 16/7$ V

The p.d. across the whole group is the same as the p.d. across each individual resistor, so you can use this to find the current through the 15 Ω resistor:

$I = V/R = (16/7) / 15 = \mathbf{0.15\ A\ (to\ 2\ s.f.)}$

Practice Questions

Q1 Write Kirchhoff's first and second laws.

Q2 State the formulas used to combine resistors in series and in parallel.

Q3 Find the current through and potential difference across each of two resistors, each with a conductance of 0.2 S, when they are placed in a circuit containing a 5 V battery, and are wired: a) in series, b) in parallel.

Exam Question

Q1 For the circuit on the right:

a) Calculate the total effective resistance of the three resistors in this combination. [2 marks]

b) Calculate the main current, I_3. [1 mark]

c) Calculate the potential difference across the 4.0 Ω resistor. [1 mark]

d) Calculate the potential difference across the parallel pair of resistors. [1 mark]

e) Using your answer from part d), calculate the currents I_1 and I_2. [2 marks]

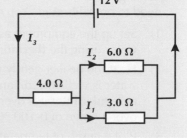

This is a very purple page — needs a bit of yellow I think...

V = IR is the formula you'll use most often in these questions. Make sure you know whether you're using it on the overall circuit, or just one specific component. It's amazingly easy to get muddled up — you've been warned.

The Potential Divider

Potential dividers are used in light sensors (photoconductive sensors), displacement sensors, heat sensors and so much more. They can even let you crank up the volume when you're listening to a spot of Kylie on your stereo...

Use a **Potential Divider** to Get a **Fraction** of an **Input Voltage**

1) At its simplest, a **potential divider** is a circuit with a **voltage source** and a couple of **resistors** in series.

2) The **potential difference** of the voltage source (e.g. a power supply) is **divided** in the **ratio** of the **resistances**. As an equation: $\frac{V_1}{V_2} = \frac{R_1}{R_2}$
   So, if you had a **2 Ω** resistor and a **3 Ω** resistor, you'd get **2/5** of the p.d. across the **2 Ω** resistor and **3/5** across the **3 Ω**.

   This rearranges to give $V_1/R_1 = V_2/R_2$. As $I = V/R$ this just means the current is the same through both resistors, which you know from page 36.

3) That means you can **choose** the **resistances** to get the **voltage** you **want** across one of them.

   In the circuit shown, R_2 has $\frac{R_2}{R_1 + R_2}$ of the total resistance. So:

   $$V_{out} = \frac{R_2}{R_1 + R_2} V_{in}$$

   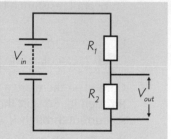

   E.g. if $V_{in} = 9$ V and you want V_{out} to be 6 V, then you need: $\frac{R_2}{R_1 + R_2} = \frac{6}{9}$, which gives $R_2 = 2R_1$. So you could have, say, $R_1 = 100\ \Omega$, $R_2 = 200\ \Omega$

4) This circuit can be used for **calibrating voltmeters**, which have a **very high resistance**.

5) If you put something with a **relatively low resistance** across R_2 though, you start to run into **problems**. You've **effectively** got **two resistors** in **parallel**, which will **always** have a **total** resistance **less** than R_2. That means that V_{out} will be **less** than you've calculated, and will depend on what's connected across R_2. Hrrumph.

Add an **LDR** or **Thermistor** for a **Light** or **Temperature Sensor**

1) Potential dividers can be made into sensors by including components whose resistance changes with external factors, for example light dependent resistors and thermistors (p.31). This means **V_{out} varies** with light or heat, so you can make a potential divider that works as a light or heat **sensor**.

2) The **circuit** needs to be **calibrated** so you know how the voltage across the component and V_{out} varies as external conditions change. E.g. knowing the voltage across a thermistor at a given temperature.

3) You can use an experiment like the one below to plot a calibration curve of voltage against an external factor:

Example: Calibration of an electronic thermometer.

Here's a potential divider using an **NTC thermistor**.

Think about safety before you start — keep the rest of the circuit as far away from the Bunsen burner and the water bath as possible.

This kind of circuit could form part of the circuit for a **thermostat** in a central heating system, or the basis of an **electronic thermometer**. First, the circuit would need to be **calibrated**. You can do this using the equipment shown on the right:

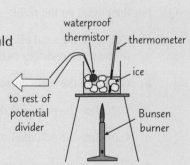

1) Set up the equipment as shown, then measure the **temperature** of the water using the **thermometer**, and record the **voltage** across the resistor.

2) **Heat** the beaker **gently** using the Bunsen burner (make sure the water is well-stirred), and record the temperature and the voltage at **regular intervals** over a **suitable range** (e.g. at 5 °C intervals over a range of 0-100 °C).

3) Plot a **graph** of temperature against voltage from your results. This graph is the thermistor's **calibration curve**. You can use it to find the temperature of the thermistor from the voltage across it, without needing the thermometer — the thermistor and the calibration curve together are effectively **another thermometer**.

Pick your fixed resistor carefully — if its resistance is too high, V_{out} won't vary enough with temperature, and if it's too low, V_{out} might vary over a bigger range than your voltmeter can handle.

The Potential Divider

A *Potentiometer* Uses a *Variable Resistor* to Give a *Variable Voltage*

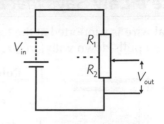

1) A **potentiometer** has a **variable resistor** replacing R_1 and R_2 of the potential divider, but it uses the **same idea** (it's even sometimes **called** a potential divider just to confuse things).

2) You move a **slider** or turn a knob to **adjust** the **relative sizes** of R_1 and R_2. That way you can vary V_{out} from 0 V up to the input voltage, V_{in}.

3) This is dead handy when you want to be able to **change** a **voltage continuously**, like in the **volume control** of a stereo.

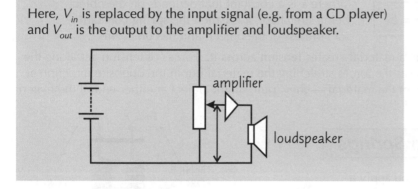

Here, V_{in} is replaced by the input signal (e.g. from a CD player) and V_{out} is the output to the amplifier and loudspeaker.

I've often wished bagpipes had a volume control. Or just an off switch.

Practice Questions

Q1 Write down the equation linking output p.d., input p.d., and component resistance for a potential divider circuit.

Q2 Draw the circuit diagram for a potential divider that works as a light sensor, where the output p.d. increases when the light level increases.

Q3 Explain how you could calibrate a circuit containing a thermistor.

Q4 What is a potentiometer?

Exam Questions

Q1 Two resistors, A and B, are connected in series as shown in the circuit diagram. Resistor A has a resistance of 35 Ω and resistor B has a resistance of 45 Ω.

a) Given that the potential difference across resistor B is 6.75 V, calculate the potential difference across resistor A. [1 mark]

b) Calculate the input p.d. supplied by the battery. [1 mark]

c) Resistor A is removed, and replaced with a 75 Ω resistor. Calculate the new potential difference across resistor B. [1 mark]

Q2 Look at the circuit on the right.

a) Calculate the p.d. between A and B as shown by a high resistance voltmeter placed between the two points. [1 mark]

b) A 40 Ω resistor is now placed between points A and B. Calculate the p.d. across AB and the current flowing through the 40 Ω resistor. [4 marks]

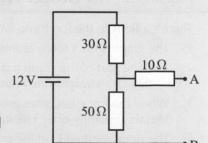

OI...YOU... [bang bang bang]... turn that potentiometer down...

Potentiometers come up a lot in experiments to do with electricity, so like them or not, you'd better get used to them. I can't stand the things myself, but then lab and me don't mix — it's all far too technical I'm afraid.

Hooke's Law

Hooke's law applies to all materials, but only up to a point...

Hooke's Law Says that Extension is Proportional to Force

If a **metal wire** is supported at the top and then a weight attached to the bottom, it **stretches**. The weight pulls down with force **F**, producing an equal and opposite force at the support.

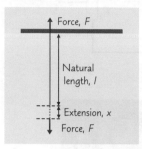

The material will only deform (stretch, bend, twist etc.) if there's a pair of opposite forces acting on it.

1) **Robert Hooke** discovered in the 17th century that the extension of a stretched wire, **x**, is **proportional** to the load or force, **F**. This relationship is now called **Hooke's law**.

2) Hooke's law can be written:

$$F = kx$$

Where **k** is a constant that depends on the object being stretched. **k** is called the **spring constant** (or **stiffness** of the object) and has units Nm^{-1}.

3) Stretching a material creates **tension** across it. Forces of tension act along the same line as the forces stretching the material but in the opposite direction at each end of the material — they 'pull' on the object at either end of the material.

Hooke's Law Also Applies to Springs

A metal spring also changes length when you apply a **pair of opposite forces**.

1) The **extension** of a spring is **proportional** to the **force** applied — so Hooke's law applies. If the forces are **compressive**, the spring is **squashed** and the extension is negative.

> Hooke's law works just as well for **compressive** forces as **tensile** forces. For a spring, **k** has the **same value** whether the forces are tensile or compressive (that's not true for all materials).

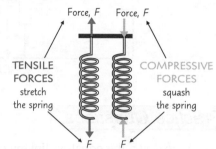

Tensile forces create <u>tension</u> in a stretched spring. Compressive forces create compression in a squashed spring. Tensile or compressive forces in the spring act in the opposite direction to the tensile or compressive forces stretching or squashing it.

2) **Hooke's Law** doesn't just apply to metal **springs** and **wires** — all **other materials** obey it up to a point.

> **Example:**
> a) A force is applied to a spring, causing the spring to be stretched by 5.0 mm. The spring constant of the spring is 9800 Nm^{-1}. Calculate the magnitude of the applied force.
>
> $F = kx$ so $F = 9800 \times 0.005 = $ **49 N**
>
> b) If the same force was applied to a spring with a spring constant of 5.2 Nmm^{-1}, how much would the spring extend by?
>
> $x = F \div k$ so $x = 49 \div 5200 = 0.00942... = 0.0094$ m = **9.4 mm (to 2 s.f.)**

Convert the spring constant into more appropriate units first: 5.2 Nmm^{-1} = 5200 Nm^{-1}

Hooke's Law Stops Working when the Load is Great Enough

There's a **limit** to the force you can apply for Hooke's law to stay true.

1) The graph shows force against extension for a **typical metal wire** or **spring**.

2) The first part of the graph (up to point P) shows Hooke's law being obeyed — there's a **straight-line relationship** between **force** and **extension**.

3) When the force becomes great enough, the graph starts to **curve**. **Metals** generally obey Hooke's law up to the **limit of proportionality**, **P**.

4) The point marked **E** on the graph is called the **elastic limit**. If you exceed the elastic limit, the material will be **permanently stretched**. When all the force is removed, the material will be **longer** than at the start.

5) Beyond the elastic limit, the material will **stretch further** for a given force.

6) Be careful — there are some materials, like **rubber**, that only obey Hooke's law for **really small** extensions.

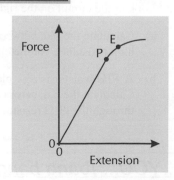

Hooke's Law

A Stretch can be Elastic or Plastic

A material will show elastic deformation **up to** its **elastic limit**, and plastic deformation **beyond** it.
If a **deformation** is **elastic**, the material returns to its **original shape** once the forces are removed.

1) When the material is put under **tension**, the **atoms** of the material are **pulled apart** from one another.
2) Atoms can **move** slightly relative to their **equilibrium positions**, without changing position in the material.
3) Once the **load** is **removed**, the atoms **return** to their **equilibrium** distance apart.

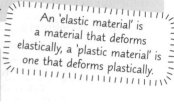

An 'elastic material' is a material that deforms elastically, a 'plastic material' is one that deforms plastically.

If a deformation is **plastic**, the material is **permanently stretched**.

1) Some atoms in the material move position relative to one another.
2) When the load is removed, the **atoms don't return** to their original positions.

You can Investigate Extension by Stretching an Object

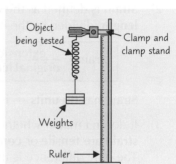

Object being tested — Clamp and clamp stand — Weights — Ruler

1) Set up the experiment shown in the diagram. Support the object being tested at the top (e.g. with a clamp) and measure its original length with a ruler.
2) Add masses one at a time to the bottom of the object.
3) After each weight is added, measure the new length of the object, then **calculate the extension**:

extension = new length – original length

4) Plot a graph of **force** (weight) against **extension** for your results.
Where the line of best fit is **straight**, then the object obeys Hooke's law and the gradient = **k** (as $F = kx$). If you've loaded the object beyond its limit of proportionality, the graph will start to curve.
5) Make sure you carry out the experiment **safely**. You should be **standing up** so you can get out of the way quickly if the weights fall, and wearing **safety goggles** to protect your eyes in case the object snaps.

Practice Questions

Q1 State Hooke's law and explain what is meant by the elastic limit of a material.
Q2 Define tension and compression in terms of the forces acting on a spring.
Q3 From studying the force-extension graph for a material as it is loaded and unloaded, how can you tell:
a) if Hooke's law is being obeyed, b) if the elastic limit has been reached?
Q4 What is meant by elastic and plastic deformation of a material?
Q5 Describe how you could investigate the effect of force on extension for a length of wire.

Exam Questions

Q1 A metal guitar string stretches 4.0 mm when a 10 N force is applied.

a) Calculate the force constant for the string, and calculate how far the string will stretch when a 15 N force is applied. [2 marks]

b) The string is then stretched beyond its elastic limit, without snapping. Describe the effect this will have on the string. [1 mark]

Q2 A rubber band is 6.0 cm long. When it is loaded with 2.5 N, its length increases to 10.4 cm. Increasing the load to 5.0 N further increases the length to 16.2 cm. State whether the rubber band will obey Hooke's law when the force on it is 5.0 N. Explain your answer. [2 marks]

Sod's Law — if you don't learn it, it'll be in the exam...

Three things you didn't know about Robert Hooke — he was the first person to use the word 'cell' (as in biology, not prisons), he helped Christopher Wren with his designs for St. Paul's Cathedral and no-one's sure what he looked like. I'd like to think that if I did all that stuff, then someone would at least remember what I looked like — poor old Hooke.

Stress, Strain and Elastic Energy

How much a material stretches for a particular applied force depends on its dimensions.
If you want to compare one material to another, you need to use stress and strain instead.
A stress-strain graph is the same for any sample of a particular material — the size of the sample doesn't matter.

A Stress Causes a Strain

As you saw on page 40, a material subjected to a pair of **opposite forces** might **deform**, i.e. **change shape**. If the forces **stretch** the material, they're **tensile**. If the forces **squash** the material, they're **compressive**.

1) **Stress** is defined as the **tension** (the **force applied**) divided by the **cross-sectional area**:

$$\text{stress} = \frac{\text{tension}}{\text{cross-sectional area}}$$

The **units** of stress are Nm^{-2} or pascals, **Pa**.

2) **Strain** is defined as the **extension**, i.e. the **change in length**, divided by the **original length** of the material:

$$\text{strain} = \frac{\text{extension}}{\text{original length}}$$

Strain has **no units** — it's given as a **number** or **percentage**.

3) It doesn't matter whether the forces producing the **stress** and **strain** are **tensile** or **compressive** — the **same equations** apply. The only difference is that you tend to think of **tensile** forces as **positive**, and **compressive** forces as **negative**, and causing negative extension.

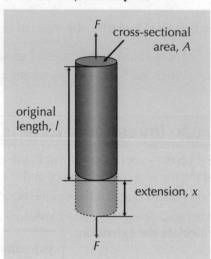

A Stress Big Enough to Break a Material is Called the Fracture Stress

As a greater and greater tensile **force** is applied to a material, the **stress** on it **increases**.

1) The effect of the **stress** is to start to **pull** the **atoms apart** from one another.

2) Eventually the stress becomes **so great** that atoms **separate completely**, and the **material fractures** (breaks). This is shown by point **B** on the graph. The stress at which this occurs is called the **fracture stress**.

3) The point marked **UTS** on the graph is called the **ultimate tensile strength**. This is the **maximum stress** that the material can withstand before breaking.

4) **Engineers** have to consider the **UTS** and **fracture stress** of materials when designing a **structure**.

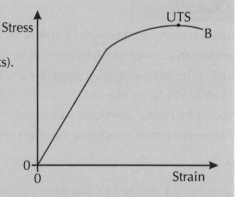

Elastic Strain Energy is the Energy Stored in a Stretched Material

When a material is **stretched** or **compressed**, **work** is done in **deforming** the material.

1) On a **graph** of **force against extension**, the **work done** is given by the **area under the graph**.

2) **Before** the **elastic limit**, all the **work done** in stretching or compressing the material is **stored** as **energy** in the material.

3) This stored energy is called **elastic strain energy**. There's more about how to calculate elastic strain energy on the next page.

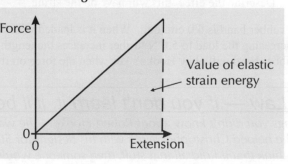

Stress, Strain and Elastic Energy

You can Calculate the **Energy Stored** in an **Elastic Material**

Provided a material obeys Hooke's law, the **strain energy** stored inside it can be **calculated** quite easily.

1) The **work done** on an elastic material in stretching it is **equal** to the **energy stored** in the material as **elastic strain energy**.

2) **Work done** equals **force × displacement**.

3) However, the **force** on the material **isn't constant**. It rises from zero up to force *F*. To calculate the **work done**, use the average force between zero and *F*, i.e. ½*F*.

$$\text{work done} = \tfrac{1}{2}Fx$$

This is the triangular area under the force-extension graph — see previous page.

4) Then the **elastic strain energy**, *E*, is: $E = \tfrac{1}{2}Fx$

5) Because Hooke's law is being obeyed, $F = kx$, which means *F* can be replaced in the equation to give:

$$E = \tfrac{1}{2}kx^2$$

6) If the material is stretched beyond the **elastic limit**, some work is done separating atoms. This energy will **not** be **stored** as elastic strain energy, and so isn't released when the force is removed.

Practice Questions

Q1 Write a definition for the stress of a material being stretched by applying a load.
Q2 Explain what is meant by the strain on a material.
Q3 What is meant by the fracture stress of a material?
Q4 How can the work done in stretching a material be found from the force against extension graph of the material?
Q5 The work done is usually calculated as force multiplied by displacement. Explain why the work done in stretching a wire is ½*Fx*.

Exam Questions

Q1 A steel wire is 2.00 m long. When a 300 N force is applied to the wire, it stretches 4.0 mm. The wire has a circular cross-section with a diameter of 1.0 mm.
a) Calculate the strain of the wire. [1 mark]
b) Calculate the stress on the wire. [2 marks]

Q2 A copper wire (which obeys Hooke's law) is stretched by 3.0 mm when a force of 50 N is applied.
a) Calculate the force constant for this wire in Nm⁻¹. [1 mark]
b) Calculate the value of the elastic strain energy in the stretched wire. [1 mark]

Q3 A pinball machine contains a spring which is used to fire a small, 12.0 g metal ball to start the game. The spring has a spring constant of 40.8 Nm⁻¹. It is compressed by 5.00 cm and then released to fire the ball.

Calculate the maximum possible speed of the ball. [3 marks]

UTS a laugh a minute, this stuff...

Bet you thought I was going to make a joke about this being stressful then, didn't you? There's a pile of equations to learn on these pages, as well a couple of graphs to drill into your brain, and they all might come up in the exam, so you need to learn the lot I'm afraid. Plus, it'll come in handy if you ever want to, I dunno, build a skyscraper or something.

The Young Modulus

Busy chap, Thomas Young. He did this work on tensile stress as something of a sideline. Light was his main thing. He proved that light behaved like a wave, explained how we see in colour and worked out what causes astigmatism.

The **Young Modulus** is Stress ÷ Strain

When you apply a **load** to stretch a material, it experiences a **stress** and a **strain**.

1) Up to a point called the **limit of proportionality** (see p.40), the stress and strain of a material are proportional to each other.

2) So below this limit, for a particular material, stress divided by strain is a constant. This constant is called the **Young modulus, E**.

$$\text{Young modulus} = E = \frac{\text{stress}}{\text{strain}}$$

The Young Modulus is a measurement of the stiffness of a material (p.46).

3) The **units** of the Young modulus are the same as stress (**Nm⁻²** or pascals), since strain has no units.

4) The Young modulus is used by **engineers** to make sure their materials can withstand sufficient forces.

To **Find** the Young Modulus, You Need a **Very Long Wire**

This is the experiment you're most likely to do in class:

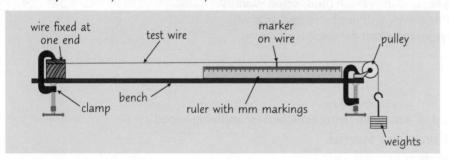

wire fixed at one end · test wire · marker on wire · pulley · clamp · bench · ruler with mm markings · weights

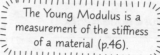

"Okay, found one. Now what?"

1) The test wire should be thin, and as long as possible. The **longer and thinner** the wire, the more it **extends** for the same force. This reduces the **uncertainty** (p.12) in your measurements.

2) First you need to find the **cross-sectional area** of the wire. Use a **micrometer** to measure the **diameter** of the wire **three times** in different places along the wire, before taking an **average** of your results. By assuming that the cross-section is **circular**, you can use the formula for the area of a circle: ⟹

If you're doing this experiment, make sure you're standing up so you can get out of the way quickly if the weights fall. And wear safety goggles — if the wire snaps, it could get very messy...

$$\text{area of a circle} = \pi r^2$$

3) **Clamp** the wire to the bench (as shown in the diagram above) so you can hang **weights** off one end of it. Start with the **smallest weight** necessary to **straighten** the wire. (**Don't** include this weight in your final calculations.)

4) Measure the **distance** between the **fixed end of the wire** and the **marker** — this is your unstretched length.

5) Then if you increase the weight, the **wire stretches** and the **marker moves**.

6) **Increase** the **weight** in steps (e.g. 1 N intervals), recording the marker reading each time — the **extension** is the **difference** between this reading and the **unstretched length**. Use a **mass meter** or a set of **digital scales** to accurately find the weight you add at each step.

7) You can use your results from this experiment to calculate the **stress** and **strain** on the wire and plot a stress-strain graph (see next page).

To reduce random errors you should use a thin marker on the wire, and always look from directly above the marker and ruler when measuring the extension.

As you unload the wire, re-measure the extension for each weight to make sure you haven't gone past the wire's elastic limit.

(The other standard way of measuring the Young modulus in the lab is using **Searle's apparatus**. This is a bit more accurate, but it's harder to do and the equipment's more complicated.)

You can also use this apparatus to find the **fracture stress** of a material. Do a preliminary experiment where you add weights to the wire to **roughly** find the force required to **break** the wire. **Repeat** the experiment with an **identical wire**, but this time add weights in small increments as the force applied approaches the force that previously broke the wire. This will help you find the breaking force (and fracture stress) more **accurately**. Then all you need to do is calculate the fracture stress from the breaking force.

The Young Modulus

Plot a **Stress-Strain Graph** of Your Results to Find **E**

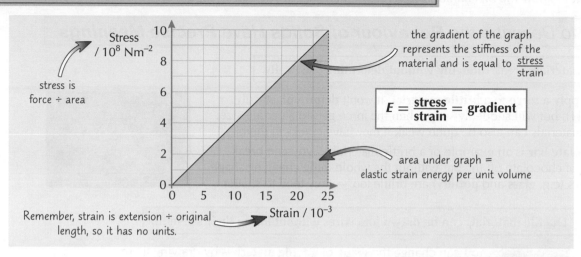

Stress / 10^8 Nm^{-2}

stress is force ÷ area

the gradient of the graph represents the stiffness of the material and is equal to $\frac{\text{stress}}{\text{strain}}$

$$E = \frac{\text{stress}}{\text{strain}} = \text{gradient}$$

area under graph = elastic strain energy per unit volume

Remember, strain is extension ÷ original length, so it has no units.

Strain / 10^{-3}

1) The **gradient** of the graph gives the Young modulus, *E*.
2) The **area under the graph** gives the **elastic strain energy** (or energy stored) **per unit volume** (i.e. the energy stored per 1 m^3 of wire).

Example: The stress-strain graph above is for a thin metal wire. Find the Young modulus of the wire from the graph.

E = stress ÷ strain = gradient

The gradient of the graph = $\frac{\Delta \text{stress}}{\Delta \text{strain}} = \frac{10 \times 10^8}{25 \times 10^{-3}}$

$$= 4 \times 10^{10} \text{ Nm}^{-2}$$

Practice Questions

Q1 Define the Young modulus for a material.

Q2 What are the units of the Young modulus?

Q3 Describe an experiment to find the Young modulus of a test wire. Explain why a thin test wire is used.

Q4 How could you adapt the experiment to find the fracture stress of a wire?

Q5 How would you calculate the stiffness of a material from a stress-strain graph for that material?

Exam Questions

Q1 The Young modulus for copper is 1.3×10^{11} Nm^{-2}.

a) The stress on a copper wire is 2.6×10^8 Nm^{-2}. Calculate the strain of the wire. [2 marks]

b) The load applied to the copper wire is 100 N. Calculate the average cross-sectional area of the wire. [1 mark]

Q2 A steel wire is stretched elastically. For a load of 80 N, the wire extends by 3.6 mm. The original length of the wire is 2.50 m and its average diameter is 0.6 mm. Calculate the value of the Young modulus for steel. [5 marks]

Q3 An aluminium wire is elastically stretched.
The graph of stress against strain is plotted and shown on the right.
Estimate the Young modulus for aluminium. [1 mark]

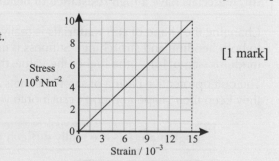

Stress / 10^8 Nm^{-2}

Strain / 10^{-3}

Learn that experiment — it's important...

Getting back to the good Dr Young... As if ground-breaking work in light, the physics of vision and materials science wasn't enough, he was also a well-respected physician, a linguist and an Egyptologist. He was one of the first to try to decipher the Rosetta stone (he didn't get it right, but nobody's perfect). Makes you feel kind of inferior, doesn't it?

Mechanical Properties of Solids

You wouldn't try doing surgery with scalpels made out of marshmallows, just as you wouldn't make a glass crash mat. It's important to know the mechanical properties of materials so you can select the best ones to suit your needs.

Terms to Describe the *Behaviour of Solids* Have *Precise Meanings*

Brittle materials break suddenly without deforming plastically.

If you apply a force to a brittle material, it won't deform plastically (see p.41), but will suddenly snap when the force gets to a certain size. Brittle materials can also be quite weak if they have cracks in them.

A chocolate bar is an example of a brittle material — you can break chunks of chocolate off the bar without the whole thing changing shape. Ceramics (e.g. glass and pottery) are brittle too — they tend to shatter.

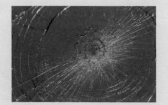

Ductile materials can be drawn into wires without losing their strength.

You can change the shape of ductile materials by drawing them into wires or other shapes. The important thing is that they keep their strength when they're deformed like this.

Copper is ductile, and with its high electrical conductivity this means that it's ideal for electric wires. A ductile material has been used for the cables supporting the ski lift in the photo — it's been drawn into long wires, but kept its strength.

Strong materials can withstand high stresses without deforming or breaking.

Strength is a measure of how much a material can resist being deformed (bent, stretched, fractured etc.) by a force without breaking. This can be resisting a pulling force (tensile strength) or a squeezing force (compressive strength).

Steel beams used to create structures like bridges are very strong — they withstand the force caused by lots of vehicles going over them without bending or breaking.

Hard materials are very resistant to cutting, indentation and abrasion.

If you try to cut, dent or scratch a hard material, you'll probably have very little effect. Their structure means hard materials are resistant to cutting, indentation (becoming dented) and abrasion (scratching).

Cutting tools (e.g. chisels) need to be harder than the stuff they're cutting — they're often made from hardened steel. Diamond is just about the hardest material there is — it's often used to reinforce the tips of drill bits.

Stiff materials have a high resistance to bending and stretching.

Changing the shape of stiff materials is really difficult as they are resistant to both bending and stretching. Stiffness is measured by the Young modulus (see p.44) — the higher the value, the stiffer the material.

The outer protective casing of safety helmets and safety boots need to be very stiff so that they keep their shape and don't crush onto your body when something impacts on them.

Tough materials are really difficult to break.

Toughness is a measure of the energy a material can absorb before it breaks. Really tough materials can absorb a lot of energy so are very difficult to break.

Some polymers, including certain types of polythene, are very tough. The hull of this kayak is made of a tough material so it won't break on rocks.

Mechanical Properties of Solids

Stress-Strain Graphs for Ductile Materials Curve

It turns out that because different solids have different properties, their stress-strain graphs look different too. The diagram shows a **stress-strain graph** for a typical **ductile** material — e.g. a copper wire.

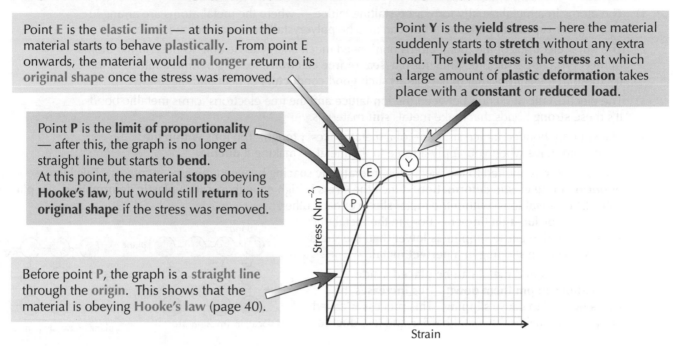

Point **E** is the **elastic limit** — at this point the material starts to behave **plastically**. From point E onwards, the material would **no longer** return to its **original shape** once the stress was removed.

Point **Y** is the **yield stress** — here the material suddenly starts to **stretch** without any extra load. The **yield stress** is the **stress** at which a large amount of **plastic deformation** takes place with a **constant** or **reduced load**.

Point **P** is the **limit of proportionality** — after this, the graph is no longer a straight line but starts to **bend**. At this point, the material **stops** obeying **Hooke's law**, but would still **return** to its **original shape** if the stress was removed.

Before point **P**, the graph is a **straight line** through the **origin**. This shows that the material is obeying **Hooke's law** (page 40).

Brittle materials (e.g. glass, Perspex®, cast iron, chocolate chip cookies... mmmm... cookies) **don't** tend to behave plastically. They **fracture** before they reach the elastic limit.

Practice Questions

Q1 Write short definitions of the following terms: ductile, stiff, tough, strong.

Q2 Give examples of materials which are: brittle, strong, hard and ductile.

Q3 Why does a kayak need to be made out of tough material?

Q4 What properties of a material are tested by finding the fracture stress needed to break a material?

Q5 What is the difference between the limit of proportionality and the elastic limit?

Q6 Define the yield stress of a material.

Q7 Sketch a stress-strain graph of a typical ductile material.

Exam Questions

Q1 A material is being chosen to create support beams for a small bridge. Choose a suitable material for this purpose from the table and explain your choice.

Material	Strength (MPa)	Toughness (kJm⁻²)
A	4	10
B	30	3
C	2000	1
D	20	0.005

[3 marks]

Q2 Riding helmets are designed to protect a rider's head from injury should they fall off their horse. Describe three properties of a material that would be suitable for a riding helmet and explain why each of these properties is advantageous.

[6 marks]

My brain must be stiff — it's resistant to being stretched...

Make sure you learn all of those definitions of material properties and an example of when each property is useful. It might just pick you up some easy marks in the exam. Then practice drawing the stress-strain graph for ductile materials.

Structures of Materials

The reason materials are flexible or tough is down to their structure.
When the going gets tough, the tough get going to page 46 to look up the definition of tough...

Metals — Positive Ions in a 'Sea' of Free Electrons

1) The atoms in a metal usually form a **crystalline** lattice — where the metal atoms are arranged in a **regular repeating pattern**. (They can also be **polycrystalline** — see below).

2) The outer electrons of the metal atoms don't need much energy to be able to desert their atoms in this crystalline structure. They form a 'sea' of **free electrons**, leaving behind a lattice of ions. It's these free electrons that make metals such **good conductors** of heat and electricity.

3) The electrostatic attraction between the ion lattice and the free electrons forms metallic bonds. It's these **strong** bonds that make metals **stiff** materials.

4) The strongly bonded lattice structure of a metal makes it **tough**. The ions within the lattice can **move** when you apply a force to the metal — making it **ductile**.

5) When a **force** is applied to the metal, the **interatomic spacing** between the ions increases. This increase is **uniform** during **elastic deformation**. Once the **stress** is high enough to cause **plastic deformation**, the **planes** ('sheets' of metal ions) within the metal **slip** over each other.
If there is a **dislocation** (imperfection) in the metal, the **stress** needed to cause slipping is **lower** than the stress needed to cause slipping in a **perfect metal**.

6) **Atoms** of a **second metal can be placed inside dislocations** to **pin them down**. This **increases** the **stress** needed to cause **slipping**. This process is called **alloying** and makes the metal **harder** and less **ductile**.

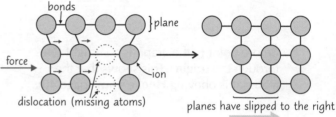

Ceramics — Giant Rigid Structures

1) Ceramics like **pottery**, **brick** and **glass** are made by melting certain materials, and then letting them cool.

2) The arrangement of atoms in a ceramic can be **crystalline** or **polycrystalline** — where there are many regions (or **grains**) of crystalline structure. The atoms in each grain line up in the same direction.

3) Some ceramics like **glass** are **amorphous** — there's no overall pattern; the atoms are arranged at **random**. The **quicker** a molten ceramic material is cooled, the more likely it is to be amorphous.

4) This **random** atomic bonding means that there are **no slip planes** in ceramic lattices. They also don't have **mobile dislocations** (dislocations which can **move**) — meaning that ceramic materials rarely deform **plastically** before they **fracture** (p.42).

5) However they're arranged, the atoms in a ceramic are either **ionically** or **covalently** bonded in a **giant rigid structure**. The **strong bonds** between the atoms make ceramics **stiff**, while the **rigid** structure means that ceramics are very **brittle** materials.

6) Ceramics being **brittle** means that **cracks spread** through them when they **fracture**. This is because the applied **force** acts on a **small area** (the **tip** of the crack) so the **stress** is high.

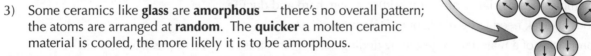

a grain

Polymers — Lots of Monomers Joined Together

1) A **polymer** is a molecular **chain**, made up of a **single repeating unit** called a **monomer**.

2) You get **natural** polymers like rubber, as well as a whole host of **man-made** ones like polythene.

3) The monomers in a polymer chain are **covalently** bonded together, and so are very hard to separate. This means even the thin polymer material used to make carrier bags is still pretty **strong**.

4) The **polymer chains** are often **entangled** (twisted and scrunched together), and can be **unravelled** by **rotating** about their bonds when you pull them. This is what makes polymer materials **flexible**. The more easily the monomers can **rotate**, the more the **chains** will **untangle** and the more **flexible** the polymer will be.

5) The strength and number of bonds **between** the chains also affect a polymer's flexibility. The stronger the cross-linking bonds, and the more cross-linking bonds you've got, the more **rigid** the material.

monomer

monomers can rotate about their bonds

MODULE 3: SECTION 3 — MECHANICAL PROPERTIES OF MATERIALS

Structures of Materials

Rayleigh Estimated Atom Sizes with Oil Drops...

1) One of the first experiments used to calculate atomic size was **Rayleigh's oil drop experiment** in 1890.

2) Olive oil was released, one drop at a time, into a **tub of water** until it **just** covered the **entire surface**. Rayleigh assumed the oil would **spread** as much as it could, so this **thickness** would be the **size** of one **molecule of oil**.

3) By knowing the **surface area** of the tub and the **volume** of the oil dropped, the **thickness** of the oil film could be found. The **size of an atom** is roughly equal to the size of an **oil molecule** divided by the **number of atoms** in an oil molecule, so Rayleigh could use his measurements to find an **upper limit** for the size of the **individual atoms**.

...Now We Use Other Methods

1) There are loads of ways of measuring both the size of atoms and their spacing.

2) **X-ray crystallography** involves firing X-rays at a sample and using their **diffraction patterns** (see page 57) to investigate atomic spacing and structure.

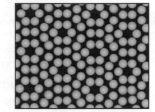
Scanning Tunnelling Microscopes can produce images of atoms.

3) **Scanning Tunnelling Microscopes** (STM) have a very fine tip which a voltage is applied to. **Electrons** from the sample surface **tunnel** (you don't need to know how this works) from the **surface** to the **tip** and cause a **current** to flow. The tip is moved across the surface of the sample, and the **height** of the tip is adjusted to keep the current **constant**, meaning that any small **bumps** or **dips** in the surface can be detected. An STM has such a **fine resolution** that **individual atoms** can be resolved and their **size** and **spacing** measured.

4) **Scanning Electron Microscopes** (SEM) and **Atomic Force Microscopes** (AFM) can also be used to measure atomic sizes. They don't let you 'see' a material's surface directly, but can be used to build up an **atom-by-atom** image of the surface on a **computer screen**. By knowing the **magnification** of the **image** on the computer screen and the size of the 'blobs' representing each atom, the sizes of the **atoms** can be calculated.

5) Modern techniques give the diameter of an atom as **0.1–0.5 nm**, depending on the atom being measured. This is much more **accurate** than the values Rayleigh **estimated** from his experiment.

Practice Questions

Q1 Describe the structure of metals.

Q2 Explain, in terms of its structure, what makes a metal stiff and what makes a metal tough.

Q3 Describe, in terms of interatomic spacing, what happens to the ions in a metal as it undergoes elastic deformation.

Q4 Describe the structure of ceramics and the directions of atoms in a polycrystalline ceramic.

Q5 Explain why there are no slip planes in ceramic materials.

Q6 Why do cracks spread through ceramics when a force is applied to them?

Exam Questions

Q1 Stress is applied to a sample of iron which contains dislocations.
The sample begins to plastically deform at a lower stress than expected.

a) Explain what is happening to the ions in the iron as it plastically deforms and comment on why plastic deformation occurred at a lower stress than expected. [2 marks]

b) Describe alloying and what effect it would have on the sample. [4 marks]

Q2 Select the statement that does **not** correctly describe polymers:

A Monomers are covalently bonded together to create a polymer.
B Polymer chains are tangled together.
C The more cross-linking bonds there are, the more flexible a polymer is.
D Polymers are unravelled when you pull on them, causing the monomers to rotate. [1 mark]

Q3 Describe how our knowledge of atomic size and spacing have changed over the past 150 years.
You should include a description of at least two methods of measuring atomic size in your answer. [6 marks]

And that's why shops don't make their bags out of clay...

It's true what they say — it's what's on the inside that counts... and it's no different for bricks. Make sure you get to grips with the structure of each class of materials so you can explain why materials have certain properties.

Superposition and Coherence

When two waves get together, it can be either really impressive or really disappointing.

Superposition Happens When Two or More Waves Pass Through Each Other

1) At the **instant** the waves **cross**, the **displacements** due to each wave **combine**. Then **each wave** goes on its merry way. You can **see** this if **two pulses** are sent **simultaneously** from each end of a rope.

2) The **principle of superposition** says that when two or more **waves cross**, the **resultant** displacement equals the **vector sum** of the **individual** displacements.

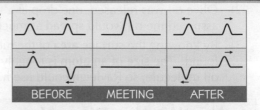

BEFORE   MEETING   AFTER

Interference can be Constructive or Destructive

1) A **crest** plus a **crest** gives a **big crest**. A **trough** plus a **trough** gives a **big trough**. These are both examples of **constructive interference**.

2) A **crest** plus a **trough** of equal size gives... **nothing**. The two displacements **cancel each other out** completely. This is called **total destructive interference**.

3) If the **crest** and the **trough** aren't the **same size**, then the destructive interference **isn't total**. For the interference to be **noticeable**, the two **amplitudes** should be **nearly equal**.

Graphically, you can superimpose waves by adding the individual displacements at each point along the x-axis, and then plotting them.

"Superposition" means "one thing on top of another thing". You can use the same idea in **reverse** — a complex wave can be **separated out** mathematically into several simple sine waves of various sizes.

You Can Use Phasors to Show Superposition

You can use little rotating arrows to represent the phase (see below) of each point on a wave. These arrows are called **phasors**. The phasor **rotates anticlockwise** through one whole turn as the wave completes a full cycle.

The length of the arrow shows the amplitude of the wave.

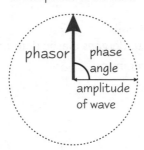

To superimpose waves using phasors, just add the arrows tip to tail:

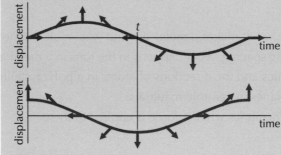

To find the resultant at time *t*, add the phasors tip to tail:

$$\leftarrow + \downarrow = \boxtimes$$

(So in this case, the resultant wave has a greater amplitude than the component waves and is 45° out of phase with both.)

In Phase Means In Step

1) Two points on a wave are **in phase** if they are both at the **same point** in the **wave cycle**.

2) It's mathematically **handy** to show one **complete cycle** of a wave as an **angle of 360° (2π radians)**, the angle a phasor will travel through.

3) **Points** that have a **phase difference** of **zero** or a **multiple of 360°** are **in phase** — their phasors point in the **same direction**.

4) **Points** with a **phase difference** of **odd-number multiples** of **180° (π radians)** are **exactly out of phase**, called **antiphase**. Their phasors point in **opposite directions**. And there's not just phase and antiphase — points can have a **phase difference** of **any** angle.

5) You can also talk about two **different waves** being in phase. **In practice** this happens because **both** waves came from the **same oscillator**. In **other** situations there will nearly always be a **phase difference** between two waves.

Displacement

position

360° 720°

Points A and B are in phase

A B

Resultant phasor

Points A and C are in antiphase

A C

Phasors cancel

Superposition and Coherence

To Get *Interference Patterns* the *Two Sources* Must Be *Coherent*

Interference **still happens** when you're observing waves of **different wavelength** and **frequency** — but it happens in a **jumble**. In order to get clear **interference patterns**, the two or more sources must be **coherent**.

> Two sources are coherent if they have the **same wavelength** and **frequency** and a **fixed phase difference** between them.

In exam questions, the 'fixed phase difference' is almost certainly going to be zero. The two sources will be in phase.

Constructive or *Destructive* Interference Depends on the *Path Difference*

1) Whether you get **constructive** or **destructive** interference at a **point** depends on how **much further one wave** has travelled than the **other wave** to get to that point (assuming the sources are **coherent** and **in phase**).

2) The **amount** by which the path travelled by one wave is **longer** than the path travelled by the other wave is called the **path difference**.

Constructive Interference — at any point an **equal** distance from both sources (that are coherent and in phase), or where the path difference is a **whole number** of **wavelengths**.

> **path difference** $= n\lambda$ (where n is an integer)

Total Destructive Interference — at any point where the path difference is an **odd** number of **half wavelengths**.

> **path difference** $= \dfrac{(2n + 1)\lambda}{2} = (n + \frac{1}{2})\lambda$

You Can Observe Interference With Sound Waves

1) Connect two **speakers** to the same oscillator (so they're **coherent** and **in phase**) and place them in line with each other.

2) Slowly move a **microphone** in a **straight line** parallel to the line of the speakers.

3) Using a data logger and a computer, you can see where the sound is **loudest** and **quietest** — the locations of maximum **constructive** and **destructive** interference.

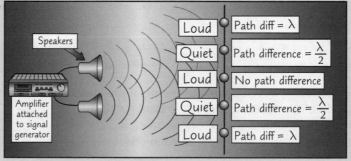

Speakers

Amplifier attached to signal generator

Loud	Path diff = λ
Quiet	Path difference = $\frac{\lambda}{2}$
Loud	No path difference
Quiet	Path difference = $\frac{\lambda}{2}$
Loud	Path diff = λ

Practice Questions

Q1 What is the principle of superposition?

Q2 When does the interference between two waves produce a clear pattern?

Q3 If two points on a wave have a phase difference of 1440°, are they in phase?

Q4 Define coherence.

Q5 Describe briefly an experiment to show interference using sound waves.

Exam Question

Q1 Sound waves that are coherent and in phase, each with a wavelength of 0.6 m, are produced by two speakers.

a) State whether maximum constructive or destructive interference would occur at a distance away from the speaker where the path difference between the two sound waves was 10.2 m. [1 mark]

b) At a point of total destructive interference, the phasor describing one of the waves at that point is shown. Draw the phasor describing the second sound wave at that point and state whether its magnitude is bigger than, smaller than or the same as the first sound wave. [2 marks]

Learn this and you'll be in a super position to pass your exam...   ...I'll get my coat.

There are a few really crucial concepts here: a) interference can be constructive or destructive, b) the sources must be coherent and in phase, c) constructive interference happens when the path difference is a whole number of wavelengths.

Standing Waves

Standing waves are waves that... er... stand still... well, not still exactly... I mean, well... they don't go anywhere... um...

You get a Standing Wave When a **Progressive Wave** is **Reflected** at a **Boundary**

A standing wave is the **superposition** of **two progressive waves** with the **same wavelength**, moving in **opposite directions**.

1) Unlike progressive waves, **no energy** is transmitted by a standing wave.

2) You can demonstrate standing waves by setting up a **driving oscillator** at one end of a **stretched string** with the other end fixed. The wave generated by the oscillator is **reflected** back and forth.

3) For most frequencies the resultant **pattern** is a **jumble**. However, if the oscillator happens to produce an **exact number of waves** in the time it takes for a wave to get to the **end** and **back again**, then the **original** and **reflected** waves **reinforce** each other.

4) At these **"resonant frequencies"** you get a **standing wave** where the **pattern doesn't move** — it just sits there, bobbing up and down. Happy, at peace with the world...

A sitting wave.

Standing Waves in **Strings** Form **Oscillating "Loops"** Separated by **Nodes**

1) Take a piece of string and **fix** it in place at **one end**.

2) Attach the other end to an **oscillator**.

3) Adjust the **frequency** of the oscillator, until a **standing wave** is formed.

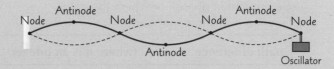

4) This is when the wave is **reflected** back on itself and **interferes**, causing "loops" to form, with **antinodes** (positions of **maximum** amplitude) and **nodes** (positions of **zero** amplitude).

5) You can then use an **oscilloscope** (see next page) to calculate the **resonant frequency**.

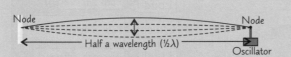

The standing wave above is vibrating at the **lowest possible** resonant frequency (the **fundamental frequency**). This is the **first harmonic**. It has **one "loop"** with a **node at each end**.

This is the **second harmonic** (or **first overtone**). It is **twice** the **fundamental frequency**. There are two **"loops"** with a **node** in the **middle** and **one at each end**.

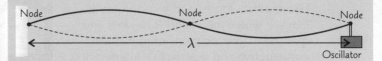

The **third harmonic** (or **second overtone**) is **three times** the fundamental frequency. **1½ wavelengths** fit on the string.

The **Notes** Played by **Stringed** and **Wind Instruments** are Standing Waves

Transverse standing waves form on the strings of **stringed instruments** like **violins** and **guitars**. Your finger or the bow sets the **string vibrating** at the point of contact. Waves are sent out in **both directions** and **reflected** back at both ends.

Longitudinal Standing Waves Form in a **Wind Instrument** or Other Air **Column**

1) If a source of sound is placed at the open end of a flute, piccolo, oboe or other column of air, there will be some frequencies for which resonance occurs and a standing wave is set up.

2) If the instrument has a closed end, a node will form there. You get the lowest resonant frequency when the length, *l*, of the pipe is a quarter wavelength.

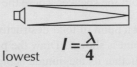

$$l = \frac{\lambda}{4}$$

3) Antinodes form at the open ends of pipes. If both ends are open, you get the lowest resonant frequency when the length, *l*, of the pipe is a half wavelength.

$$l = \frac{\lambda}{2}$$

Remember, the sound waves in wind instruments are <u>longitudinal</u> — they don't actually look like these diagrams.

MODULE 4: SECTION 1 — WAVES AND QUANTUM BEHAVIOUR

Standing Waves

You Can Calculate **Frequency** with an **Oscilloscope**

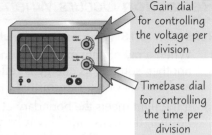

Gain dial for controlling the voltage per division

Timebase dial for controlling the time per division

1) A cathode ray **oscilloscope** (CRO) measures **voltage**. It **displays** waves from an **oscillator** as a function of **voltage** over **time**.

2) The screen is split into squares called **divisions**.

3) The vertical axis shows the **voltage**, and the **gain dial** controls the voltage represented by each **division**.

4) The horizontal axis shows **time**, and the **timebase dial** controls the time represented by each **division**.

5) To calculate the **frequency** of the wave, first you must find the **period**, T. Do this by counting how many **horizontal squares** one **wavelength** covers.

6) **Multiply** this number by the **timebase** value you set on the oscilloscope. This gives the **period**.

7) Use $f = \frac{1}{T}$ to calculate the **frequency** of the wave being **generated** by the **oscillator**.

You can Use **Standing Waves** to **Measure** the **Speed of Sound**

1) You can create a resonance tube by placing a hollow tube into a measuring cylinder of water.

2) Choose a tuning fork and note down the frequency of sound it produces (it'll be stamped on the side of it).

3) Gently tap the tuning fork and hold it just above the hollow tube. The sound waves produced by the fork travel down the tube and get reflected (and form a node) at the air/water surface.

4) Move the tube up and down until you find the shortest distance between the top of the tube and the water level that the sound from the fork resonates at. This will be when the sound appears loudest.

5) Measure the distance between the air/water surface and the tuning fork — just like with any closed pipe, this distance is a quarter of the wavelength of the standing sound wave.

6) Once you know the frequency and wavelength of the standing sound wave, you can work out the speed of sound (in air), v, using the equation $v = f\lambda$.

7) Then, repeat this experiment using tuning forks with different frequencies. You could also move the tuning fork higher above the cylinder until you find the next harmonic (equal to three quarters of the wavelength).

tuning fork

$\frac{\lambda}{4}$

node

water

measuring cylinder

hollow plastic tube

Practice Questions

Q1 How do standing waves form?

Q2 At four times the fundamental frequency, how many half wavelengths fit on a violin string?

Q3 Describe an experiment to find the speed of sound in air using standing waves.

Exam Question

Q1 a) A standing wave of three times the fundamental frequency is formed on a stretched string of length 1.2 m. Sketch a diagram showing the form and length of the wave. [2 marks]

b) Calculate the wavelength of the standing wave. [1 mark]

c) Explain how the amplitude varies along the string and how this compares to a progressive wave. [2 marks]

d) An oscilloscope is connected to the oscillator used to produce the standing wave. The seconds per division is set at 2 ms per division. One wavelength spans 4 squares on the oscilloscope display. Calculate the frequency of the wave. [2 marks]

CGP — putting the FUN back in FUNdamental frequency...

Resonance was a big problem for the Millennium Bridge in London. The resonant frequency of the bridge was roughly normal walking pace, so as soon as people started using it they set up a huge standing wave. An oversight, I feel...

Refraction and Refractive Index

The stuff on the next two pages explains why your legs look short in a swimming pool.

Refraction Occurs When the Medium a Wave is Travelling in Changes

Refraction (p.18) is the way a wave **changes direction** as it enters a **different medium**.

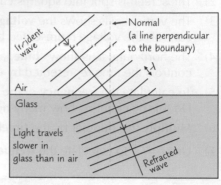

1) When a ray of light meets a boundary between one medium and another, some of its energy is **reflected** back into the first medium and the rest of it is **transmitted** through into the second medium.

2) If the light meets the boundary at an angle to the normal, the transmitted ray is bent or "**refracted**" as it travels at a **different speed** in each medium.

3) When the speed changes, the **frequency** stays **constant**, so the **wavelength** changes too ($v = f\lambda$).

4) If the ray bends **towards** the normal — it is **slowing** down. The ray is going from a **less** optically dense material to a **more** optically dense material. The wavelength **decreases**.

5) If the ray bends **away** from the normal — the wave is **speeding up**. It is going from a more optically **dense** material to a **less** optically dense material. The wavelength **increases**.

The Refractive Index of a Material Measures How Much It Slows Down Light

Light goes fastest in a **vacuum**. It **slows down** in other materials, because it **interacts** with the particles in them. The more **optically dense** a medium is, the more light slows down when it enters it.

The **absolute refractive index** of a medium, **n**, is a measure of **optical density**. It is found from the **ratio** between the **speed of light** in a **vacuum**, **c**, and the speed of light in that **medium**, c_{medium}.

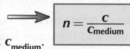

$$n = \frac{c}{c_{medium}}$$

$c = 3.00 \times 10^8 \text{ ms}^{-1}$

> **Example:** Light enters a material A, where it travels at a speed of 1.9×10^8 ms^{-1}. It then enters a second material B, which has a refractive index of 2.1. Determine whether the light ray is bent towards or away from the normal when it travels from material A to material B.

First, calculate the refractive index for material A:

$$n = \frac{c}{c_{medium}} = \frac{3.00 \times 10^8}{1.9 \times 10^8} = 1.57...$$

As the refractive index of material A is lower than that of material B, A is less optically dense than B. This means the light wave will slow down when it travels from A to B and will bend towards the normal.

Snell's Law uses Angles to Calculate the Refractive Index

When a ray of light is refracted at a boundary between two materials:

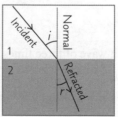

1) The light is crossing a **boundary**, going from medium 1 with refractive index n_1 to medium 2 with refractive index n_2.

2) The **angle** the **incoming light** makes to the **normal** is called the **angle of incidence**, **i**.

3) The **angle** the **refracted ray** makes with the **normal** is the **angle of refraction**, **r**.

4) n_1, n_2, i and r are related by **Snell's law**:

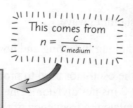

This comes from $n = \frac{c}{c_{medium}}$.

$$\frac{\sin i}{\sin r} = \frac{n_2}{n_1} \quad \text{or} \quad \frac{\sin i}{\sin r} = \frac{c_{1st\ medium}}{c_{2nd\ medium}}$$

The equivalent angles between the wavefronts and the boundary line can sometimes also be labelled as r and i.

5) The **speed of light** in **air** is only a **tiny** bit smaller than c. This means you can assume the **refractive index** of air is **1** ($n_{air} \approx c \div c$). So for an **air-to-material** boundary, Snell's law becomes:

$$n = \frac{\sin i}{\sin r}$$

where n is the refractive index of the material

Refraction and Refractive Index

You Can **Calculate** the **Refractive Index** of a **Transparent Block**

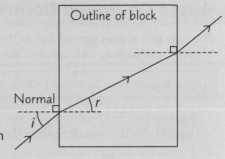

1) Place a glass block on a piece of paper and draw around it.
2) Use a **ray box** to shine a beam of light into the glass block. Turn off any other lights so you can see the path of the light beam through the block clearly.
3) **Trace** the path of the **incoming** and **outgoing** beams of light either side of the block.
4) Remove the block and join up the two paths you've drawn with a **straight line**. The line will follow the path the light beam took through the glass block. You should be able to see from your drawing how the path of the ray **bent** when entering and leaving the block.
5) Measure the angles of **incidence** and **refraction** where the light enters the block.
6) Use **Snell's law** for an **air-to-material** boundary to calculate the refractive index of the block.

Example: Light is shone through a transparent block. The angle of incidence at the air/material boundary is 30° and the angle of refraction is 25°. Calculate the refractive index of the block.

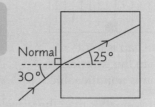

Using Snell's law for an air/material boundary:

$$n = \frac{\sin i}{\sin r} = \frac{\sin(30°)}{\sin(25°)} = 1.18... = \mathbf{1.2 \text{ (to 2 s.f.)}}$$

Practice Questions

Q1 What is refraction?

Q2 Why does light go fastest in a vacuum and slow down in other media?

Q3 Give the equation for the absolute refractive index of a material.

Q4 Write down Snell's law for an air-to-material boundary.

Q5 Describe an experiment for calculating the refractive index of a transparent block.

Exam Questions

Q1 a) Light travels in diamond at 1.24×10^8 ms^{-1}. Calculate the refractive index of diamond. [1 mark]

   b) Calculate the angle of refraction if light strikes a facet of a diamond ring at an angle of 50° (to 2 s.f.) to the normal of the air/diamond boundary. [2 marks]

Q2 Light travels from air, through a cube of material A (refractive index 1.4) and into a cube of material B.

   a) As the light ray travels from air into the block of material A, it enters at an angle of 40° (to 2 s.f.) to the normal and creates an angle of refraction of 27° to the normal. Calculate the speed of the light ray as it travels through material A. [2 marks]

   b) Light travels at 1.7×10^8 ms^{-1} in material B. Calculate the refractive index of material B. [1 mark]

   c) Calculate the angle of refraction as the light ray passes from material A to material B. [2 marks]

I don't care about expensive things — all I care about is wave speed...

Physics examiners are always saying how candidates do worst in the waves bit of the exam. You'd think they'd have something more important to worry about — poverty, war, their favourite band splitting up... but apparently not.

Diffraction

Astronomers trying to observe radio waves have to battle diffraction. They've been known to cheat and set up a network of telescopes around the world to get a good image. All that trouble because of diffraction... but it has its uses too.

Waves Go **Round Corners** and **Spread out** of **Gaps**

The way that **waves spread out** as they come through a **narrow gap** (aperture) or go round obstacles is called **diffraction**. **All** waves diffract, but it's not always easy to observe.

Use a Ripple Tank To Show Diffraction of Water Waves

You can make diffraction patterns in ripple tanks. The **amount** of diffraction depends on the **wavelength** of the wave compared with the **size of the gap**.

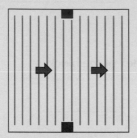

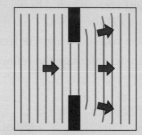

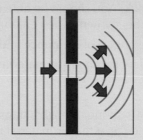

When the gap is **a lot bigger** than the **wavelength**, diffraction is **unnoticeable**.

You get **noticeable diffraction** through a gap **several** wavelengths wide.

You get the **most diffraction** when the gap is **the same** size as the **wavelength**.

If the gap is **smaller** than the wavelength, the waves are mostly just **reflected back**.

When **sound** passes through a **doorway**, the **size of gap** and the **wavelength** are usually roughly **equal**, so **a lot** of **diffraction** occurs. That's why you have no trouble **hearing** someone through an **open door** to the next room, even if the other person is out of your **line of sight**. The reason that you can't **see** him or her is that when **light** passes through the doorway, it is passing through a **gap** around a **hundred million times bigger** than its wavelength — the amount of diffraction is **tiny**.

Demonstrate **Diffraction** in **Light** Using **Laser Light**

1) Diffraction in **light** can be demonstrated by shining a **laser light** through a very **narrow slit** onto a screen (see the next page). You can alter the amount of diffraction by changing the width of the slit.

2) You can do a similar experiment using a **white light** source instead of the laser (which is monochromatic) and a set of **colour filters**. The size of the slit can be kept constant while the **wavelength** is varied by putting different **colour filters** over the slit.

Warning. Use of coloured filters may result in excessive fun.

You Get a **Similar** Effect Around an Obstacle

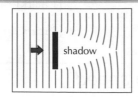

When a wave meets an **obstacle**, you get diffraction around the edges. Behind the obstacle is a '**shadow**', where the wave is blocked. The **wider** the obstacle compared with the wavelength of the wave, the less diffraction you get, and so the **longer** the shadow.

Diffraction

With *Light Waves* you get a *Pattern* of *Light* and *Dark Fringes*

1) If the wavelength of a light wave is roughly similar to the size of the aperture, you get a diffraction pattern of light and dark fringes.

2) The pattern has a bright central fringe with alternating dark and bright fringes on either side of it.

3) The central fringe is the most intense — there are more incident photons per unit area in the central fringe than in the other bright fringes. (See page 62 for more on light as photons).

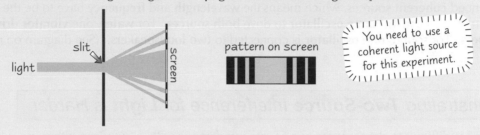

You need to use a coherent light source for this experiment.

4) The narrower the slit, the wider the diffraction pattern.

You can Explain *Diffraction Patterns* Using *Phasors*

1) The **brightest** point of a diffraction pattern is where light passes in a straight line from the slit to the screen. All the light waves that arrive there are **in phase**.

2) At all other bright points where light hits the screen, there is a **constant phase difference** between the waves arriving there, so the phasors point in slightly different directions and form a **smaller resultant**.

3) **Dark fringes** on the screen are where the phase difference between the light waves means their phasors add to form a **loop**, giving a **resultant of zero**.

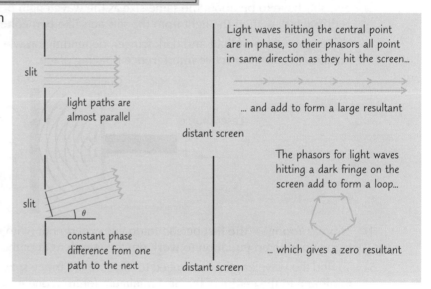

Practice Questions

Q1 What is diffraction?

Q2 Sketch what happens when plane waves meet an obstacle about as wide as one wavelength.

Q3 For a long time some scientists argued that light couldn't be a wave because it did not seem to diffract. Suggest why they might have got this impression.

Q4 Describe in terms of phasors why diffraction patterns are made up of bright and dark fringes.

Exam Question

Q1 A mountain lies directly between you and a radio transmitter.

Explain using diagrams why you can pick up long-wave radio broadcasts from the transmitter but not short-wave radio broadcasts.

[4 marks]

Even hiding behind a mountain, you can't get away from long-wave radio...

Diffraction crops up again and again, so you really need to understand it — learn it, learn it, learn it. (And then learn it again.)

Two-Source Interference

That Young chap gets everywhere... and here he is again. Young was a doctor, and nowadays you probably wouldn't trust a doctor who started telling you he was right and other physicists including Newton were wrong... I mean Newton's Mr Gravity for goodness' sake. But it turned out he was right... and this was the experiment that helped him show it.

Demonstrating Two-Source Interference in **Water** and **Sound** is Easy

1) It's **easy** to demonstrate **two-source interference** for either **sound** or **water** because they've got **wavelengths** of a handy **size** that you can **measure**.

2) You need **coherent** sources, which means the **wavelength** and **frequency** have to be the **same**. The trick is to use the **same oscillator** to drive **both sources**. For **water**, one **vibrator** drives two **dippers**. For sound, **one oscillator** is connected to **two loudspeakers**. (See diagram on page 51).

Demonstrating **Two-Source** Interference for **Light** is Harder

Light is more difficult to demonstrate two-source interference with — you can either use **two coherent light sources**, or use a single **laser** and shine it through **two slits**... clever, huh. It's called **Young's double-slit experiment**, and you need to learn it...

1) Laser light is **coherent** and **monochromatic** (there's only **one wavelength** present).

2) The slits have to be about the same size as the wavelength of the laser light so that it is **diffracted** — then the light from the slits acts like **two coherent point sources**.

3) You get a pattern of light and dark **fringes**, depending on whether constructive or destructive **interference** is taking place.

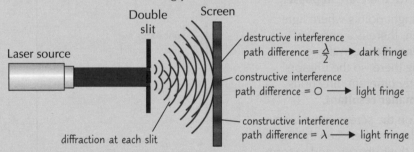

4) Thomas Young — the first person to do this experiment (with the Sun rather than a laser) — came up with an **equation** to **work out** the **wavelength** of the **light** from this experiment (see p.59).

5) To find the wavelength, you'll need to measure the **fringe spacing** — the distance from the **centre** of one **minimum** to the centre of the next minimum (or from one **maximum** centre to the next maximum centre).

You Can Do a **Similar** Experiment with **Microwaves**

1) To see interference patterns with **microwaves**, you can **replace** the laser and slits with two microwave **transmitter cones** attached to the **same signal generator**.

2) You also need to replace the screen with a microwave **receiver probe**.

3) If you move the probe along the path of the green arrow, you'll get an **alternating pattern** of **strong** and **weak** signals — just like the light and dark fringes on the screen.

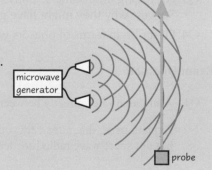

Two-Source Interference

Work Out the Wavelength with Young's Double-Slit Formula

1) The fringe spacing (**X**), wavelength (**λ**), spacing between slits (**d**) and the distance from slits to screen (**D**) are all related by **Young's double-slit formula**, which works for all waves (you need to be able to derive this, see p.61).

$$\text{Fringe spacing, } X = \frac{D\lambda}{d}$$

2) Since the wavelength of light is so small you can see from the formula that a high ratio of **D / d** is needed to make the fringe spacing **big enough to see**.

3) Rearranging, you can use $\lambda = Xd / D$ to **calculate the wavelength** of light.

4) The fringes are **so tiny** that it's very hard to get an **accurate value of X**. It's easier to measure across **several** fringes then **divide** by the number of **fringe widths** between them. Doing this helps to lower the **percentage error** — see p.8 for more about this.

Always check your fringe spacing.

Young's Experiment was Evidence for the Wave Nature of Light

1) Towards the end of the **17th century**, two important **theories of light** were published — one by Isaac Newton and the other by a chap called Huygens. **Newton's** theory suggested that light was made up of tiny particles, which he called "**corpuscles**". And **Huygens** put forward a theory using **waves**.

2) The **corpuscular theory** could explain **reflection** and **refraction**, but **diffraction** and **interference** are both **uniquely** wave properties. If it could be **shown** that light showed interference patterns, that would help settle the argument once and for all.

3) **Young's** double-slit experiment (over 100 years later) provided the necessary evidence. It showed that light could both **diffract** (through the narrow slits) and **interfere** (to form the interference pattern on the screen).

Of course, this being Physics, nothing's ever simple — give it another 100 years or so and the debate would be raging again.

Practice Questions

Q1 In Young's experiment, why do you get a bright fringe at a point equidistant from both slits?

Q2 Write down Young's double-slit formula.

Q3 What does Young's experiment show about the nature of light?

Exam Questions

Q1 a) The diagram on the right shows waves from two slits on a screen, S_1 and S_2. Behind the screen is a laser light. Sketch the interference pattern, marking on constructive and destructive interference. [2 marks]

b) If S_1 and S_2 were changed to two separate light sources, what condition must be met in order to still observe an interference pattern? [1 mark]

Q2 In an experiment to study sound interference, two loudspeakers are connected to an oscillator emitting sound at 1320 Hz and set up as shown in the diagram below. They are 1.5 m apart and 7 m away from the line AC. A listener moving from A to C hears minimum sound at A and C and maximum sound at B. (You may assume that Young's double-slit formula can be used in this calculation).

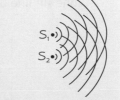

a) Calculate the wavelength of the sound waves if the speed of sound in air is taken to be 330 ms⁻¹. [1 mark]

b) Calculate the separation of points A and C. [2 marks]

Young's double-slit experiment — what bright spark came up with that name?

Be careful when you're calculating the fringe spacing by averaging over several fringes. Don't just divide by the number of bright lines. Ten bright lines will only have nine fringe-widths between them, not ten. You have been warned.

Diffraction Gratings

Diffraction gratings are pretty amazing. If you want to know what a star's made of you obviously can't just go there with your bucket and spade. Luckily astronomers can tell just by looking at light emitted from the star using one of these babies what the star's atmosphere's made of... genius.

Interference Patterns Get **Sharper** When You Diffract Through **More Slits**

1) You can repeat **Young's double-slit** experiment (see p.58) with **more than two equally spaced** slits. You get basically the **same shaped** pattern as for two slits — but the **bright bands** are **brighter** and **narrower** and the **dark areas** between are **darker**.

2) When **monochromatic light** (one wavelength) is passed through a **grating** with **hundreds** of slits per millimetre, the interference pattern is **really sharp** because there are so **many beams reinforcing** the **pattern**.

3) Sharper fringes make for more **accurate** measurements.

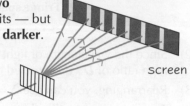

screen

diffraction grating

Monochromatic Light on a Diffraction Grating gives Sharp Lines

1) For **monochromatic** light, all the **maxima** are sharp lines. (It's different for white light — see next page.)

2) There's a line of **maximum brightness** at the centre called the **zero order** line.

3) The lines just **either side** of the central one are called **first order lines**. The **next pair out** are called **second order** lines and so on.

4) For a grating with slits a distance **d** apart, the angle between the **incident beam** and **the nth order maximum** is given by:

$$d \sin \theta = n\lambda$$

5) So by observing **d**, **θ** and **n** you can **calculate the wavelength** of the light.

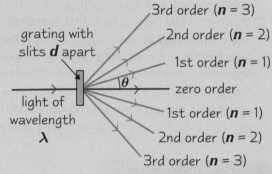

If the grating has N slits per metre, then the slit spacing, *d*, is just 1/*N* metres.

DERIVING THE EQUATION:

1) At **each slit**, the incoming waves are **diffracted**. These diffracted waves then **interfere** with each other to produce an **interference pattern**.

2) Consider the **first order maximum**. This happens at the **angle** when the waves from one slit line up with waves from the **next slit** that are **exactly one wavelength** behind.

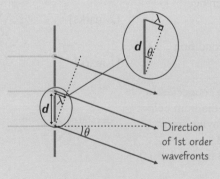

Direction of 1st order wavefronts

3) Call the **angle** between the **first order maximum** and the **incoming light** θ.

4) Now, look at the **triangle** highlighted in the diagram. The angle is θ (using basic geometry), **d** is the slit spacing and the **path difference** is λ.

5) So, for the first maximum, using trig: **d** sin θ = λ

6) The other maxima occur when the path difference is 2λ, 3λ, 4λ, etc. So to make the equation **general**, just replace λ with **n**λ, where **n** is an integer — the **order** of the maximum.

You can draw the following conclusions from *d* sin θ = *n*λ:

1) If **λ** is **bigger**, **sin θ** is **bigger**, and so **θ** is **bigger**. This means that the larger the **wavelength**, the more the pattern will **spread out**.

2) If **d** is **bigger**, **sin θ** is **smaller**. This means that the **coarser** the **grating**, the **less** the pattern will **spread out**.

3) Values of **sin θ** greater than **1** are **impossible**. So if for a certain **n** you get a result of **more than 1** for **sin θ** you know that that order **doesn't exist**.

Diffraction Gratings

You can *Derive* the *Fringe Spacing* from *d sin θ = nλ*

You have to be able to derive Young's double-slit formula for **fringe spacing** from page 59.

For the first order maximum ($n = 1$) the angle θ is small. This means you can use the **small angle approximations** of $\tan\theta \approx \theta$ and $\sin\theta \approx \theta$.

$\tan\theta$ is equal to $\dfrac{\text{opposite}}{\text{adjacent}}$, so in the triangle shown $\tan\theta = \dfrac{X}{D}$ ($\approx \theta \approx \sin\theta$).
(X is fringe spacing and D is the distance from the grating to the screen).

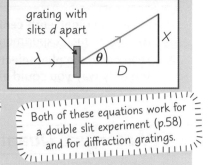

grating with slits d apart

This means you can substitute $\dfrac{X}{D}$ into $d \sin\theta = n\lambda$ to get $\dfrac{Xd}{D} = \lambda$.

Remember, $n = 1$ here.

Rearrange for X and you get $\boxed{X = \dfrac{D\lambda}{d}}$

Both of these equations work for a double slit experiment (p.58) and for diffraction gratings.

Shining *White Light* Through a *Diffraction Grating* Produces *Spectra*

1) **White light** is really a **mixture** of **colours**. If you **diffract** white light through a **grating** then the patterns due to **different wavelengths** within the white light are **spread out** by **different** amounts.

2) Each **order** in the pattern becomes a **spectrum**, with **red** on the **outside** and **violet** on the **inside**. The **zero order maximum** stays **white** because all the wavelengths just pass straight through.

3) **Astronomers** and **chemists** often need to study spectra to help identify elements. They use diffraction gratings rather than prisms because they're **more accurate**.

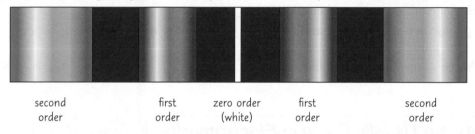

| second order | first order | zero order (white) | first order | second order |

Practice Questions

Q1 How is the diffraction grating pattern for white light different from the pattern for laser light?

Q2 What difference does it make to the pattern if you use a finer grating?

Q3 What equation is used to find the angle between the nth order maximum and the incident beam for a diffraction grating?

Q4 From this, derive Young's double-slit formula.

Exam Questions

Q1 Yellow laser light of wavelength 600 nm (6.00×10^{-7} m) is transmitted through a diffraction grating of 4.0×10^5 lines per metre.

    a) At what angle to the normal are the first and second order bright lines seen? [4 marks]

    b) Is there a fifth order line? [1 mark]

Q2 Visible, monochromatic light is transmitted through a diffraction grating of 3.7×10^5 lines per metre. The first order maximum is at an angle of 14.2° to the incident beam.

    Find the wavelength of the incident light. [2 marks]

Ooooooooooooooo — pretty patterns...

Three important points for you to take away — the more slits you have, the sharper the image, one lovely equation to learn and white light makes a pretty spectrum. Make sure you get everything in this section — there's some good stuff coming up in the next one and I wouldn't want you to be distracted.

Light — Wave or Particle?

You probably already thought light was a bit weird — but oh no... being a wave that travels at the fastest speed possible isn't enough for light — it has to go one step further and act like a particle too...

Light Behaves Like a *Wave*... or a *Stream of Particles*

1) In the **late nineteenth century**, if you asked what light was, scientists would happily show you lots of nice experiments showing how light must be a **wave** (see pages 54–61).

2) Then came the **photoelectric effect** (pages 64–65), which mucked up everything. The only way you could explain this was if light acted as a **particle** — called a **photon**.

A *Photon* is a *Quantum* of *EM Radiation*

1) When Max Planck was investigating **black body radiation** (don't worry — you don't need to know about that right now), he suggested that **EM waves** can **only** be **released** in **discrete packets**, called **quanta**. A single packet of **EM radiation** is called a **quantum**.

   The **energy carried** by one of these **wave-packets** had to be:

   $$E = hf = \frac{hc}{\lambda}$$

   where h = the Planck constant = 6.63×10^{-34} Js,
   f = frequency (Hz), λ = wavelength (m) and
   c = speed of light in a vacuum = 3.00×10^8 ms^{-1}

2) So, the **higher** the **frequency** of the electromagnetic radiation, the more **energy** its wave-packets carry.

3) **Einstein** went **further** by suggesting that **EM waves** (and the energy they carry) can only **exist** in discrete packets. He called these wave-packets **photons**.

4) He believed that a photon acts as a **particle**, and will either transfer **all** or **none** of its energy when interacting with another particle, e.g. an electron.

5) Photons have **no charge** — they are **neutral**, like neutrons.

Photon Energies are Usually Given in *Electronvolts*

1) The **energies involved** when you're talking about photons are **so tiny** that it makes sense to use a more **appropriate unit** than the **joule**. Bring on the **electronvolt**...

2) When you **accelerate** an electron between two electrodes, it transfers some electrical potential energy (eV) into kinetic energy.

   $$eV = \tfrac{1}{2}mv^2$$

   e is the size of the charge on an electron: 1.60×10^{-19} C.

3) An electronvolt is defined as:

   > The **kinetic energy gained** by an **electron** when it is **accelerated** through a **potential difference** of **1 volt**.

4) So 1 electron volt = $e \times V = 1.60 \times 10^{-19}$ C $\times$ 1 JC^{-1}. $\Longrightarrow$ $\boxed{\textbf{1 eV} = \textbf{1.60} \times \textbf{10}^{-19} \textbf{ J}}$

The *Threshold Voltage* is Used to Find the *Planck Constant*

1) The Planck constant comes up everywhere — but it's not just some random number plucked out of the air. You can find its value by doing a simple experiment with **light-emitting diodes (LEDs)**.

2) Current will only pass through an LED after a **minimum voltage** is placed across it — **the threshold voltage V_0**.

3) This is the voltage needed to give the electrons the **same energy** as a photon emitted by the LED. **All** of the electron's **kinetic energy** after it is accelerated over this potential difference is **transferred** into a **photon**.

4) So by finding the threshold voltage for a particular wavelength LED, you can estimate the Planck constant.

   $$E = \frac{hc}{\lambda} = eV_0 \Longrightarrow h = \frac{(eV_0)\lambda}{c}$$

Module 4: Section 1 — Waves and Quantum Behaviour

Light — Wave or Particle?

You can Use LEDs to Estimate the Planck Constant

You've just seen the **theory** of how to find the **Planck constant** — now it's time for the **practicalities**.

Experiment to Measure the Planck Constant

1) Connect an LED of known wavelength in the electrical circuit shown.

2) Close any blackout blinds and place a shaded tube over the LED to look through. The room should be as dark as possible so you can see when the LED first begins to emit light.

3) Start off with no current flowing through the circuit, then adjust the variable power source until a current just begins to flow through the circuit and the LED lights up.

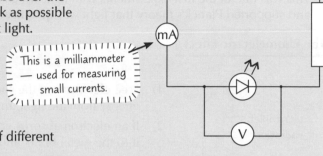
This is a milliammeter — used for measuring small currents.

4) Record the voltage (V_0) across the LED.

5) Repeat this experiment with a number of LEDs of different colours that emit light at different wavelengths.

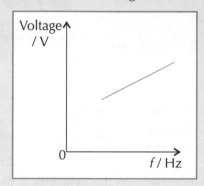

6) Plot a graph of threshold voltages (V_0) against frequency ($f = c/\lambda$) (where λ is the wavelength of light emitted by the LED in metres).

7) You should get a straight line graph with a gradient of h/e — which you can then use to find the value of h.

E.g. gradient $= \dfrac{h}{e} = 4.13 \times 10^{-15}$ so $h = 4.13 \times 10^{-15}e$

$= (4.13 \times 10^{-15}) \times (1.6 \times 10^{-19}) = 6.608 \times 10^{-34}$

$= \mathbf{6.6 \times 10^{-34}}$ **Js (to 2 s.f.)**

8) Repeat the experiment to find an average value of h.

If your straight line doesn't go through the origin, there could be some systematic errors you need to account for. You can do this by adding or taking away the difference between the origin and the vertical intercept from all of your data.

After careful measurements, Fluffles determined that her plank was indeed constant.

Practice Questions

Q1 Give two different ways to describe the nature of light.

Q2 What is a photon?

Q3 Write down the two formulas you can use to find the energy of a photon. Include the meanings of all the symbols you use.

Q4 What is an electronvolt? What is 1 eV in joules?

Q5 Describe an experiment to determine the Planck constant using different coloured LEDs.

Exam Question

Q1 An LED is tested and found to have a threshold voltage of 1.74 V.

a) Calculate the energy of the photons emitted by the LED. Give your answer in joules. [1 mark]

b) The LED emits light with a wavelength of 700 nm, given to 3 significant figures. Use your answer from a) to calculate an estimate for the value of the Planck constant. [2 marks]

c) Other LEDs are tested and a graph of threshold voltage against frequency is plotted. The intercept with the vertical axis is at 0.0400 V. Estimate the Planck constant taking this into account. [2 marks]

Millions of light particles are hitting your retinas as you read this... PANIC...

I hate it in physics when they tell you lies, make you learn it, and just when you've got to grips with it they tell you it was all a load of codswallop. It just makes me doubt all the other things they say. I bet the Earth isn't even round.
Adjusts tin foil hat. Ahem. This actually is the real deal folks — light isn't just the nice wave you've always known...

The Photoelectric Effect

If light has enough energy, it can actually cause electrons to be kicked out of a metal. Parts of the experiment that shows this can't be explained with wave theory — but the photon model does a pretty good job...

The **Photoelectric Effect** Shows **Particle Behaviour** of Light

1) The **photoelectric effect** is when a light with a **high enough frequency** is shone onto the **surface of a metal**, and causes **electrons** to be **emitted**. For **most** metals, this **frequency** falls in the **U.V.** range.

2) This was one of the first experiments with light which couldn't be explained with **wave theory** and supported Planck's theory that light was **quantised** (p.62).

The Photoelectric Effect

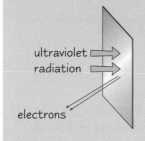

ultraviolet radiation

electrons

1) **Free electrons** on the **surface** of the metal **absorb energy** from the light, making them **vibrate**.

2) If an electron **absorbs enough** energy, the **bonds** holding it to the metal **break** and the electron is **released**.

3) This is called the **photoelectric effect** and the electrons emitted are called **photoelectrons**.

The electric photo effect is a whole other story.

You don't need to know the details of any experiments on this
— you just need to learn the **three main conclusions**:

Conclusion 1:	For a given metal, **no photoelectrons are emitted** if the radiation has a frequency **below** a certain value — called the **threshold frequency**.
Conclusion 2:	The photoelectrons are emitted with a variety of kinetic energies ranging from zero to some maximum value. This value of **maximum kinetic energy** increases with the **frequency** of the radiation, and is **unaffected** by the **intensity** (photons per unit area) of the radiation.
Conclusion 3:	The **number** of photoelectrons emitted per second is **proportional** to the **intensity** of the radiation.

These are the two that had scientists puzzled.

More on intensity of light on p.15.

The **Photoelectric Effect Couldn't** be Explained by **Wave Theory**

According to wave theory:

1) For a particular frequency of light, the **energy** carried is **proportional** to the **intensity** of the beam.

2) The energy carried by the light would be **spread evenly** over the wavefront.

3) **Each** free electron on the surface of the metal would gain a **bit of energy** from each incoming wave.

4) Gradually, each electron would gain **enough energy** to leave the metal.

For a comparison between wave theory and particle theory, see page 73.

SO...

• If the light had a **lower frequency** (i.e. was carrying less energy) it would take **longer** for the electrons to gain enough energy — but it would happen eventually. There is **no explanation** for the **threshold frequency**.

• The **higher the intensity** of the wave, the **more energy** it should transfer to each electron — the kinetic energy should increase with **intensity**. There's **no explanation** for the **kinetic energy** depending only on the **frequency**.

The Photoelectric Effect

The **Photon Model** Explained the **Photoelectric Effect** Nicely

According to the photon model (see page 62):
1) When light hits its surface, the metal is **bombarded** by photons.
2) If one of these photons is **absorbed** by a free electron, the electron will gain energy equal to *hf*. So a higher **frequency** will result in a **higher kinetic energy**.
3) Each electron only **absorbs one** photon at a time, so all the **energy** it needs to gain before it can be released must come from that **one photon**.
4) So an **increase** in the **intensity** of the light (i.e. **more photons**) won't affect the **kinetic energy** of the electrons — only the **frequency** will.

Before an electron can **leave** the surface of the metal, it needs enough energy to **break the bonds holding it there**. This energy is called the **work function energy** (symbol ϕ, phi) and its **value** depends on the **metal**.

It also Explained the **Threshold Frequency**

1) If the energy **gained** by an electron (on the surface of the metal) from a photon is **greater** than the **work function**, the electron is **emitted**.
2) If it **isn't**, the metal will heat up, but **no electrons** will be emitted.
3) Since, for **electrons** to be released, $hf \geq \phi$, the **threshold frequency** must be:

Remember, h is the Planck constant — 6.63×10^{-34} Js⁻¹.

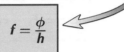

$$f = \frac{\phi}{h}$$

Example: A metal has a work function of 3.2 eV. Light is incident on the metal which has just enough energy to release electrons. Calculate the energy of the incoming light and the threshold frequency.

$$E = hf = \phi, \text{ so } f = \frac{\phi}{h} = \frac{3.2 \times 1.60 \times 10^{-19}}{6.63 \times 10^{-34}}$$

*The energy must **equal** the work function as it's **just** enough to release electrons.*

$$f = 7.72... \times 10^{14} = \textbf{7.7} \times \textbf{10}^{14} \textbf{ Hz (to 2 s.f.)}$$

Remember to convert back to joules. 1 eV = 1.60 × 10⁻¹⁹ J.

Practice Questions

Q1 State the main three conclusions which can be drawn from the photoelectric effect.
Q2 Briefly describe the wave theory of light.
Q3 Explain why the photoelectric effect suggested light wasn't a wave.
Q4 What is the equation for calculating the threshold frequency of a metal?

Exam Questions

$h = 6.63 \times 10^{-34}$ Js; 1 eV = 1.60 × 10⁻¹⁹ J

Q1 The work function of calcium is 2.9 eV. Calculate the threshold frequency of radiation needed for the photoelectric effect to take place. [2 marks]

Q2 Photons with an energy *E* of 9.0 eV strike a metal, causing it to emit electrons with kinetic energies of 3.6 eV.

a) Define the work function of a metal. [1 mark]

b) Calculate the threshold frequency of the metal. [3 marks]

Q3 Explain why the photoelectric effect only occurs after the incident light has reached a certain frequency. [3 marks]

I'm so glad we got that all cleared up...

Yep, the photoelectric effect is a bit tricky. The most important bit here is why wave theory doesn't explain the phenomenon, and why photon theory does. A good way to learn conceptual stuff like this is to try to explain it to someone else. If you need to use any formulas (e.g. for frequency), they'll be in your handy data and formulae booklet.

Energy Levels and Photon Emission

Hot gas doesn't sound like one of the nicest discussion points, but look how pretty it is.
All together now: red and yellow and pink and green, orange and purple and bluuuuuuuuuuuuuuuuuuuuuue...

Electrons in Atoms Exist in Discrete Energy Levels

1) **Electrons** in an **atom** can **only exist** in certain **well-defined energy levels**. Each level is given a **number**, with $n = 1$ representing the **ground state**.

2) Electrons can **move down** an energy level by **emitting** a **photon**.

3) Since these **transitions** are between **definite energy levels**, the **energy of each photon** emitted can **only** take a **certain allowed value**.

4) The diagram on the right shows the **energy levels** for **atomic hydrogen**.

5) The **energy** carried by each **photon** is **equal** to the **difference in energies** between the **two levels**. The equation below shows a **transition** between levels $n = 2$ and $n = 1$:

$$\Delta E = E_2 - E_1 = hf = \frac{hc}{\lambda}$$

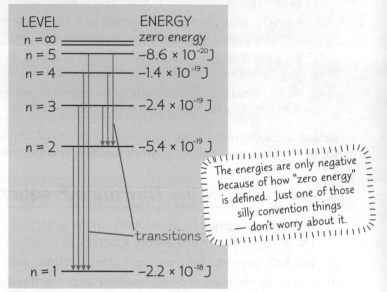

LEVEL	ENERGY
$n = \infty$	zero energy
$n = 5$	-8.6×10^{-20} J
$n = 4$	-1.4×10^{-19} J
$n = 3$	-2.4×10^{-19} J
$n = 2$	-5.4×10^{-19} J
$n = 1$	-2.2×10^{-18} J

transitions

The energies are only negative because of how "zero energy" is defined. Just one of those silly convention things — don't worry about it.

Example: An excited electron moves from the $n = 2$ level of an atom, which has an energy of $E = -1.2$ eV, to the ground state, which has an energy of -6.6 eV. Calculate the wavelength of the photon that is emitted as the electron makes this transition.

$\Delta E = E_2 - E_1 = -1.2$ eV $- -6.6$ eV $= 5.4$ eV

Convert this to joules: $5.4 \times 1.60 \times 10^{-19} = 8.64 \times 10^{-19}$ J

$\Delta E = \frac{hc}{\lambda}$ so $\lambda = \frac{hc}{\Delta E} = \frac{6.63 \times 10^{-34} \times 3.00 \times 10^8}{8.64 \times 10^{-19}} = 2.302... \times 10^{-7} = \mathbf{2.3 \times 10^{-7} m}$ (to 2 s.f.)

1 eV = 1.60 $\times 10^{-19}$ J
c = 3.00 $\times 10^8$ ms^{-1}
h = 6.63 $\times 10^{-34}$ Js.

Hot Gases Produce Line Emission Spectra

1) If you heat a gas to a high temperature, many of its electrons move to higher energy levels (this is known as excitation — the atom becomes excited).

2) As they fall back to the ground state, these electrons emit energy as photons.

3) If you split the light from a hot gas with a prism or a diffraction grating (see pages 60-61), you get a line spectrum.

4) A line spectrum is seen as a series of bright lines against a black background, as shown on the right.

5) Each line on the spectrum corresponds to a particular wavelength of light emitted by the source. Since only certain photon energies are allowed, you only see the corresponding wavelengths.

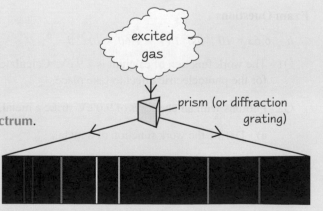

excited gas

prism (or diffraction grating)

Energy Levels and Photon Emission

Shining *White Light* through a *Cool Gas* gives an *Absorption Spectrum*

Continuous Spectra Contain All Possible Wavelengths

1) The **spectrum** of **white light** is **continuous**.

2) If you **split** the **light** up with a **prism**, the **colours** all **merge** into each other — there **aren't** any **gaps** in the spectrum.

3) **Hot things** emit a **continuous spectrum** in the visible and infrared parts of the **spectrum**.

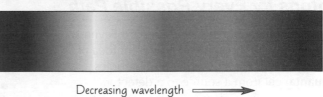

Decreasing wavelength ⟹

Cool Gases Remove Certain Wavelengths from the Continuous Spectrum

1) You get a **line absorption spectrum** when **light** with a **continuous spectrum** of **energy** (white light) passes through a cool gas.

2) At **low temperatures**, **most** of the **electrons** in the **gas atoms** will be in their **ground states**.

3) **Photons** of the **correct wavelength** are **absorbed** by the **electrons** to **excite** them to **higher energy levels**.

4) These **wavelengths** are then **missing** from the **continuous spectrum** when it **comes out** the other side of the gas.

5) You see a **continuous spectrum** with **black lines** in it corresponding to the **absorbed wavelengths**.

6) If you **compare** the **absorption** and **emission** spectra of a **particular gas**, the **black lines** in the **absorption spectrum match up** to the **bright lines** in the **emission spectrum**.

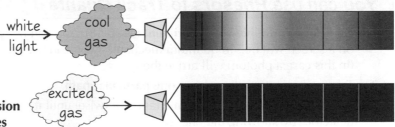

Practice Questions

Q1 Describe line absorption and line emission spectra. How are these two types of spectra produced?

Q2 Why do different excited gases glow different colours?

Exam Question

Q1 An electron has a kinetic energy of 2.04×10^{-18} J. This electron hits a hydrogen atom and excites it.

a) Explain what is meant by excitation. [1 mark]

b) Using the energy values on the right, work out to which energy level the electron in the hydrogen atom is excited. [1 mark]

c) Draw all the possible transitions the atom might undergo to return to a de-excited state. [2 marks]

d) Assume multiple electrons excite multiple atoms and all of the transitions you drew in c) occur. State how many spectral lines would appear on the emission spectra. [1 mark]

e) Calculate the frequency of the photon produced as an atom transitions from the $n = 3$ level to the $n = 1$ level. [2 marks]

$n = 5$ ———— -8.65×10^{-20} J
$n = 4$ ———— -1.36×10^{-19} J
$n = 3$ ———— -2.40×10^{-19} J
$n = 2$ ———— -5.45×10^{-19} J
$n = 1$ ———— -2.18×10^{-18} J

I can honestly say I've never got so excited that I've produced light...

This is heavy stuff, it really is. Quite interesting though, as I was just saying to Dom a moment ago. He's doing a psychology book. Psychology's probably quite interesting too — but it won't help you become an astrophysicist.

The "Sum Over Paths" Theory

So... you've got to grips with phasors... now here's where the really weird stuff kicks in. Buckle your seatbelts... and prepare to be amazed as the magical world of quantum reveals why light travels in straight lines, and why probability is a bit more useful than guessing what coloured ball you're likely to pick out of a bag...

Photons *try Every Possible Path*

1) A rather clever bloke called Richard Feynman came up with a completely different idea of how photons (or any subatomic particles, **quanta**) get from a source to a detector.

2) Feynman reckoned that instead of just taking one route to the detector, a photon will take **all** of the **possible paths** to the detector in one go. You can keep track of this photon whizzing along every possible route using **phasors** (see p.50).

> A phasor shows the amplitude (size) and phase (direction) of a point on a wave.

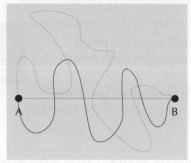

And all means <u>all</u> — the paths between A and B can be as squiggly as you like.

Andrew wasn't lost, he was just trying every path.

You can use *Phasors* to *Track Quanta*

1) Take **Young's double-slit experiment** (see p.58). You can use **phasors** to show how light or dark a certain spot on a screen will be. In quantum mechanics, you can use phasors to tell you how **probable** it is that a quantum (in this case a photon) will arrive there.

2) Take a photon travelling down **one particular path**.

3) As it travels, its phasor will rotate (anticlockwise) until it reaches the detector. By knowing the energy of the photon, you can work out the **frequency** of the phasor's rotation, f, by rearranging Planck's formula.

$$f = \frac{E}{h}$$

> Remember — E is the photon's energy and h is Planck's constant.

4) You want to **record** the position of the phasor at the **end** of every path — you could then **sum** these phasors to find the **resultant phasor** for the photon making the journey from a source to a detector.

5) Of course you can't find the final phasor for every path as there's an **infinite** number of them. When you do the maths, nearly all the phasors cancel each other out — so you only need to consider the straightest/quickest possible paths (see next page).

Young's Double-Slit Experiment (again...)

1) Imagine that a photon is emitted by the source and hits point X on the screen. Take two of its possible paths and say it follows **both** of them, as shown.

2) The **phasor** of the photon along each path rotates at the **same rate** (because it's the **same photon** so the phasors will have the same frequency).

3) Because the photon has to travel slightly **further** on the green path, it takes slightly **longer** to reach point X. This means the final phasor for the green path will have **rotated** slightly **further** than that for the blue path.

4) You can find the **resultant** phasor arrow for the photon reaching point X by **adding** the final phasor position for each path, **tip-to-tail** (just like a normal vector sum (see p.74)).

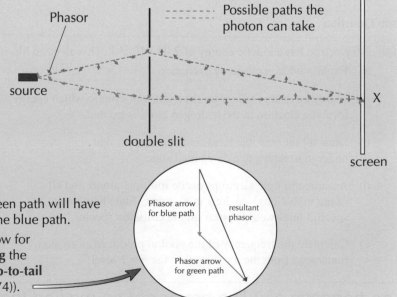

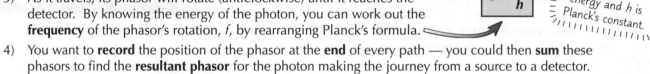

The "Sum Over Paths" Theory

You can Calculate *Probability* from the *Resultant Phasor*

1) You can find the **probability** that a quantum will arrive at a point from **squaring** the **resultant phasor amplitude**.

$$\text{Probability} \propto (\text{Resultant phasor})^2$$

2) The **resultant phasor amplitude** has nothing to do with the **amplitude** of the light wave hitting the area, only the **probability** that a particle will arrive there.

3) The **higher** the probability, the **more likely** the particle will arrive there (well duh....).

4) If the **photon** is your quantum of choice, you can think of the **probability** and the **brightness** of the area as pretty much the same thing — the more **probable** it is that a photon will arrive at a point, the **brighter** it will appear.

Example: The resultant phasor amplitudes are shown for the paths a photon could take to points X and Y. How many times brighter does point X appear than point Y? Explain your answer.

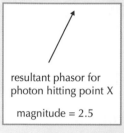

resultant phasor for photon hitting point X

magnitude = 2.5

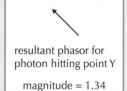

resultant phasor for photon hitting point Y

magnitude = 1.34

Square the magnitude of each phasor to find a number proportional to the probability of the photon arriving at each point.

Probability of photon hitting point X $\propto (2.5)^2 = $ **6.25**

Probability of photon hitting point Y $\propto (1.34)^2 = 1.7956$
$$= \textbf{1.80 (to 3 s.f.)}$$

The more probable a photon will arrive at a point, the brighter it will be. So the relative probability of a photon arriving at the two points will be the relative brightness between the points.

So, point X appears $6.25 \div 1.7956 = 3.48... = $ **3.5 times (to 2 s.f.)** brighter than point Y.

The *Path* that gives the *Highest Probability* is the *Quickest Route*

1) The sum over paths rule (finding the path with the **highest probability**) predicts all sorts of physics laws we take for granted. And each time it seems to be down to the **same reason**:

The final phasor of the **quickest path** will contribute the **most** to the **resultant amplitude** and the **probability** of a quantum arriving at a point.

2) It even predicts one of the most fundamental light behaviours — that **light** travels in a **straight line**. As a **straight line** is the shortest (and therefore **quickest**) path between two points — it provides the largest probability of a photon arriving at a particular point.

3) Obviously there are times when light **doesn't** travel in a straight line, like when it's being **refracted** — but quantum behaviour predicts that as well...

Refraction is also Predicted by Quantum Behaviour

1) Imagine spotting a pineapple at the bottom of a swimming pool. What **route** does the light take from the pineapple to your eye? Altogether now... it takes **all of them**.

2) When light travels in water, it **slows down**, but its **frequency stays the same**. This means the photons still have the **same energy**, and a photon's phasor will still have the **same amplitude** and **frequency** of rotation **whatever** material it's travelling through.

3) If you **add** up all the phasors for all the possible paths, it's the path that takes the **shortest time** that contributes the most to the **resultant amplitude** (and so gives the **highest probability** that the photon will get to your eye).

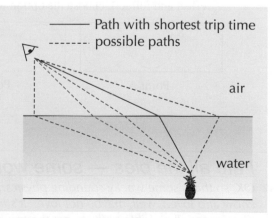

—— Path with shortest trip time
------ possible paths

air

water

The "Sum Over Paths" Theory

You Need *All Paths* to Take the *Same Time* to Focus *Quanta*

To **focus** photons (or any other quanta), you need to make sure all straight line paths (that follow the reflection or refraction rule) from the source to the focus point take the **same amount of time** — so the final phasors for every path will be in the same direction.

A Convex Lens

The paths towards the edges of the lens are longer than those that go through the middle. You make the time taken for each path the same by increasing the amount of glass in the middle part of the lens to increase the time it takes to travel along the shorter paths between the source and detector.

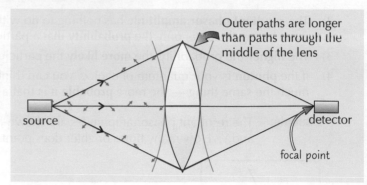

Outer paths are longer than paths through the middle of the lens

source
detector
focal point

Practice Questions

Q1 What equation would you use to find the frequency of rotation of a photon phasor?

Q2 How are two phasor arrows combined to give a resultant?

Q3 How will a point appear if the probability for a light photon is zero there?

Q4 What path gives the highest probability?

Q5 Explain why light travels in straight lines.

Q6 Describe in terms of phasors how light is focused through a convex lens.

Exam Questions

Q1 The resultant phasors for an electron reaching points A and B have magnitudes of 6.3 and 4.5 respectively. How many times more likely is it that an electron will arrive at point A than point B? [3 marks]

Q2 A light photon has a frequency of 6.0×10^{14} Hz. How many times does the photon's phasor arrow rotate as it moves along a path 120 mm long from a source to a detector? ($c = 3.0 \times 10^8$ ms^{-1}.) [2 marks]

Q3 Using the idea of phasors and the "sum over paths theory", explain why very little (if any) light would be detected around the corner from the source in the diagram shown. [3 marks]

○ light source

walls

detector

Q4 A photon takes all possible paths through a convex lens. By considering three possible straight line paths (that can reflect and refract), choose the option which correctly describes the phasors of each path at the focal point of the lens.

Point A   Point B   Point C   Point D

[1 mark]

I ate all the pies — some would call it greed, I say it's photon thinking...

OK, so that's some wacky sounding physics... but it does seem to work and agree with the standard physics laws we know and love... well, maybe not love. It's tricky, but you just need to follow the same method each time: sum the final phasors for all possible paths to get the resultant, then use the resultant to find the probability the quanta will get there.

Quantum Behaviour of Electrons

Light isn't the only thing that shows quantum behaviour — electrons do too...

De Broglie Suggested Electrons were Quantum Objects

1) Louis de Broglie made a **bold suggestion** in his **PhD thesis**:

> If 'wave-like' light showed particle properties (photons), 'particles' like electrons should be expected to show wave-like properties.

2) The **de Broglie equation** relates a **wave property** (**wavelength**, λ) to a **moving particle property** (**momentum**, p). h = Planck's constant = 6.63×10^{-34} Js.

$$\lambda = \frac{h}{p} \quad \text{or} \quad \lambda = \frac{h}{mv}$$

I'm not impressed — this is just speculation. What do you think Dad?

3) The **de Broglie wave** of a particle can be interpreted as a '**probability wave**'. You can use it to find the probability of finding an electron at a particular point (hmm, sounds familiar...).

4) Many physicists at the time **weren't very impressed** — his ideas were just **speculation**. But later experiments **confirmed** the wave nature of electrons.

Example: Electrons in a beam are travelling at a speed of 3.50×10^6 ms^{-1} and are exhibiting quantum behaviour. Calculate the de Broglie wavelength of the particles, and the speed at which protons would need to travel to have an equal de Broglie wavelength. $m_e = 9.11 \times 10^{-31}$ kg, $m_p = 1.673 \times 10^{-27}$ kg, $h = 6.63 \times 10^{-34}$ Js.

The momentum of the electrons is:

$p = mv = 9.11 \times 10^{-31} \times 3.50 \times 10^6 = 3.1885 \times 10^{-24}$ kgms^{-1}

So the de Broglie wavelength of the electrons is:

$\lambda = \dfrac{h}{p} = \dfrac{6.63 \times 10^{-34}}{3.1885 \times 10^{-24}} = 2.079... \times 10^{-10} = \mathbf{2.08 \times 10^{-10}}$ **m (to 3 s.f.)**

For the protons:

$v = \dfrac{h}{m\lambda} = \dfrac{6.63 \times 10^{-34}}{1.673 \times 10^{-27} \times 2.079... \times 10^{-10}} = 1905.8... = \mathbf{1910}$ **ms^{-1}(to 3 s.f.)**

Rearranging $\lambda = \dfrac{h}{mv}$.

The Evidence: Electron Interference and Superposition

1) You can repeat experiments like **Young's double-slit** experiment (p.58) with **electrons**. They show the same kind of **interference** and **superposition** effects as you get with photons.

2) You usually show interference and superposition patterns using a **fluorescent screen**. As an electron hits the screen, it causes a photon to be released, so you can see the location of the electron.

3) Just like photons, the **electrons try every path**:

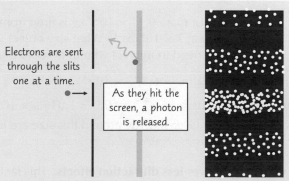

Electrons are sent through the slits one at a time.

As they hit the screen, a photon is released.

If the location of each photon that's released is recorded, gradually the interference patten builds up, showing the same bright and dark fringes as Young's double slit experiment for light.

Bright fringes in an electron interference pattern show where the probability of an electron arriving is high.
Dark fringes show where the probability of an electron hitting the screen is low.

Quantum Behaviour of Electrons

Electron Diffraction Also Supports Electrons Being Quantum Objects

1) **Diffraction patterns** are observed when **accelerated electrons** in a vacuum tube **interact** with the **spaces** in a graphite **crystal**.

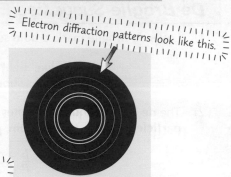

Electron diffraction patterns look like this.

2) You can think of it in exactly the same way as photon diffraction. By summing the final phasor for every possible path, you can find how **likely** it is an electron will hit the fluorescent screen at a particular point. The **higher** the **probability**, the **brighter** the point on the screen.

3) The only difference is that when finding the **frequency** and **amplitude** of the electron phasor, **E** is the **kinetic energy** of the electron.

$$f = \frac{E_{kinetic}}{h}$$

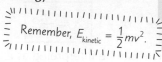

Remember, $E_{kinetic} = \frac{1}{2}mv^2$.

4) This **confirms** that **electrons** show **quantum behaviour**.

5) This was a **huge** discovery. A few years earlier, **Louis de Broglie** had **hypothesised** that electrons would show **quantum behaviour** just like **light**, but this was the first **direct evidence** for it.

6) **Increasing** the **accelerating voltage** also **increases** the **electron speed**. The diffraction pattern circles will **squash together** towards the **middle**. This fits in with the **de Broglie** equation on the previous page — if the **velocity** is **higher**, the **wavelength** is **shorter** and the **spread** of lines is **smaller**.

The race was on to squash into the best sunbathing spot.

Example: An electron has a velocity of 8.42×10^5 ms⁻¹. Calculate the frequency of the electron phasor. Electron mass = 9.11×10^{-31} kg.

$E_{kinetic} = \frac{1}{2} \times m \times v^2 = \frac{1}{2} \times 9.11 \times 10^{-31} \times (8.42 \times 10^5)^2 = 3.229... \times 10^{-19}$

$f = E_{kinetic} / h = (3.229... \times 10^{-19}) / (6.63 \times 10^{-34})$

$= 4.870... \times 10^{14} = \mathbf{4.87 \times 10^{14}}$ **Hz (to 3 s.f.)**

Electrons Don't show Quantum Behaviour All the Time

1) You **only** get **diffraction** if a particle interacts with an object of about the **same size** as its **de Broglie wavelength**.

2) A **tennis ball**, for example, with **mass 0.058 kg** and **speed 100 ms⁻¹** has a **de Broglie wavelength** of 10^{-34} m. That's 10^{19} **times smaller** than the **nucleus** of an **atom**! There's nothing that small for it to interact with.

Example: An electron of mass 9.11×10^{-31} kg is fired from an electron gun at 7×10^6 ms⁻¹. What size object will the electron need to interact with in order to diffract?

You need the de Broglie equation from the previous page, $\lambda = \frac{h}{mv}$.

Momentum of electron = $mv = 6.377 \times 10^{-24}$ kg ms⁻¹

$\lambda = h/mv = 6.63 \times 10^{-34} / 6.377 \times 10^{-24} = 1.039... \times 10^{-10} = \mathbf{1 \times 10^{-10}}$ **m (to 1 s.f.)**

Only crystals with atom layer spacing around this size are likely to cause the diffraction of this electron.

3) A **shorter wavelength** gives **less diffraction effects**. This fact is used in the **electron microscope**.

Diffraction effects **blur detail** on an image. If you want to **resolve tiny detail** in an **image**, you need a **shorter wavelength**. **Light** blurs out detail more than **electrons** do, so an **electron microscope** can resolve **finer detail** than a **light microscope**. They can let you look at things as tiny as a single strand of DNA... which is nice.

Quantum Behaviour of Electrons

All this Couldn't Be Explained By **Particle Theory**

1) Particle theory says that particles are **physical** objects which cannot **superpose** with other particles. To have **interference** patterns, you need superposition.

2) You also need at least **two slits** to create an interference pattern — classic particles would either go through **one slit** or the other, not both. However, interference patterns can be seen when only a **single electron** at a time is sent through narrow slits.

3) These experiments showed how electrons exhibited **wave-like** properties as theorised by de Broglie.

The table shows which observations are explained by each theory of light.

Phenomenon	Is it explained by...	
	...wave theory?	...particle theory?
Diffraction	Yes	No
Superposition and Interference	Yes	No
Refraction	Yes	No
Photoelectric effect	No	Yes

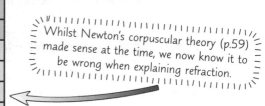

Whilst Newton's corpuscular theory (p.59) made sense at the time, we now know it to be wrong when explaining refraction.

Practice Questions

Q1 State the two equations for calculating the de Broglie wavelength and explain all of the symbols used.

Q2 What happens to the de Broglie wavelength of a particle if its velocity increases?

Q3 State one observable phenomena which supported de Broglie's theory that electrons were quantum objects.

Q4 What is the formula for calculating the phasor frequency of electrons?

Q5 What conditions must be met for electron diffraction to occur?

Q6 What were the limitations of particle theory which showed that electrons must display wave-like properties?

Exam Questions

Q1 An electron has a kinetic energy of 5.22×10^{-19} J.

a) Calculate the frequency of the electron phasor. [1 mark]

b) Calculate the atomic spacing needed to cause diffraction of the electron. [2 marks]

c) Calculate how much the velocity of the electron would need to be increased by for it to be diffracted by a lattice spacing of 2.3×10^{-10} m. [2 marks]

Q2 Electrons are accelerated through a potential difference and diffracted through a crystal lattice. The diffraction pattern is shown in Figure 1. The potential difference is then altered, and a second diffraction pattern is created, as shown in Figure 2.

Fig. 1   Fig. 2

a) State whether the accelerating voltage was increased or decreased. [1 mark]

b) Explain why the rings are closer together on the second diffraction pattern. [2 marks]

Don't look now, but... it's the ENDOFTHESECTION — YAY...

Right — I think we'll all agree that quantum physics is a wee bit strange when you come to think about it. What it's saying is that electrons and photons aren't really waves, and they aren't really particles — they're both... at the same time. It's what quantum physicists like to call a 'juxtaposition of states'. Well they would, wouldn't they...

Scalars and Vectors

Time to draw some lovely triangles. Please, don't all thank me at once...

Scalars Only Have Size, but Vectors Have Size and Direction

1) A **scalar** has **no direction** — it's **just an amount** of something, like the **mass** of a **sack of meaty dog food**.

2) A **vector** has magnitude (**size**) and **direction** — like the **velocity** (**speed and direction**) of next door's **cat** running away.

3) **Force**, **velocity** and **momentum** are all **vectors** — you need to know **which way** they're going as well as **how big** they are. Here are some of the common scalars and vectors that you'll come across in your exams:

Scalars	Vectors
mass, time, temperature, length, speed, energy	displacement, force, velocity, acceleration, momentum

You can Add Vectors to Find the Resultant

1) Adding two or more vectors is called finding the **resultant** of them. Whatever the quantity is — displacement, force, momentum, the procedure is the same.

2) You should always start by drawing a **diagram**. Draw the vectors '**tip-to-tail**'. If you're doing a **vector subtraction**, draw the vector you're subtracting with the same magnitude but pointing in the **opposite direction**.

3) If the vectors are at **right angles** to each other, then you can use **Pythagoras** and **trigonometry** to find the resultant vector.

4) If the vectors aren't at right angles, you may need to draw a **scale diagram**.

Trig's really useful in physics, so make sure you're completely okay with it. Remember SOH CAH TOA.

Example 1:   Jemima goes for a walk. She walks 3.0 m north and 4.0 m east. She has walked 7.0 m but she isn't 7.0 m from her starting point. Find the magnitude and direction of her displacement.

First, draw the vectors **tip-to-tail**. Then draw a line from the **tail** of the first vector to the **tip** of the last vector to give the **resultant**:

Because the vectors are at right angles, you get the **magnitude** of the resultant using Pythagoras:

$R^2 = 3.0^2 + 4.0^2 = 25.0$ So $R = \textbf{5.0 m}$

4.0 m

3.0 m

resultant vector, R

Jemima's 'displacement' gives her position relative to her starting point, see p.76.

Now find the **bearing** of Jemima's new position from her original position. You use the triangle again, but this time you need to use trigonometry. You know the opposite and the adjacent sides, so you can use:

$\tan \theta = 4.0\,/\,3.0$ So $\theta = \textbf{053° (to 2 s.f.)}$

4.0 m

3.0 m

θ

resultant vector magnitude = 5.0 m

Jemima

Example 2:   A van is accelerating north, with a resultant force of 510 N. A wind begins to blow on a bearing of 150°. It exerts a force of 200 N on the van. What is the new resultant force acting on the van?

A bearing is just an angle measured clockwise from the north line, represented by three digits, e.g. 10° = 010°.

The vectors **aren't** at right angles, so you need to do a scale drawing. Pick a sensible scale. Here, 1 cm = 100 N seems good.

Using a really sharp pencil, draw the initial resultant force on the van. As the van is going north, this should be a 5.1 cm long line going straight up.

The force of the wind acts on a bearing of 150°, so add this to your diagram. Using the same scale, this vector has a length of 2.0 cm.

Then you can draw on the new resultant force and measure its length. Measure the angle carefully to get the bearing.

The resultant force has a magnitude of 350 N (to 2 s.f.), acting on a bearing of 017° (to 2 s.f.).

North

150°

Wind: 2.0 cm = 200 N

Van: 5.1 cm = 510 N

New resultant force: 3.5 cm = 350 N

17° (to 2 s.f.)

Instead of a scale drawing, you could also use the sine and cosine rules.

Scalars and Vectors

It's Useful to Split a **Vector** into **Horizontal** and **Vertical Components**

This is the opposite of finding the resultant — you start from the resultant vector and split it into two **components** at right angles to each other. You're basically **working backwards** from Example 1 on the last page.

> **Resolving a vector v into horizontal and vertical components:**

You get the **horizontal** component v_h like this:

$$\cos \theta = v_h / v$$

$$\boxed{v_h = v \cos \theta}$$

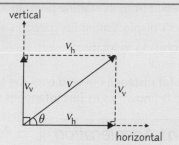

...and the **vertical** component v_v like this:

$$\sin \theta = v_v / v$$

$$\boxed{v_v = v \sin \theta}$$

Where θ is the angle from the horizontal.

Example: Charley's amazing floating home is travelling at a speed of 5 ms⁻¹ at an angle of 60° to the horizontal. Find the vertical and horizontal components.

The **horizontal** component v_h is:
$$v_h = v \cos \theta = 5 \cos 60° = \mathbf{2.5 \ ms^{-1}}$$

The **vertical** component v_v is:
$$v_v = v \sin \theta = 5 \sin 60° = \mathbf{4.3 \ ms^{-1}} \text{ (to 2 s.f.)}$$

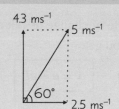

Charley's mobile home was the envy of all his friends.

Resolving is dead useful because the two components of a vector **don't affect each other**. This means you can deal with the two directions **completely separately**.

See pages 80–81 for more on resolving.

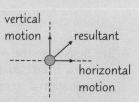

Only the vertical component is affected by gravity.

Practice Questions

Q1 What is the difference between a vector and a scalar?

Q2 Name three vector quantities and three scalar quantities.

Q3 Describe how to find a resultant vector using a scale diagram.

Q4 If a vector of magnitude L makes an angle of 30° to the horizontal, what are the horizontal and vertical components of the vector?

Exam Questions

Q1 The wind applies a horizontal force of 20 N on a falling rock of weight 75 N. Calculate the magnitude and direction of the resultant force. [2 marks]

Q2 A glider is travelling at a velocity of 20.0 ms⁻¹ at an angle of 15.0° below the horizontal. Calculate the horizontal and vertical components of the glider's velocity. [2 marks]

Q3 A remote controlled boat is placed in a river. The boat produces a driving speed of 1.54 ms⁻¹ at an angle of 60° to the current (travelling with the current). The river is flowing at 0.20 ms⁻¹. By resolving the vectors into their horizontal and vertical components, show that the resultant velocity of the boat is 1.6 ms⁻¹ at an angle of 54° to the current. [4 marks]

I think I'm a scalar quantity, my Mum says I'm completely direction-less...

Lots of different ways to solve vector problems on these pages, it must be your lucky day. Personally, I avoid doing scale drawings unless I absolutely have to (too fiddly for my liking), but if they work for you that's great. And you may get told to draw one in your exams, so you need to be prepared in case they come up.

Motion with Constant Acceleration

All the equations on this page are for motion with constant acceleration. It makes life a whole lot easier, trust me.

Learn the **Definitions** of **Speed**, **Displacement**, **Velocity** and **Acceleration**

Displacement, velocity and acceleration are all **vector** quantities (page 74), so the **direction** matters.

> **Speed** — How fast something is moving, regardless of direction (i.e. the magnitude of velocity).
> **Displacement** (s) — How far an object's travelled from its starting point in a given direction.
> **Velocity** (v) — The rate of change of an object's displacement (its speed in a given direction).
> **Acceleration** (a) — The rate of change of an object's velocity.

During a journey, the **average speed** is just the **total distance** covered over the **total time** elapsed.
The speed of an object at any given point in time is known as its **instantaneous** speed.

Uniform Acceleration is Constant Acceleration

Acceleration could mean a change in speed or direction or both.

Uniform means **constant** here. It's nothing to do with what you wear.
There are **four main equations** that you use to solve problems involving **uniform acceleration**.
You need to be able to **derive them** so make sure you learn all of these steps.

1) **Acceleration is the rate of change of velocity.**
   From this definition you get:

   $$a = \frac{(v - u)}{t} \quad \text{so} \quad \boxed{v = u + at}$$

   where:
   u = initial velocity a = acceleration
   v = final velocity t = time taken

2) **displacement = average velocity × time**
   If acceleration is constant, the average velocity is just the average of the initial and final velocities, so:

   $$\text{average velocity} = \frac{(u + v)}{2} \qquad \boxed{s = \frac{(u + v)}{2} \times t}$$

   s = displacement

3) Substitute the expression for v from equation 1 into equation 2 to give:

   $$s = \frac{(u + u + at) \times t}{2}$$
   $$= \frac{2ut + at^2}{2}$$

   $$\boxed{s = ut + \tfrac{1}{2}at^2}$$

4) You can **derive** the fourth equation from equations **1** and **2**:

   Use equation **1** in the form: $a = \dfrac{v - u}{t}$ Multiply both sides by s, where: $s = \dfrac{(u + v)}{2} \times t$

   This gives us: $\quad as = \dfrac{(v - u)}{t} \times \dfrac{(u + v)t}{2}$

   The t's on the right cancel, so:
   $2as = (v - u)(v + u)$
   $2as = v^2 - uv + uv - u^2$

   so: $\boxed{v^2 = u^2 + 2as}$

Example: A tile falls from the edge of a roof 25.0 m above ground level. Assuming it was initially at rest, calculate its speed when it hits the ground and how long it takes to fall. Take $g = 9.81$ ms^{-2}.

First of all, write out what you know:
$s = 25.0$ m
$u = 0$ ms^{-1} since the tile's stationary to start with
$a = 9.81$ ms^{-2} due to gravity
$v = ?$ $t = ?$

Usually you take upwards as the positive direction. In this question it's probably easier to take downwards as positive, so you get $g = +9.81$ ms^{-2} instead of $g = -9.81$ ms^{-2}.

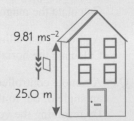
9.81 ms^{-2}
25.0 m

Then, choose an equation with only **one unknown quantity**.
So start with $v^2 = u^2 + 2as$
$v^2 = 0 + 2 \times 9.81 \times 25.0$
$v^2 = 490.5$ $v = $ **22.1 ms^{-1} (to 3 s.f.)**

Now, find t using:
$s = ut + \tfrac{1}{2}at^2$
$25.0 = 0 + \tfrac{1}{2} \times 9.81 \times t^2$
$t^2 = \dfrac{25.0}{4.905}$

Final answers:
$t = $ **2.26 s (to 3 s.f.)**
$v = $ **22.1 ms^{-1} (to 3 s.f.)**

Motion with Constant Acceleration

Example: A car accelerates steadily from rest at a rate of 4.2 ms^{-2} for 6.0 seconds.

a) Calculate the car's final speed.

b) Calculate the distance travelled by the car during the 6.0 seconds.

4.2 ms^{-2}

Remember — always start by writing down what you know.

a) $a = 4.2$ ms^{-2} choose the right equation... $v = u + at$

$u = 0$ ms^{-1} $v = 0 + 4.2 \times 6.0$

$t = 6.0$ s   **Final answer:** $v = \textbf{25.2 ms}^{-1}$

$v = ?$

b) $s = ?$ you can use: $s = \dfrac{(u + v)}{2} \times t$ **or:** $s = ut + \frac{1}{2}at^2$

$t = 6.0$ s

$u = 0$ ms^{-1}

$a = 4.2$ ms^{-2} $s = \dfrac{(0 + 25.2)}{2} \times 6.0$ $s = 0 + \frac{1}{2} \times 4.2 \times (6.0)^2$

$v = 25.2$ ms^{-1}

Final answer: $s = \textbf{75.6 m}$ $s = \textbf{75.6 m}$

It's always better to use an equation which doesn't use a value you've previously calculated.

Practice Questions

Q1 Write down the definitions of speed, velocity and displacement.

Q2 Define average speed.

Q3 Define acceleration and write down the equation that links acceleration, initial and final velocity and time.

Q4 Give the equation for calculating the average velocity.

Q5 Write down another equation of motion for constant acceleration.

Exam Questions

Q1 A skydiver steps out of an aeroplane when it is flying horizontally. She accelerates due to gravity for 5 s.
a) Calculate her maximum vertical velocity. (Assume no air resistance.)   [2 marks]
b) Calculate how far she falls in this time.   [2 marks]

Q2 A motorcyclist slows down uniformly as he approaches a red light.
He takes 3.2 seconds to come to a halt and travels 40 m in this time.
a) Calculate how fast he was travelling initially.   [2 marks]
b) Calculate his acceleration. (N.B. a negative value shows a deceleration.)   [2 marks]

Q3 The flow of a section of river provides a constant acceleration of 6 ms^{-2}. A remote controlled boat
is travelling upstream. 1.2 m upstream from the edge of a waterfall, the boat's motor cuts out.
Just before it reaches the waterfall, it is travelling at a speed of 5 ms^{-1}.
a) Calculate the boat's velocity when the motor cuts out.   [2 marks]
b) Calculate the maximum distance upstream from the waterfall the boat reaches.   [2 marks]

Q4 A cyclist is travelling at a constant speed of 3 ms^{-1} as he starts to roll down a hill. He rolls down the
hill with a constant acceleration. During the third second, he travels a distance of 6 m.
a) Calculate the cyclist's acceleration.   [3 marks]
b) Calculate how far he travels during the fourth second.   [2 marks]

Constant acceleration — it'll end in tears...

If a question talks about "uniform" or "constant" acceleration, it's a dead giveaway they want you to use one of these equations. The tricky bit is working out which one to use — start every question by writing out what you know and what you need to know. That makes it much easier to see which equation you need. To be sure. Arrr.

Acceleration of Free Fall

Ahhh acceleration due to gravity. The reason falling apples whack you on the head.

Free Fall is When There's Only Gravity and Nothing Else

Free fall is defined as the motion of an object undergoing an acceleration of 'g'. You need to remember:

1) Acceleration is a **vector quantity** — and 'g' acts **vertically downwards**.

2) The magnitude of 'g' is usually taken as **9.81 ms⁻²**, though it varies slightly at different points above the Earth's surface.

3) The **only force** acting on an object in free fall is its **weight**.

4) **All** objects free fall at the **same rate**.

5) Objects can have an initial velocity in any direction and still undergo **free fall** as long as the **force** providing the initial velocity is **no longer acting**.

You Can Calculate g By Doing an Experiment...

1) Set up the equipment shown in the diagram on the right.

2) Measure the height h from the **bottom** of the ball bearing to the **trapdoor**.

3) Flick the switch to simultaneously **start the timer** and **disconnect the electromagnet**, releasing the ball bearing.

4) The ball bearing falls, knocking the trapdoor down and **breaking the circuit** — which **stops the timer**. Record the time t shown on the timer.

5) **Repeat** this experiment three times and **average** the time taken to fall from this height. Do this for a range of **different heights**.

6) You can then use these results to find g using a **graph**.

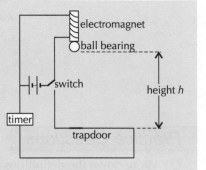

1) Use your data from the experiment to plot a graph of **height** (s) against the **time** it takes the ball to fall, **squared** (t^2). Then draw a **line of best fit**.

2) You know that with constant acceleration: $s = ut + \frac{1}{2}at^2$.

3) If you drop the ball, initial speed $u = 0$, so $s = \frac{1}{2}at^2$.

4) Rearranging this gives $\frac{1}{2}a = \frac{s}{t^2}$, or $\frac{1}{2}g = \frac{s}{t^2}$ (remember the acceleration is all due to gravity).

5) The gradient of the line of best fit $\frac{\Delta s}{\Delta t^2}$, is equal to $\frac{1}{2}g$:

$$g = 2 \times \frac{\Delta s}{\Delta t^2} = 2 \times \frac{0.44}{0.09} = 9.8 \text{ ms}^{-2} \text{ (to 2 s.f.)}$$

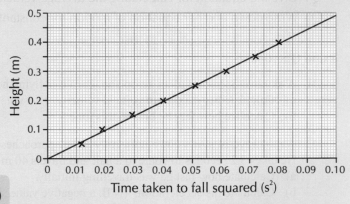

To increase the **accuracy** (see page 8) of the measurements you take you can:

- Use a **small** and **heavy** ball bearing so you can assume air resistance is so small that you can **ignore it**.

- Use a ruler with **smaller increments** and pick a certain **point** on the ball bearing to measure from to reduce the errors in measuring the **height**.

In the experiment above, using a computer to **automatically release** and **time** the ball bearing's fall **removes random error** that might arise if you timed the ball bearing manually by eye with a stopwatch, **reducing** the **uncertainty** (see page 8) in **time** measurement.

You could also do a **similar** experiment with **light gates**. **Drop** the ball bearing from a height h so it falls through a light gate. The light gate **automatically** calculates the **velocity** of the falling object.

You can then use $v^2 = u^2 + 2as$ to calculate the acceleration due to gravity, g.

Both methods give less **uncertainty** when calculating g than measuring the time manually by eye would. The light gates can calculate the velocity automatically, instead of it being calculated from time measurements, which could reduce **systematic error**. This means the main uncertainty would be caused by measuring h.

Acceleration of Free Fall

You Can Also Use *Video Techniques* to find *g*

1) Set up a **video camera** in front of a **metre rule** and record the ball as it is dropped from the top of the ruler.
2) Once the ball hits the floor, you can stop recording and analyse the video with video editing software.
3) Go through **frame by frame**, making a note of the **distance** the ball has travelled every **0.1 seconds**.
4) Create a table to calculate the ball's **velocity**. You can then calculate an average value for *g* from the **table** or plot a **graph** of **velocity** against **distance**. The **gradient** of this graph will give the **acceleration** due to gravity.

Your table should have the headings shown below:

Time (s)	Total distance fallen (m)	Change in distance (m)	Velocity (ms⁻¹)	Change in velocity (ms⁻¹)	Acceleration (ms⁻²)

You'll be measuring every 0.1 s. | This is what you measure. | This is the distance fallen in the 0.1 s interval. | This is change in distance ÷ change in time. (Which is the previous column ÷ 0.1) | This is the difference in the velocities in the current row and the previous one. | This is the change in velocity ÷ change in time (i.e. the previous column ÷ 0.1)

You can also use a **regular camera** in a **dark** room and a **strobe light** to find *g*.

Set the camera to take a **long exposure**. While the camera is taking the photo, turn on the strobe light and **drop** the ball. As the ball falls, it will be **lit up** at regular intervals by the strobe light. This means that ball will appear **multiple times** in the photograph, in a different position each time. Calculate the **change in distance** between each location of the ball and create the same **table** as above. The **frequency** that the strobe light flashes at gives you the **time interval** between distances.

1) The **main cause** of uncertainty in this experiment is in measuring the **distance** fallen by the ball — other sources of uncertainty are small because you're not timing the ball yourself (see previous page).
2) **Parallax** (systematic error due to looking at the ruler at an angle) will also affect your **distance** measurements, so make sure your camera is at a **right angle** to the ruler (and use **multiple cameras** if the ruler is large).
3) Uncertainty caused by the **time interval** between pictures can be reduced by either **increasing** the **frequency** of the strobe light, or using a camera with a **higher frame rate**.
4) **Repeating** the experiment and calculating an **average value** of *g* can also increases the accuracy of the experiment.
5) Measuring over a **larger distance** or using **smaller time increments** means you will **average** over more values, which is likely to give a more **accurate** value for *g*.

Practice Questions

Q1 What is meant by free fall?
Q2 How does the velocity of a free-falling object change with time?
Q3 Describe an experiment that uses an electromagnet and a trapdoor to calculate the value of *g*.
Q4 Describe how video techniques could be used to calculate a value of *g*.

Exam Questions

Q1 In an experiment to determine the value of *g*, a small steel ball is dropped from a range of heights. The time it takes to reach the ground when dropped from each height is recorded.

a) Explain why using a small steel ball is better than using a beach ball in this experiment. [1 mark]
b) State one random and one systematic error that could arise from this experiment and suggest ways to reduce or remove them. [4 marks]
c) A graph of the distance travelled by the ball against time taken squared is plotted. Show that the gradient of the graph is equal to half the value of *g*. [3 marks]

Q2 A video camera with a frame rate of 4 Hz is used to record the motion of a ball dropped from the edge of a tall building. Frame 2 immediately follows Frame 1. Calculate the acceleration due to gravity if the ball is travelling at 13.51 ms⁻¹ when Frame 1 is recorded.

Frame 1: 11.04 m
Frame 2: 15.03 m
[4 marks]

It's not the falling that hurts — it's the being pelted with rotten vegetables... okay, okay...

Make sure you know about all of these methods, including the uncertainties they cause and how you can fix them.

Projectile Motion

Calculators at the ready — it's time to resolve some more things into vertical and horizontal components.
It can be a bit tricky at first, but you'll soon get the hang of it. Chop chop, no time to lose.

You can just Replace a with g in the Equations of Motion

You need to be able to work out **speeds**, **distances** and **times** for objects moving vertically with an **acceleration** of g.
As g is a **constant acceleration** you can use the **equations of motion**. But because g acts downwards, you need to
be careful about directions, here we've taken **upwards as positive** and **downwards as negative**.

Case 1: No initial velocity (it's just free falling)

Initial velocity $u = 0$
Acceleration $a = g = -9.81$ ms^{-2}. Hence the equations of motion become:

$$v = gt \qquad v^2 = 2gs$$
$$s = \tfrac{1}{2}gt^2 \qquad s = \tfrac{vt}{2}$$

Case 2: An initial velocity upwards (it's thrown up into the air)

The equations of motion are just as normal,
but with $a = g = -9.81$ ms^{-2}.

> **Sign Conventions — Learn Them:**
> g is always <u>downwards</u> so it's <u>usually negative</u>
> t is <u>always positive</u>
> u and v can be either <u>positive or negative</u>
> s can be either <u>positive or negative</u>

Case 3: An initial velocity downwards (it's thrown down)

Example: Alex throws a stone downwards from the top of a cliff. She throws it with a downwards
velocity of 2.0 ms^{-1}. It takes 3.0 s to reach the water below. How high is the cliff?

1) You know: $u = -2.0$ ms^{-1}, $a = g = -9.81$ ms^{-2} and $t = 3.0$ s. You need to find s.

2) Use $s = ut + \tfrac{1}{2}gt^2 = (-2.0 \times 3.0) + \left(\tfrac{1}{2} \times -9.81 \times 3.0^2\right) = -50.145$ m. The cliff is **50 m (to 2 s.f.)** high.

s is negative because the stone ends up further down than it
started. Height is a scalar quantity, so is always positive.

You Have to Think of Horizontal and Vertical Motion Separately

Example: Sharon fires a scale model of a TV talent show presenter horizontally with a
velocity of 100 ms^{-1} (to 3 s.f.) from 1.5 m above the ground. How long does
it take to hit the ground, and how far does it travel horizontally? Assume the
model acts as a particle, the ground is horizontal and there is no air resistance.

Think about the vertical motion first:

1) It's **constant acceleration** under gravity...

2) You know $u = 0$ (no vertical velocity at first),
$s = -1.5$ m and $a = g = -9.81$ ms^{-2}. You need to find t.

$a = 0$
$u = 0$
$a = g$

3) Use $s = \tfrac{1}{2}gt^2 \Rightarrow t = \sqrt{\dfrac{2s}{g}} = \sqrt{\dfrac{2 \times -1.5}{-9.81}} = 0.55300...$ s

4) So the model hits the ground after **0.55 seconds (to 2 s.f.)**.

Then do the horizontal motion:

1) The horizontal motion isn't affected by gravity or any
other force, so it moves at a **constant speed**.

2) That means you can just use good old **speed = distance / time**.

Where v_H is the horizontal velocity, and
s_H is the horizontal distance travelled
(rather than the height fallen).

3) Now $v_H = 100$ ms^{-1}, $t = 0.55300...$ s and $a = 0$. You need to find s_H.

4) $s_H = v_H t = 100 \times 0.55300... = $ **55 m (to 2 s.f.)**

Projectile Motion

It's *Slightly Trickier* if it *Starts Off* at an *Angle*

If something's projected at an angle (like, say, a javelin) you start off with both horizontal and vertical velocity:

Method:
1) Resolve the initial velocity into horizontal and vertical components.
2) Use the vertical component to work out how long it's in the air and/or how high it goes.
3) Use the horizontal component to work out how far it goes horizontally while it's in the air.

Example: A cannonball is fired from ground height at an angle of exactly 40° to the horizontal with an initial velocity of 15 ms^{-1}. Calculate how far the cannonball travels horizontally before it hits the ground. Assume no air resistance and that the ground is level.

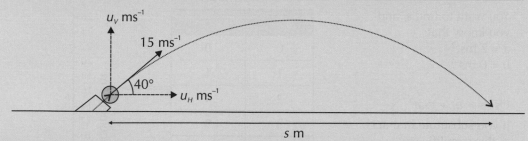

Resolve the velocity into horizontal and vertical components:
1) Horizontal component $u_H = 15 \cos 40° = 11.49...$ ms^{-1}
2) Vertical component $u_V = 15 \sin 40° = 9.64...$ ms^{-1}

Use the vertical component to work out how long the cannonball is in the air:
1) Halfway through the ball's flight, v_v will be zero. $u_V = 9.64...$ ms^{-1}, $a = -9.81$ ms^{-2}, $t = ?$.
   Use $v_v = u_v + at$: $0 = 9.64... + (-9.81 \times t) \Rightarrow t = \dfrac{9.64...}{9.81} = 0.98...$ s
2) So the time it takes to reach the ground again = $2 \times 0.98... = 1.96...$ s ⟵ You know this because of the symmetrical shape of the cannonball's path — it will reach its highest point halfway through its flight.

Use the horizontal component to work out how far it goes while it's in the air:
1) There's no horizontal acceleration, so $u_H = v_H = 11.49...$ ms^{-1}.
2) Distance = constant speed × time = $11.49... \times 1.96... = 22.58... = $ **23 m (to 2 s.f.)**

Practice Questions

Q1 What is the initial vertical velocity for an object projected horizontally with a velocity of 5 ms^{-1}?

Q2 What is the initial horizontal component of velocity of an object projected at 45° to the ground with a speed of 25 ms^{-1}?

Exam Questions

Q1 Jason stands on the edge of a vertical cliff, throwing stones into the sea below.
He throws a stone horizontally with a speed of exactly 8.0 ms^{-1}, from a point 230 m above sea level.

a) Calculate the time taken for the stone to hit the water from leaving Jason's hand.
Use $g = -9.81$ ms^{-2} and ignore air resistance. [2 marks]

b) Calculate the distance of the stone from the base of the cliff when it hits the water. [2 marks]

Q2 Robin fires an arrow into the air with a vertical component of velocity of exactly 30 ms^{-1}, and a horizontal component of velocity of exactly 20 ms^{-1}, from 1 m above the ground. Calculate the maximum height from the ground reached by his arrow to the nearest metre. Use $g = -9.81$ ms^{-2} and ignore air resistance. [3 marks]

All this physics makes me want to create projectile motions...

...by throwing my revision books out of the window. The maths on this page can be tricky, but take it slowly step by step and all will be fine. Don't worry about making Norman (the lion) wait on the next page — he's very patient.

Displacement-Time Graphs

Drawing graphs by hand — oh joy. You'd think examiners had never heard of the graphical calculator.
Ah well, until they manage to drag themselves out of the Dark Ages, you'll just have to grit your teeth and get on with it.

Acceleration Means a Curved Displacement-Time Graph

A graph of displacement against time for an **accelerating object** always produces a **curve**.
If the object is accelerating at a **uniform rate**, then the **rate of change** of the **gradient** will be constant.

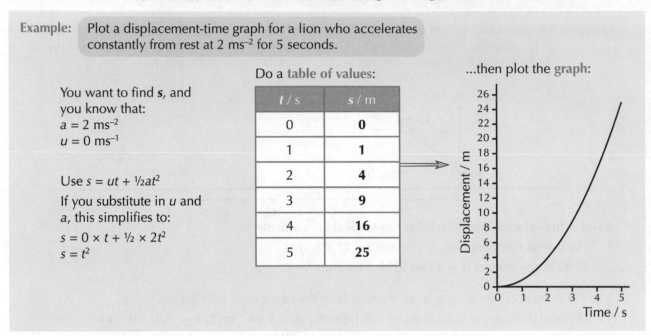

Example: Plot a displacement-time graph for a lion who accelerates constantly from rest at 2 ms^{-2} for 5 seconds.

You want to find **s**, and you know that:
$a = 2$ ms^{-2}
$u = 0$ ms^{-1}

Use $s = ut + \frac{1}{2}at^2$
If you substitute in u and a, this simplifies to:
$s = 0 \times t + \frac{1}{2} \times 2t^2$
$s = t^2$

Do a **table of values**:

t / s	s / m
0	**0**
1	**1**
2	**4**
3	**9**
4	**16**
5	**25**

...then plot the **graph**:

Different Accelerations Have Different Gradients

In the example above, if the lion has a **different acceleration** it'll change the **gradient** of the curve like this:

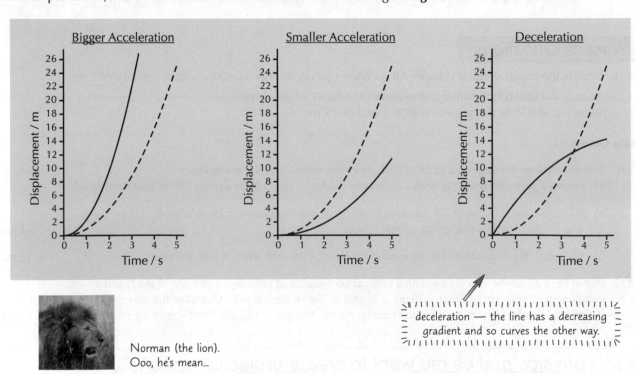

Bigger Acceleration

Smaller Acceleration

Deceleration

deceleration — the line has a decreasing gradient and so curves the other way.

Norman (the lion).
Ooo, he's mean...

Displacement-Time Graphs

The Gradient of a Displacement-Time Graph Tells You the Velocity

When the velocity is constant, the graph's a **straight line**.
Velocity is defined as...

$$\text{velocity} = \frac{\text{change in displacement}}{\text{change in time}}$$

On the graph, this is $\dfrac{\text{change in } y \, (\Delta y)}{\text{change in } x \, (\Delta x)}$, i.e. the gradient.

So to get the velocity from a displacement-time graph, just find the gradient.

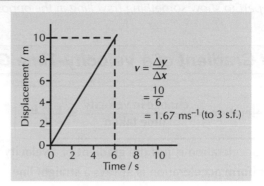

$$v = \frac{\Delta y}{\Delta x}$$
$$= \frac{10}{6}$$
$$= 1.67 \text{ ms}^{-1} \text{ (to 3 s.f.)}$$

It's the Same with Curved Graphs

If the graph is a **curve**, (i.e. the object is accelerating) then you can find its **instantaneous velocity** (i.e. its velocity at a certain point).

To find the **instantaneous velocity** at a certain point, you need to draw a **tangent** to the curve at that point and find its gradient.

To find the **average velocity** over a period of time, just divide the final (change in) displacement by the final (change in) time — it doesn't matter whether or not the graph is curved.

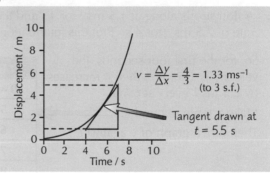

$$v = \frac{\Delta y}{\Delta x} = \frac{4}{3} = 1.33 \text{ ms}^{-1}$$
(to 3 s.f.)

Tangent drawn at $t = 5.5$ s

Practice Questions

Q1 What is given by the gradient of a displacement-time graph?

Q2 Sketch a displacement-time graph to show: a) constant velocity, b) acceleration, c) deceleration.

Exam Questions

Q1 Describe the motion of a cyclist whose journey is shown by the graph below. [4 marks]

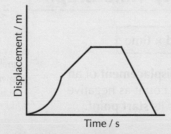

Q2 A baby crawls in a straight line. At first she crawls 5 m over 8 seconds at a constant velocity.
She then rests for 5 seconds before crawling a further 3 m in 5 seconds at a constant velocity.
Finally, she makes her way back to her starting point in 10 seconds, travelling at a constant speed all the way.

a) Draw a displacement-time graph to show the baby's journey. [4 marks]

b) Calculate her velocity during each of the four stages of her journey. [2 marks]

Be ahead of the curve, get to grips with this stuff now...

Whether it's a straight line or a curve, the steeper it is, the greater the velocity. There's nothing difficult about these graphs — the problem is that it's easy to confuse them with velocity-time graphs (next page). If in doubt, think about the gradient — is it velocity or acceleration, is it changing (curve), is it constant (straight line), is it 0 (horizontal line)...

Velocity-Time Graphs

Speed-time graphs and velocity-time graphs are pretty similar. The big difference is that velocity-time graphs can have a negative part to show something travelling in the opposite direction:

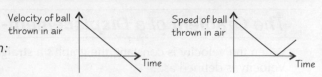

Velocity of ball thrown in air — Time

Speed of ball thrown in air — Time

The **Gradient** of a **Velocity-Time Graph** tells you the **Acceleration**

$$\text{acceleration} = \frac{\text{change in velocity}}{\text{time taken}} = \frac{v - u}{t}$$

likewise for a speed-time graph

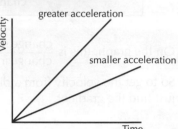

Velocity — greater acceleration — smaller acceleration — Time

So the acceleration is just the **gradient** of a **velocity-time graph**.

1) **Uniform** acceleration is always a **straight line**.

2) The **steeper** the **gradient**, the **greater** the **acceleration**.

The equation for a straight line is $y = mx + c$. You can rearrange the acceleration equation into the same form, getting $v = at + u$. So on a linear v-t graph, **acceleration**, a, is the **gradient** (m) and the **initial speed**, u, is the **y-intercept** (c).

You've seen $v = u + at$ before (p.76).

Example: A lion strolls along at 1.5 ms⁻¹ for 4 s and then accelerates uniformly at a rate of 2.5 ms⁻² for 4 s. Plot this information on a velocity-time graph.

So, for the first four seconds, the velocity is 1.5 ms⁻¹, then it increases by **2.5 ms⁻¹ every second**.

Make a table of t and v:

Then plot a graph of v against t.

t (s)	v (ms⁻¹)
0 – 4	1.5
5	4.0
6	6.5
7	9.0
8	11.5

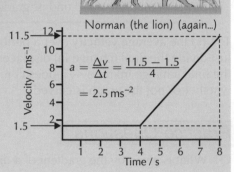

Norman (the lion) (again...)

$$a = \frac{\Delta v}{\Delta t} = \frac{11.5 - 1.5}{4} = 2.5 \text{ ms}^{-2}$$

You can see that the **gradient of the line** is **constant** between 4 s and 8 s and has a value of 2.5 ms⁻², representing the **acceleration of the lion**.

You could also draw this graph in two parts. Draw a straight horizontal line for the first 4 s, then work out his final velocity at 8 s using the equations of motion for constant acceleration. Plot this value and connect the two points with another straight line.

Displacement = **Area** under **Velocity-Time Graph**

You know that: | **distance travelled = average speed × time** |

The **area** under a velocity-time graph tells you the **displacement** of an object. Areas under any **negative** parts of the graph count as negative areas, as they show the object moving **back** towards its **start point**.

Similarly, the area under a speed-time graph is the total distance travelled.

Example: A racing car on a straight track accelerates uniformly from rest to 40 ms⁻¹ in 10 s. It maintains this speed for a further 20 s before coming to rest by decelerating at a constant rate over the next 15 s. Draw a velocity-time graph for this journey and use it to calculate the final displacement of the racing car.

Plot a graph of the information and split it into **sections**: A, B and C.

Calculate the **area** of each and **add** the three results together.

A: Area = ½ base × height = ½ × 10 × 40 = 200 m

B: Area = $b \times h$ = 20 × 40 = 800 m

C: Area = ½ $b \times h$ = ½ × 15 × 40 = 300 m

Final displacement = 200 + 800 + 300 = 1300 m

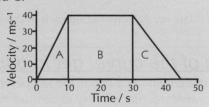

Velocity-Time Graphs

Non-Uniform Acceleration is a Curve on a V-T Graph

1) If the acceleration is changing, the gradient of the velocity-time graph will also be changing — so you **won't** get a **straight line**.

2) **Increasing acceleration** is shown by an **increasing gradient** — like in curve ①.

3) **Decreasing acceleration** is shown by a **decreasing gradient** — like in curve ②.

Simple enough...

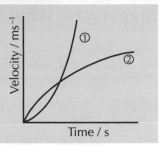

Estimate the Area to Find Displacement from a Curved V-T Graph

As the velocity-time graph is no longer a simple straight line, you have to **estimate** the area under the curve. If the graph is on **squared paper**, an easy way to do this is just **count** the squares under the curve. Another way is to split the curve up into **trapeziums**, calculate the **area** of each one and then **add** them all up.

Example: A car accelerates from rest. It decreases its acceleration as it approaches 15 ms⁻¹. Estimate the car's displacement between 0 and 3 seconds, using the velocity-time graph.

Split the area under the curve up into trapeziums and a triangle.

0-1 s — estimate the area using a triangle.
The height of the triangle is about 4. $A = \frac{1}{2}(1 \times 4) = 2 \text{ m}$
The base of the triangle is 1.

1-2 s — estimate the area using a trapezium.   Area $= \frac{1}{2}(a + b)h$
a is the length of the first side, $a \approx 4$
b is the length of the second side, $b \approx 7$ $A = \frac{1}{2}(4 + 7) \times 1 = 5.5 \text{ m}$
h is the width of each strip, so $h = 1$

2-3 s — another trapezium, $a \approx 7$, $b \approx 9$, $h = 1$ $A = \frac{1}{2}(7 + 9) \times 1 = 8 \text{ m}$

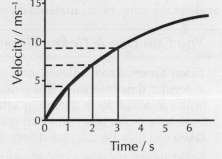

Now add the areas together — total area = 2 + 5.5 + 8 = 15.5 m

So the estimated overall displacement of the car is 15.5 m = **16 m (to 2 s.f.)**

Practice Questions

Q1 How do you calculate acceleration from a velocity-time graph?

Q2 How do you calculate the distance travelled from a speed-time graph?

Q3 Sketch velocity-time graphs for constant velocity and constant acceleration.

Q4 Three trapeziums are drawn side by side on a v-t graph to estimate the area under a curve. They have equal widths of 2 s, and side lengths of 1, 3, 7 and 9 ms⁻¹. Show that the displacement shown by this area is about 30 m.

Exam Question

Q1 A skier accelerates uniformly from rest at 2 ms⁻² down a straight slope.

a) Sketch a velocity-time graph for the first 5 s of his journey. [2 marks]

b) Use a constant acceleration equation to calculate his displacement at $t = 1, 2, 3, 4$ and 5 s, and plot this information onto a displacement-time graph. [4 marks]

c) Suggest another method of calculating the skier's displacement after each second and use this to check your answers to part b). [2 marks]

Still awake — I'll give you five more minutes...

There's a lovely sunset outside my window. It's one of those ones that makes the whole landscape go pinky-yellowish. And that's about as much interest as I can muster on this topic. Normal service will be resumed on page 87, I hope.

Motion Experiments and Models

It's all getting a bit hi-tech now — using light gates and video cameras to look at how an object's velocity changes as it rolls down a ramp or crashes into something. Who doesn't love a good motion experiment...

You Can **Investigate** What **Affects** the **Motion** of a Trolley on a Slope

1) To investigate how the distance a trolley has rolled affects its speed, set up the experiment shown in the diagram.

2) Measure the length of the trolley.

3) Mark a start line on the ramp to make sure the trolley always starts from the same position.

4) Measure the angle of the ramp, θ, and the distance from the start line to the light gate, d.

5) Place the trolley on the ramp and line it up with the start line. Let go of it so its initial velocity, u, is 0.

6) The data logger will record the time taken for the trolley to pass through the light gate and calculate the velocity of the trolley as it passes through the gate.

7) Change the starting position of the trolley, so d is varied.

8) Repeat this experiment for each distance 3 times and average the recorded velocities to reduce the error in your final result.

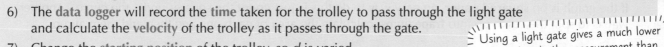

Using a light gate gives a much lower uncertainty in the measurement than using a stopwatch and calculating the velocity manually.

You can use the same set-up as above to investigate other factors. For example, you could change the **angle** of the ramp or the **material** it's made from, or change the **mass**, **size** or **shape** of the trolley.

You Can Use A **Ticker Timer** Instead of a **Data Logger**

10 dots = 1/5th of a second.

Ticker timers create **holes** in (or make **dots** on) a long piece of **paper** (**ticker tape**) at **regular time intervals**. This is usually about **every 50th** of a second. You can **calculate** how long it takes a trolley to travel down a ramp by **attaching ticker tape** to the back of the trolley and threading it through the timer. Switch the ticker timer **on** when you **release** the trolley, and **off** when it reaches the **end** of the **ramp**. The **time taken** can then be calculated from the **number of holes** punched into the ticker tape (50 holes = 1 second).

Ticker timers are able to measure time very **accurately** but rely on **manually** turning on and off the machine, which will add **uncertainty** to the measurements e.g. human error/reaction time. Uncertainty can also be introduced when having to **count** the **total number** of dots.

Data loggers do not have this **human error** and can calculate the **velocity** and display it in **real time** — saving **time** and allowing **comparisons** between experiments to be easily made.

You Can Also **Investigate** How **Collisions** Affect the **Motion** of an Air Glider

Air gliders have **minimal friction**, as they're not in contact with a surface as they move. You can investigate what happens when **two** gliders collide using the experiment below.

• Set up the experiment shown in the diagram below, with a **video camera** positioned side-on to the motion of the gliders.

• Measure the **length** and **mass** of both gliders.

• Turn on the video camera and **start recording**.

• **Push** one glider so it hits the second glider.

• When both gliders have come to a stop, stop recording.

If you use the velocities you find to work out the total momentum before and after the collision, you should find it is the same (see p.92).

1) You can use this experiment to investigate how the **mass** and **velocity** of a glider just **before** a collision **affect** the **velocities** of both gliders after the **collision**.

2) Using **video analysis** software, you can view your videos **frame by frame**. Pick a **point of reference** on the metre rule and count how many **frames** it takes a glider to pass that point.

3) By knowing how many **frames per second** the video is shot at (the frame rate of the video), you can calculate the **time taken** (t) for a whole glider to pass that point. You recorded the **length** (L) of each glider, and so you can calculate their **velocities**.

Time taken (t) for a glider to pass a point	=	Number of frames for glider to pass a point	×	$\dfrac{1 \text{ second}}{\text{Frame rate of camera}}$

$$\text{velocity} = \frac{L}{t}$$

Motion Experiments and Models

Motion can be *Modelled* Using *Iterative Methods*

You can *Model* Using a *Spreadsheet*...

Using the **equations of motion** for **constant acceleration** (p.76) you can **model** how a uniformly accelerating body's **velocity** and **displacement** vary over time. To do this, use an **iterative method**, where **velocity** and **displacement** are calculated over **lots** of **small time increments** to model their behaviour over a **longer time period**. Create a **spreadsheet** like the one shown (which models motion for a body accelerating from rest at 4 ms^{-2} over increments of 1 s).

1) For each row, the change in velocity, Δv will be constant (as $\Delta v = a\Delta t = 4 \times 1 = 4$ ms^{-1}).

2) **Add** this Δv to the velocity, v, from the **previous** row, giving you the **new velocity** for each increment.

3) To find the **change in displacement**, Δx, for each row use $\Delta x = u\Delta t + \frac{1}{2}a(\Delta t)^2$ (where u is the value of v from the previous row). Add this to the previous x value to get the new **displacement** at the **end** of each time interval.

t (s)	Δt (s)	Δv (ms^{-1})	v (ms^{-1})	Δx (m)	x (m)
0	-	-	0	-	0
1	1	4	4	2	2
2	1	4	8	6	8
3	1	4	12	10	18

4) **Repeat** this to build up a full model of the body's motion over time. If you enter the correct formulas into the spreadsheet, then it can automatically complete as many rows (iterations) as you want.

5) You can then **plot a graph** of v against t (which should be a **straight line** through the origin with **gradient** equal to the body's **acceleration**) and x against t (which should be a **curve** similar to the one shown on page 82).

...Or by *Drawing Vectors*

(This method is useful for visualising motion in 2 dimensions.)

For each interval:
— starting velocity
— final velocity
— change in velocity

1) Consider an object fired horizontally, so that it begins to move with **projectile motion** (see p.80) under the influence of gravity.

2) Initially, the object has horizontal speed v_0 and vertical speed 0. Following the first time increment, the object still has horizontal speed v_0, but its **vertical speed** has **increased by Δv**. This gives a resultant velocity of v_1, as shown.

Each resultant velocity has the same horizontal width since Δt is constant, but a greater vertical component than the previous one.

3) Following the second increment, the horizontal speed has remained constant and the vertical speed has again **increased by Δv**. The new resultant velocity is $v_1 + \Delta v = v_2$.

4) This pattern **continues** for each time increment. The resultant velocity **increases** for each increment (the blue arrow gets longer each time), as the object is **accelerating**.

Draw a grid (or use graph paper). Each horizontal increment represents an increment of time. The increments on the vertical axes often represent Δv.

Practice Questions

Q1 Describe an experiment you could do to investigate the motion of a trolley on a slope.

Q2 Explain how a ticker timer works. State one advantage of using a data logger instead of a ticker timer.

Q3 Describe how you could use a spreadsheet to model displacement and velocity of a constantly accelerating object.

Exam Questions

Q1 A video recording is made of two 15 cm long trollies. Trolley 1 is pushed and then allowed to collide with trolley 2. The frame rate of the camera is 26 frames per second.

a) The video is analysed and after the collision, trolley 2 takes a little less than one frame to fully pass a reference point. It is assumed the trolley takes exactly one frame to pass the reference point. Estimate the velocity of trolley 2. [3 marks]

b) Suggest and explain one change which could be made to the experiment that could give more precise velocity measurements. [2 marks]

Q2 A projectile is fired diagonally upwards from ground level, with an initial vertical velocity of 35 ms^{-1} and an initial horizontal velocity of 20 ms^{-1}. Taking the acceleration due to gravity to be 10 ms^{-2} downwards, sketch a series of velocity vectors at 1 second intervals to model the first 6 seconds of the motion of the projectile. [3 marks]

Investigating motion — not an excuse to throw out your physics books...

So many ways to investigate motion. You can roll trolleys, push air gliders, use ticker tape or video techniques, or decide to theoretically model it on a spreadsheet... just make sure you can explain all of them.

Forces

Remember the vector stuff from the beginning of the section? Good, you're going to need it...

Free-Body Force Diagrams show All Forces on a Single Body

1) **Free-body force** diagrams show a **single body** on its own.

2) The diagram should include all the **forces** that **act on** the body, but **not** the **forces it exerts** on the rest of the world.

3) Remember **forces** are **vector quantities** and so the **arrow labels** should show the **size** and **direction** of the forces.

4) If a body is in **equilibrium** (i.e. not accelerating) the **forces** acting on it will be **balanced**.

Drawing free-body force diagrams isn't too hard — you just need practice. Here are a few **examples**:

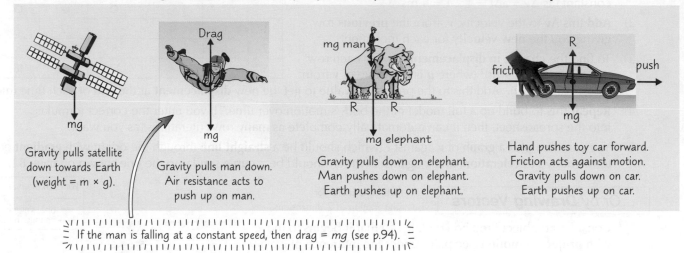

Gravity pulls satellite down towards Earth (weight = m × g).

Gravity pulls man down. Air resistance acts to push up on man.

Gravity pulls down on elephant. Man pushes down on elephant. Earth pushes up on elephant.

Hand pushes toy car forward. Friction acts against motion. Gravity pulls down on car. Earth pushes up on car.

If the man is falling at a constant speed, then drag = *mg* (see p.94).

Resolving a Force means Splitting it into Components

1) Forces can be in **any direction**, so they're not always at right angles to each other. This is sometimes a bit **awkward** for **calculations**.

2) To make an 'awkward' force easier to deal with, you can think of it as two **separate**, **independent** forces, acting at **right angles** to each other.

3) These two forces have **no effect** on each other as they are **perpendicular**. E.g. a horizontal force will have no vertical effect, and vice-versa.

The force *F* has exactly the same effect as the horizontal and vertical forces, F_H and F_V.

Replacing *F* with F_H and F_V is called **resolving the force *F***.

4) To find the **size** of a **component** force in a particular **direction**, you need to use trigonometry (see page 74). Forces are vectors, so you treat them in the same way as velocity or displacement — put them end to end.

So this... 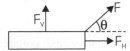 ...could be drawn like this:

Using trigonometry you get:

$$\frac{F_H}{F} = \cos\theta \quad \text{or} \quad F_H = F\cos\theta$$

And:

$$\frac{F_V}{F} = \sin\theta \quad \text{or} \quad F_V = F\sin\theta$$

Remember that cos 90° = 0, so forces which act at an angle of **90°** to each other are **independent** (i.e. they have **no effect** on each other).

Example: A tree trunk is pulled along the ground by an elephant exerting a force of 1200 N at an angle of 25° to the horizontal. Calculate the components of this force in the horizontal and vertical directions.

Horizontal force:
1200 × cos 25° = 1087.5...
= **1100 N (to 2 s.f.)**

Vertical force:
1200 × sin 25° = 507.1...
= **510 N (to 2 s.f.)**

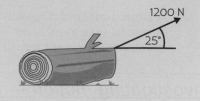

Forces

You *Add* the *Components Back Together* to get the *Resultant Force*

1) If **two forces** act on an object, you find the **resultant** (total) **force** by adding the **vectors** together and creating a **closed triangle**, with the resultant force represented by the **third side**.

2) Forces are vectors (as you know), so use **vector addition** — draw the forces as vector arrows 'tip-to-tail'.

3) Then it's yet more trigonometry to find the **angle** and the **length** of the third side.

Example: Two dung beetles roll a dung ball along the ground at a constant velocity. Beetle A applies a force of 0.5 N northwards while beetle B exerts a force of only 0.2 N eastwards. What is the resultant force on the dung ball?

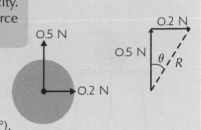

By Pythagoras, $R^2 = 0.5^2 + 0.2^2 = 0.29$
$R = \sqrt{0.29} = 0.538... = \textbf{0.54 N (to 2 s.f.)}$

$\tan\theta = \frac{0.2}{0.5}$ so $\theta = \tan^{-1}\left(\frac{0.2}{0.5}\right) = 21.8°... = \textbf{22° (to 2 s.f.)}$

So the resultant force is **0.54 N** at an angle of **22° to the vertical** (a bearing of 022°).

Choose *Sensible* Axes for *Resolving*

Use directions that **make sense** for the situation you're dealing with. If you've got an object on a slope, choose your directions **along the slope** and **at right angles to it**. You can turn the paper to an angle if that helps.

Always choose sensible axes

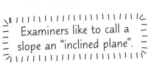
Examiners like to call a slope an "inclined plane".

Example

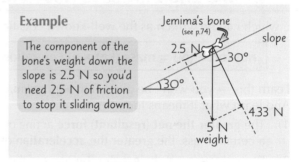

The component of the bone's weight down the slope is 2.5 N so you'd need 2.5 N of friction to stop it sliding down.

Practice Questions

Q1 Sketch a free-body force diagram for an ice hockey puck moving across horizontal ice (assuming no friction).

Q2 What are the horizontal and vertical components of a force F if it is applied at an angle of θ to the horizontal?

Q3 Explain why perpendicular forces are independent of each other.

Exam Questions

Q1 An 8 kg picture is suspended from a hook as shown in the diagram. Calculate the tension force, T, in the string.

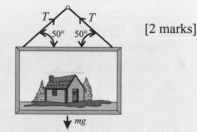

[2 marks]

Q2 Two elephants pull a tree trunk as shown in the diagram. Calculate the resultant force on the tree trunk. Both values given are correct to 3 s.f.

[2 marks]

Free-body force diagram — sounds like a dance competition...

Remember those $F\cos\theta$ and $F\sin\theta$ bits. Write them on bits of paper and stick them to your wall. Scrawl them on your pillow. Tattoo them on your brain. Whatever it takes — you just have to learn them.

Newton's Laws of Motion

You did most of this at GCSE, but that doesn't mean you can just skip over it now.
You'll be kicking yourself if you forget this stuff in the exam — it's easy marks...

Newton's 1st Law says that a Force is Needed to Change Velocity

1) **Newton's 1st law of motion** states the **velocity** of an object will **not change** unless a **resultant force** acts on it.

2) This means a body will remain at rest or moving in a **straight line** at a **constant speed**, unless acted on by a **resultant force**.

An apple sitting on a table won't go anywhere because the forces on it are balanced.

$$\text{reaction } (R) \quad = \quad \text{weight } (mg)$$

(table pushing up on apple) (gravity pulling apple down)

3) If any forces acting on a body **aren't balanced**, the **overall resultant force** will cause the body to **accelerate**. If you gave the apple on the left a shove, there'd be a resultant force acting on it and it would roll off the table.

4) Acceleration can mean a change in **direction**, or **speed**, or both.

Newton's 2nd Law says Acceleration is Proportional to Force

...which can be written as the well-known equation:

net force (N) = mass (kg) × acceleration (ms⁻²) or $F = ma$

From this equation, $1 \text{ N} = 1 \text{ kg ms}^{-2}$. This is the definition of a newton. $F = ma$ is a special case of Newton's second law — the mass is constant. For the momentum version see p.93.

Learn this — you won't be given it in your exam. And learn what it means too:

1) The **greater the net (resultant) force** acting on a body of a certain mass, the **greater** the **acceleration** of the body.

2) For a given force, the **greater** the **mass** of the body it acts on, the **less acceleration** the body will experience.

REMEMBER:
1) The resultant force is the vector sum of all the forces.
2) The force is always measured in newtons.
3) The mass is always measured in kilograms.
4) The acceleration is always in the same direction as the resultant force and is measured in ms⁻².

All Objects Fall at the Same Rate (if you Ignore Air Resistance)

1) On Earth, the force that causes objects to accelerate towards the ground is the **gravitational pull** of the Earth. The gravitational field strength on Earth, **g**, is pretty much **constant** — so all objects should **accelerate** towards the ground at the **same rate**, no matter what their mass is.

You've already seen free fall on p.78–79.

2) Newton's 2nd law explains it neatly — consider two balls dropped at the same time — ball **1** being heavy, and ball **2** being light. Then use Newton's 2nd law to find their acceleration.

mass = m_1
resultant force = F_1
acceleration = a_1

By Newton's Second Law:

$$F_1 = m_1 a_1$$

Ignoring air resistance, the only force acting on the ball is weight, given by $W_1 = m_1 g$ (where g = gravitational field strength = 9.81 Nkg⁻¹).

So: $F_1 = m_1 a_1 = W_1 = m_1 g$
So: $m_1 a_1 = m_1 g$
m_1 cancels out to give: $a_1 = g$

mass = m_2
resultant force = F_2
acceleration = a_2

By Newton's Second Law:

$$F_2 = m_2 a_2$$

Ignoring air resistance, the only force acting on the ball is weight, given by $W_2 = m_2 g$ (where g = gravitational field strength = 9.81 Nkg⁻¹).

So: $F_2 = m_2 a_2 = W_2 = m_2 g$
So: $m_2 a_2 = m_2 g$
m_2 cancels out to give: $a_2 = g$

Newton's Laws of Motion

Newton's *3rd Law* is a *Consequence* of the *Conservation of Momentum*

There are a few different ways of stating Newton's 3rd law, but the clearest way is:

> **If an object A EXERTS a FORCE on object B, then
> object B exerts AN EQUAL BUT OPPOSITE FORCE on object A.**

You'll also hear the law as "every action has an equal and opposite reaction". But this confuses people who wrongly think the forces are both applied to the same object. (If that were the case, you'd get a resultant force of zero and nothing would ever move anywhere...)

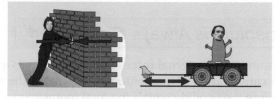

The two forces actually represent the **same interaction**, just seen from two **different perspectives**:

1) If you **push against a wall**, the wall will **push back** against you, **just as hard**. As soon as you stop pushing, so does the wall. Amazing...

2) If you **pull a cart**, whatever force **you exert** on the rope, the rope exerts the **exact opposite** pull on you.

3) When you go **swimming**, you push **back** against the water with your arms and legs, and the water pushes you **forwards** with an equal-sized force. So, the **backward momentum** of the water is equal to your **forward momentum**.

This looks like Newton's 3rd law...

Gravity pulls down on book

But it's <u>NOT</u>.

Table pushes upwards on book

...because both forces are acting on the book, and they're not of the same type. This is two separate interactions. The forces are equal and opposite, resulting in zero acceleration, so this is showing Newton's 1st law.

Newton's 3rd law applies in **all situations** and to all **types of force**. But the pairs of forces are always the **same type**, e.g. both gravitational or both electrical.

Newton's 3rd law is a consequence of the **conservation of momentum** (page 92). A **resultant force** acting means a change in **mass** or **acceleration** ($F = ma$) — which means a **change in momentum**.

Momentum is always **conserved** when no external force acts, so whenever one object exerts a force on another (and changes its momentum), the second object must exert an **equal-sized** force back on the first object so that the **overall** change in momentum is **zero**.

Practice Questions

Q1 State Newton's 1st, 2nd and 3rd laws of motion, and explain what they mean.

Q2 Write out the formula which describes a special case of Newton's 2nd law.

Q3 Sketch a force diagram of a book resting on a table to illustrate Newton's 3rd law.

Exam Questions

Q1 A parachutist with a mass of 78 kg steps out of a plane. As she falls, she accelerates.

    a) Use Newton's 2nd law to explain why she initially accelerates.   [2 marks]

    b) What is the initial vertical force on the parachutist? Use $g = 9.81$ ms^{-2}.   [1 mark]

Q2 A 250 kg boat is moving across a river. The engines provide a force of 500 N at right angles to the flow of the river, and the boat experiences a drag of 100 N in the opposite direction. The force on the boat due to the flow of the river is 300 N. Show that the magnitude of the acceleration of the boat is 2 ms^{-2}.   [3 marks]

Newton's three incredibly important laws of motion...

These equations may not really fill you with a huge amount of excitement (and I hardly blame you if they don't)... but it was pretty fantastic at the time — suddenly people actually understood how forces work, and how they affect motion.

Momentum and Impulse

Linear momentum is just momentum in a straight line (not a circle or anything complicated like that).

Understanding **Momentum** helps you do **Calculations** on **Collisions**

The **momentum** of an object depends on two things — its **mass** and **velocity**:

> **momentum** (in kg ms⁻¹) = **mass** (in kg) × **velocity** (in ms⁻¹)
>
> or in symbols: $p = mv$

Momentum is a vector quantity (see p.74), so just like velocity, it has size and direction.

*Momentum is Always **Conserved***

1) Assuming **no external forces** act, momentum is always **conserved** (this is the **principle of conservation of momentum**). This means the **total momentum** of two objects **before** they collide **equals** the total momentum **after** the collision.

2) This is really handy for working out the **velocity** of objects after a collision (as you do...):

> **Example:** A skater of mass 75 kg and velocity 4 ms⁻¹ collides with a stationary skater of mass 50 kg. The skaters join together and move off in the same direction. Calculate their velocity after impact.
>
> BEFORE   AFTER
>
>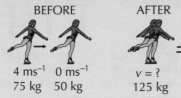
>
> 4 ms⁻¹ 0 ms⁻¹   v = ?
> 75 kg   50 kg   125 kg
>
> Before you start a momentum calculation, always draw a quick sketch.
>
> Momentum of skaters before = Momentum of skaters after
> $(75 \times 4) + (50 \times 0) = 125v$
> $300 = 125v$
> So... $v = \textbf{2.4 ms}^{-1}$

3) The same principle can be applied in **explosions**. E.g. if you fire an **air rifle**, the **forward momentum** gained by the pellet **equals** the **backward momentum** of the rifle, and you feel the rifle recoiling into your shoulder.

*Collisions can be **Elastic** or **Inelastic***

A **perfectly elastic** collision is one where **momentum** is **conserved** and **kinetic energy** is **conserved** — i.e. no energy is dissipated as heat, sound, etc. If a collision is **inelastic** it means that some of the kinetic energy is converted into other forms during the collision. But **momentum is always conserved.**

You can use the **principle of conservation of momentum**, (and the conservation of kinetic energy in elastic collisions) to predict the behaviour of real-world objects, for example balls in sports games.

> **Example:** A toy lorry (mass 2.0 kg) travelling at 3.0 ms⁻¹ crashes into a smaller toy car (mass 800 g to 2 s.f.), travelling in the same direction at 2.0 ms⁻¹. The velocity of the lorry after the collision is 2.6 ms⁻¹ in the same direction. Calculate the new velocity of the car and the total kinetic energy (KE) before and after the collision.
>
> 2.0 kg, 3.0 ms⁻¹ 800 g, 2.0 ms⁻¹   2.6 ms⁻¹   v = ?
>
>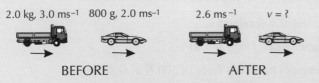
>
> BEFORE   AFTER
>
> Momentum before collision = Momentum after collision
> $(2.0 \times 3.0) + (0.80 \times 2.0) = (2.0 \times 2.6) + (0.80v)$
> $7.6 = 5.2 + 0.80v$
> $2.4 = 0.80v$ so $v = \textbf{3.0 ms}^{-1}$
>
> KE before = KE of lorry + KE of car
> $= \frac{1}{2}mv^2_{(lorry)} + \frac{1}{2}mv^2_{(car)}$
> $= \frac{1}{2}(2.0 \times 3.0^2) + \frac{1}{2}(0.80 \times 2.0^2)$
> $= 9 + 1.6 = \textbf{10.6 J}$
>
> KE after $= \frac{1}{2}(2.0 \times 2.6^2) + \frac{1}{2}(0.80 \times 3.0^2)$
> $= 6.76 + 3.6 = \textbf{10.4 J (to 3 s.f.)}$
>
> The KE before is different to the KE after — so this is an <u>inelastic</u> collision. The difference in the two values is the amount of energy <u>dissipated</u> as heat or sound, or in damaging the vehicles.

Momentum and Impulse

Newton's 2nd Law says that Force is the Rate of Change of Momentum

Newton's 2nd law states that:

"The **rate of change of momentum** of an object is **directly proportional** to the **net force** which acts on the object."   or $F = \dfrac{\Delta(mv)}{\Delta t}$

If mass is constant, this can be written as:

net force = mass × acceleration   or $F = ma$

Remember this equation — it's not given in the exam. If you forget, the equation above is given and you should know that acceleration is rate of change of velocity.

(As you saw on page 90.)

F = ma Doesn't Apply if the Mass is Changing

$F = ma$ is a special case of Newton's 2nd law. If the **mass** of the object is **changing** — e.g. if it is accelerating at close to the **speed of light** — then you **can't** use $F = ma$. (You don't need to know why this happens.)

Don't worry though — **Newton's 2nd law still applies**, it's just that the 'rate of **change of momentum**' bit refers to a **change in mass and velocity**.

Daisy always knew she was special.

Impulse = Change in Momentum

1) Newton's second law says **force = rate of change of momentum** (see above), or $F = \Delta mv \div \Delta t$.

2) **Rearranging** Newton's 2nd law gives:
Impulse is defined as **average force × time**, $F\Delta t$.
The units of impulse are **newton seconds**, Ns.

$$F\Delta t = \Delta mv$$
so **impulse = change of momentum**

3) Impulse is the change in momentum of **one** object, whilst conservation of momentum applies to the **whole system**. So the impulse of an object can **change** while momentum is **conserved**.

Practice Questions

Q1 Write down the formula for calculating momentum.

Q2 What is the difference between elastic and inelastic collisions?

Q3 Give the equation for calculating the net force on an object which relates mass, velocity and time.

Q4 What is impulse? Write down the equation for calculating impulse, defining all symbols used.

Q5 A 20 N force acting on a moving mass causes an impulse of 80 Ns. Show that the force acts for 4 seconds.

Exam Question

Q1 A snooker ball of mass 0.145 kg moving at 1.94 ms⁻¹ collides with a stationary snooker ball of mass 0.148 kg. The first ball rebounds along its initial path at 0.005 ms⁻¹, and the second ball moves off in the opposite direction.

     a) Calculate the velocity of the second ball immediately after the collision.   [2 marks]

     b) State whether or not the collision is perfectly elastic. Support your answer with a calculation.   [3 marks]

     c) The first ball then hits the cushion at the edge of the table and comes to a stop. The collision takes 0.15 seconds. Calculate the average force experienced by the ball in this collision.   [2 marks]

Momentum will never be an endangered species — it's always conserved...

...unlike exams which, one day, will be done forever and you'll never have to revise ever again. But if you don't get momentum and impulse nailed now, you'll forever be looking back and wishing you had — so go learn it well good like.

Terminal Velocity

If you jump out of a plane at 2000 metres, you want to know that you're not going to be accelerating all the way.

Friction is a Force that Opposes Motion

There are two main types of friction:

1) **Contact friction** between **solid surfaces** (which is what we usually mean when we just use the word 'friction'). You don't need to worry about that too much for now.

2) **Fluid friction** (known as **drag** or fluid resistance or air resistance).

> **Fluid Friction or Drag:**
> 1) 'Fluid' is a word that means either a **liquid or a gas** — something that can **flow**.
> 2) The force depends on the thickness (or **viscosity**) of the fluid.
> 3) It **increases** as the **speed increases** (for simple situations it's directly proportional, but you don't need to worry about the mathematical relationship).
> 4) It also depends on the **shape** and **size** of the object moving through it — the larger the **area** pushing against the fluid, the greater the resistance force.

Things you need to remember about frictional forces:

1) They **always** act in the **opposite direction** to the **motion** of the object.

2) They can **never** speed things up or start something moving.

3) They convert **kinetic energy** into **heat**.

Terminal Velocity — when the Friction Force Equals the Driving Force

You will reach a **terminal velocity** at some point, if you have:

1) a **driving force** that stays the **same** all the time

2) a **frictional** or **drag force** (or collection of forces) that increases with speed

There are **three main stages** to reaching terminal velocity:

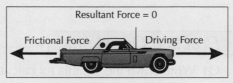

The car **accelerates** from **rest** using a constant driving force.

As the **velocity increases**, the **resistance forces increase** (because of things like turbulence — you don't need the details). This **reduces the resultant force** on the car and hence **reduces its acceleration**.

Eventually the car reaches a velocity at which the **resistance forces are equal to the driving force**. There is now **no resultant force** and **no acceleration**, so the car carries on at **constant velocity**.

Sketching a Graph for Terminal Velocity

You need to be able to **recognise** and **sketch** the graphs for **velocity against time** and **acceleration against time** for the **terminal velocity** situation.

> Nothing for it but practice — shut the book and sketch them from memory. Keep doing it till you get them right every time.

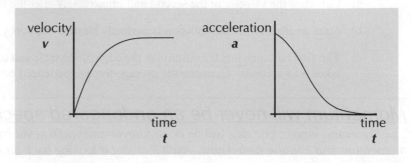

Terminal Velocity

Things **Falling** through **Air** or **Water** Reach a **Terminal Velocity** too

When something's falling through air, the weight of the object is a **constant** force accelerating the object downwards. Air resistance is a frictional force opposing this motion, which **increases** with **speed**.

So before a parachutist opens the parachute, exactly the same thing happens as with the car example:

1) A skydiver leaves a plane and will **accelerate** until the **air resistance** equals his **weight**.

2) He will then be travelling at a **terminal velocity**.

But... the terminal velocity of a person in free fall is too great to land **safely**. The **parachute increases** the **air resistance massively**, which slows him down to a lower terminal velocity:

3) Before reaching the ground he will **open his parachute**, which immediately **increases the air resistance** so it is now **bigger** than his **weight**.

4) This **slows him down** until his speed has dropped enough for the **air resistance** to be **equal to his weight** again. This new terminal velocity is small enough to survive landing.

The *v-t* graph is a bit different, because you have a new terminal velocity being reached after the parachute is opened:

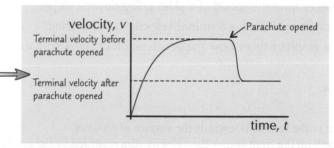

Measure the Terminal Velocity of a Ball Bearing

You don't have to use elastic bands — you could also use insulation tape or another marker for your intervals.

You can calculate the terminal velocity of a **ball bearing** (a little steel ball) in a **viscous** (thick) liquid by setting up an experiment like this:

1) Put **elastic bands** around the tube of viscous liquid at **fixed distances** using a **ruler**.

2) **Drop** a ball bearing into the tube, and use a **stopwatch** to record the time at which it reaches **each band**. Record your results in a **table** (see below).

3) **Repeat** this a few times to reduce the effect of **random errors** (see p.12) on your results. You can use a **strong magnet** to remove the ball bearing from the tube.

4) **Calculate** the times taken by the ball bearing to travel between consecutive elastic bands and calculate an **average** for each reading. Use the **average times** and the **distance between bands** to calculate the **average velocity** between **each pair** of elastic bands.

5) You should find that the average velocity **increases** at first, then **stays constant** — this is the ball bearing's **terminal velocity** in the viscous liquid used.

Elastic band	Time / s	Time from last band / s	Average time / s	Average velocity / ms^{-1}
2	1			
	2			
	3			
3	1			
	2			
	3			

If your stopwatch has a lap timer, you might be able to measure these times directly.

You could also investigate terminal velocity by dropping paper cones through air and using a light gate to get more accurate velocity readings.

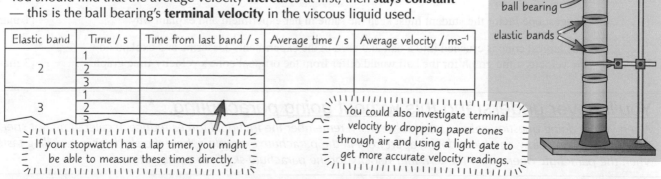

Terminal Velocity

You can Work Out what **Affects** Terminal Velocity

1) Use your average velocity data from the experiment on page 95 to plot a graph of **velocity** against **time**. Draw a smooth curve and use it to estimate the terminal velocity.

2) You might be asked to draw **force diagrams** for the ball bearing as it falls. Remember that the forces are balanced when the ball reaches terminal velocity.

3) You can change parts of your experiment to see what effect they have on terminal velocity and the time taken to reach terminal velocity. For example you could:

- Change the **liquid** — the terminal velocity will be **lower** in more viscous (thicker) liquids because the drag is **greater**. Try mixing water into wallpaper paste and see how much the terminal velocity increases when the drag is lower.

- Change the **size** of the ball. What happens if the ball is larger? Or smaller?

- Change the **shape** of the thing you are dropping. The drag force will be greater on **less streamlined** shapes.

- Change the **mass** of the thing you are dropping, while keeping the **size** the **same** (this might be a bit tricky). You should find that **heavier objects** reach a **faster** terminal velocity because a **greater drag force** is needed to balance the extra weight. (Remember, objects with different masses only fall at the same rate if drag is ignored — p.90.)

Prof. Fraise dedicated his life to investigating terminal velocity in fluids.

Turn back to p.84–85 for more on velocity-time graphs.

Practice Questions

Q1 What forces limit the speed of a skier going down a slope?

Q2 What conditions cause a terminal velocity to be reached?

Q3 Sketch a graph to show how the acceleration changes with time for an object falling through air.

Exam Questions

Q1 A space probe free-falls towards the surface of a planet.
The graph on the right shows the velocity data recorded by the probe as it falls.

velocity, v

time, t

a) The planet does not have an atmosphere. Explain how you can tell this from the graph. [2 marks]

b) Sketch the v-t graph you would expect to see if the planet did have an atmosphere. [2 marks]

c) Explain the shape of the graph you have drawn. [3 marks]

Q2 A student is investigating how the terminal velocity of paper cones varies with cone size. She drops weighted cones of base diameter 5 cm, 10 cm and 15 cm point-down from a height of 2 m and uses a video camera and video analysis software to obtain data on the displacement of the cone at certain times. She then plots a displacement-time graph to calculate the terminal velocity. You may assume that the weights of the cones are negligible compared to that of the weights used to stabilise them, and that each cone is weighted by the same amount.

a) State which size of cone you expect to have the lowest terminal velocity. Explain your answer. [2 marks]

b) Sketch a graph of velocity against time for the three cones. Put all three curves on the same axes. [3 marks]

c) Suggest one factor the student must keep the same in her experiment and explain why. [1 mark]

d) The largest cone is crushed into a ball and used in the experiment. Describe and explain how the velocity-time graph for the ball would differ from the original cone's velocity-time graph. [3 marks]

You'll never understand this without going parachuting...*

When you're doing questions about terminal velocity, remember the frictional forces reduce acceleration, not speed. They usually don't slow an object down, apart from in the parachute example, where the skydiver is travelling faster when the parachute opens than the terminal velocity for the parachute-skydiver combination.

* No. 37 in a series of the 100 least convincing excuses for an interesting holiday.

Work and Power

As everyone knows, work in Physics isn't like normal work. It's harder. Work also has a specific meaning that's to do with movement and forces. You'll have seen this at GCSE — now it's time to have a look at it in more detail.

Work is Done Whenever Energy is Transferred

This table gives you some examples of **work being done** and the **energy changes** that happen.

Activity	Work Done Against	Final Energy Form
Lifting up a box.	Gravity	Gravitational potential energy
Pushing a chair across a level floor.	Friction	Heat and sound
Pushing two magnetic north poles together.	Magnetic force	Magnetic Energy
Stretching a spring.	Stiffness of spring	Elastic strain energy

1) Usually you need a force to move something because you're having to **overcome another force**.

2) The thing being moved has **kinetic energy** while it's **moving**.

3) The kinetic energy has been transferred to **another form of energy** when the movement stops.

The word **'work'** in Physics means the **amount of energy transferred** from one form to another when a force causes a movement of some sort.

Work = Force × Distance

When a car tows a caravan, it applies a force to the caravan to move it to where it's wanted. To **find out** how much **work** has been **done**, you need to use the **equation**:

$$\Delta E = F\Delta s \quad \text{or} \quad \textbf{work done = force causing motion} \times \textbf{distance moved}$$

...where ΔE is measured in joules (J), F is measured in newtons (N) and Δs is measured in metres (m).

Example: A student moves a book from a shelf to the shelf above. She exerts 1.96 N to do this. The shelves are 0.30 metres apart. Calculate the work done by the student in moving the book and state what the work was done against.

$\Delta E = F \times \Delta s$ so $\Delta E = 1.96 \times 0.30 = 0.588$
$$= \textbf{0.59 J (to 2 s.f.)}$$

As the book was lifted through a gravitational field, the work was done against gravity.

You might also see the equation for work written as $W = Fx$, where W is work, F is the force and x is the distance moved.

Points to remember:

1) **Work** is the **energy** that's been **changed** from one form to another — it's not necessarily the **total** energy. E.g. moving a book from a low shelf to a higher one will increase its gravitational potential energy, but it had some potential energy to start with. Here, the **work done** would be the **increase** in potential energy, **not the total** potential energy.

2) Remember the distance needs to be measured in metres — if you have **distance in centimetres or kilometres**, you need to **convert** it to metres first.

3) The force F will be a **fixed** value in any calculations, either because it's **constant** or because it's the **average** force.

4) The equation assumes that the **direction of the force** is the **same** as the **direction of movement**.

5) The equation gives you the **definition** of the joule (symbol J): 'One joule is the work done when a force of 1 newton moves an object through a distance of 1 metre'.

MODULE 4: SECTION 2 — SPACE, TIME AND MOTION

Work and Power

The Force isn't always in the Same Direction as the Displacement

Sometimes the **direction of movement** is **different** from the **direction of the force**.

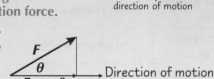

direction of force on sledge

rosebud

direction of motion

1) To calculate the work done in a situation like the one on the right, you need to consider the horizontal and vertical components of the force.

2) The only displacement is in the horizontal direction. This means the vertical force is not causing any displacement (and hence not doing any work) — it's just balancing out some of the weight, meaning there's a smaller reaction force.

3) The horizontal force is causing the displacement — so to calculate the work done, this is the only force you need to consider. Which means you get:

$$\Delta E = F\Delta s \cos\theta$$

F
θ
$F\cos\theta$ → Direction of motion

Where θ is the angle between the direction of the force and the direction of displacement. See page 88–89 for more on resolving forces.

Power = Rate of Energy Transfer

Power means many things in everyday speech, but in physics (of course!) it has a special meaning. Power is the **rate of doing work** — in other words it's the **amount of energy transferred** from one form to another **per second.**
You **calculate power** from this equation:

$$P = \frac{\Delta E}{t}$$

Power = work done ÷ time

...where P is measured in watts (W), ΔE is measured in joules (J) and t is measured in seconds (s).

The **watt** (symbol W) is defined as a **rate of energy transfer** equal to **1 joule per second** (Js^{-1}).

Example: a) Brian is doing the shopping. He pushes a 15 kg cart with a force of 45 N and his arms make an angle of 20.0° to the horizontal. If it takes him 7 seconds to reach the end of a 10.0 m aisle, calculate the power he outputs to do so.

The horizontal component of the pushing force is given by $F\cos\theta$
So $\Delta E = F \times \Delta s \times \cos\theta = 45 \times 10.0 \times \cos(20°)$
$$= 422.861... \text{ J}$$

20°

Power is $P = \frac{\Delta E}{t} = \frac{422.861...}{7}$
$$= 60.408... = \textbf{60 W (to 2 s.f.)}$$

b) Brian later sees that chocolate biscuits are on sale on a shelf 5.0 m away. He races to get the last pack, exerting the twice as much force as in part a) and keeping his arms in the same position as before. He outputs 211 W of power to get to the biscuits. Calculate the time it takes him to reach them.

The force applied is doubled, but the distance over which it is applied is halved, so the work is still $\Delta E = 422.861...$

The time taken, $t = \frac{\Delta E}{P} = \frac{422.861...}{211}$
$$= 2.004... = \textbf{2.0 s (to 2 s.f.)}$$

Work and Power

Power is also Force × Velocity (P = Fv)

Sometimes, it's **easier** to use **this version** of the power equation. This is how you get it:

1) You **know** $P = \Delta E \div t$.
2) You also **know** $\Delta E = F\Delta s$, which gives $P = F\Delta s \div t$.
3) But $v = \Delta s \div t$, which you can substitute into the above equation to give: $\boxed{P = Fv}$
4) It's easier to use this if you're given the **speed** in the question.
   Learn this equation as a **shortcut** to link **power** and **speed**.

> **Example:** A car is travelling at a speed of $10\,\text{ms}^{-1}$ and is kept going against
> frictional forces by a driving force of $500\,\text{N}$ in the direction of motion.
> Find the power supplied by the engine to keep the car moving.
>
> Use the shortcut $P = Fv$, which gives: $P = 500 \times 10 = \textbf{5000 W}$

If the force and motion are in different directions, you can replace F with $F\cos\theta$ to get: $\boxed{P = Fv\cos\theta}$

You **aren't** expected to **remember** this equation, but it's made up of bits that you
are supposed to know, so be ready for the possibility of calculating **power** in a
situation where the **direction of the force and direction of motion are different**.

Practice Questions

Q1 Define 'work' in terms of transferring energy.

Q2 Write down the equation for calculating work when the force, F,
acts in the same direction as the change in displacement, Δs.

Q3 An engine applies a force perpendicular to a change in displacement. How much work does it do?

Q4 Write down the equation for calculating work when the motion is horizontal
and the applied force is at an angle θ to the horizontal.

Q5 Define power and state the unit it is measured in.

Q6 Write down the equation linking power to work done and time.

Q7 From this, show that power = force × velocity.

Exam Questions

Q1 The motor in a model train does 7.5 J of work to move the train 3.6 m in a straight line.
Calculate the force applied by the motor. You may assume that frictional losses are negligible. [2 marks]

Q2 A traditional narrow boat is drawn by a horse walking along the towpath.
The horse pulls the boat at a constant speed between two locks which
are 1500 m apart. The tension in the rope is 100 N at 40° (both to 2 s.f.)
to the direction of motion.

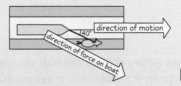

a) Calculate the work done on the boat. [2 marks]

b) The boat moves at 0.80 ms⁻¹. Calculate the power supplied to the boat in the direction of motion. [1 mark]

Q3 A motor is used to lift a 20.0 kg load a height of 3.00 m. *(g = 9.81 Nkg⁻¹)*

a) Calculate the work done in lifting the load. [1 mark]

b) The speed of the load during the lift is 0.25 ms⁻¹. Calculate the power delivered by the motor. [1 mark]

Work — there's just no getting away from it...

Loads of equations to learn. Well, that's what you came here for, after all. Can't beat a good bit of equation-learning,
as I've heard you say quietly to yourself when you think no one's listening. Aha, can't fool me. Aahahahahahahaha.

Conservation of Energy

Energy can never be lost. I repeat — energy can never be lost. Which is basically what I'm about to take up two whole pages saying. But that's, of course, because you need to do exam questions on this as well as understand the principle.

Learn the **Principle** of **Conservation** of **Energy**

The **principle of conservation of energy** says that:

Energy **cannot be created** or **destroyed**. Energy **can be transferred** from one form to another but the total amount of energy in a closed system will not change.

You can talk about how well energy is transferred in terms of **efficiency**:

$$\text{efficiency} = \frac{\text{useful energy output}}{\text{energy input}}$$

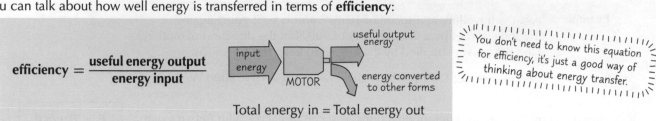

Total energy in = Total energy out

You don't need to know this equation for efficiency, it's just a good way of thinking about energy transfer.

You need it for **Questions** about **Kinetic** and **Potential Energy**

The principle of conservation of energy nearly always comes up when you're doing questions about **changes** between **kinetic** and **potential energy**. A quick reminder:

1) **Kinetic energy** is the energy of anything due to its **motion**, which you work out from:

$$\text{kinetic energy} = \tfrac{1}{2}mv^2$$

m is the mass of the object (kg) and v is its velocity (ms^{-1})

2) There are **different types of potential energy** — e.g. gravitational and elastic.

3) **Gravitational potential energy** is the energy something gains if you lift it up, where:

$$\text{gravitational potential energy} = mgh$$

g is the acceleration due to gravity, $g = 9.81 \ \text{ms}^{-2}$ and h is the height (m)

*Make sure you **know** the equations for kinetic and gravitational potential energy. You won't be given them in your exam.*

4) **Elastic strain energy** (elastic stored energy) is the energy you get in, say, a stretched rubber band or spring. If the object obeys Hooke's law (see p.40), you work this out using:

$$\text{elastic strain energy} = \tfrac{1}{2}kx^2$$

x is the extension of the spring (m) and k is the spring constant (Nm^{-1})

These pictures show you three **examples** of changes between kinetic and potential energy.

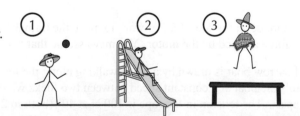

1) As Becky throws the **ball upwards**, **kinetic energy** is converted into **gravitational potential energy**. When it **comes down** again, that **gravitational potential** energy is **converted back** into **kinetic** energy.

2) As Dominic goes **down the slide**, **gravitational potential energy** is converted to **kinetic energy**.

3) As Simon bounces upwards from the trampoline, **elastic strain energy** is converted to **kinetic energy**, to **gravitational potential energy**. As he comes back down again, that **gravitational potential** energy is **converted back** to **kinetic** energy, to **elastic strain** energy, and so on.

In **real life** there are also **frictional forces** — Simon would have to exert some **force** from his **muscles** to keep **jumping** to the **same height** above the trampoline each time. Each time the trampoline **stretches**, some **heat** is generated in the trampoline material. You're usually told to **ignore friction** in exam questions — this means you can **assume** that the **only forces** are those that provide the **potential or kinetic energy** (in this example that's **Simon's weight** and the **tension** in the springs and trampoline material).

If you're ignoring friction, you can say that the **sum of the kinetic and potential energies is constant**.

Conservation of Energy

Use Conservation of Energy to **Solve Problems**

You need to be able to **use** conservation of mechanical energy (change in potential energy = change in kinetic energy) to solve problems. The classic example is the **simple pendulum**.

In a simple pendulum, you assume that all the mass is in the **bob** at the end.

Example: A simple pendulum has a mass of 0.70 kg and a length of 50.0 cm.
It is pulled out to an angle of 30° (to 2 s.f.) from the vertical.

a) Find the gravitational potential energy stored in the pendulum bob.

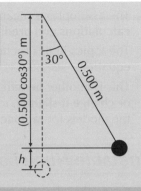

You can work out the increase in height, h, of the end of the pendulum using trig.

Gravitational potential energy = mgh

$= 0.70 \times 9.81 \times (0.500 - 0.500 \cos 30°)$

$= 0.4600... = \textbf{0.46 J (to 2 s.f.)}$

b) The pendulum is released. Find the maximum speed of the pendulum bob as it passes the vertical position.

To find the maximum speed, assume no air resistance.
The conservation of energy principle then gives $mgh = \frac{1}{2}mv^2$.

You can then work out the speed in two ways:

$$\frac{1}{2}mv^2 = 0.4600...$$

$$v = \sqrt{\frac{2 \times 0.4600...}{0.70}}$$

$$= 1.1464... = \textbf{1.1 ms}^{-1} \textbf{ (to 2 s.f.)}$$

OR

Cancel the m's and rearrange to give:
$v^2 = 2gh$
$= 2 \times 9.81 \times (0.500 - 0.500 \cos 30°)$
$= 1.31429...$

$v = 1.146... = \textbf{1.1 ms}^{-1} \textbf{ (to 2 s.f.)}$

Practice Questions

Q1 State the principle of conservation of energy.

Q2 What are the equations for calculating kinetic energy and gravitational potential energy?

Q3 Show that, if there's no air resistance and the mass of the string is negligible, the speed of a pendulum is independent of the mass of the bob.

Exam Questions

$g = 9.81 \, Nkg^{-1}$

Q1 A skateboarder is on a half-pipe. He rides the board down one side of the ramp and up the other. The height of the ramp is 2.0 m. Assuming there is no friction, calculate his speed at the lowest point of the ramp. [3 marks]

Q2 A 0.020 kg rubber ball is released from a height of 8.0 m. (Assume that the effect of air resistance is negligible.)

a) Find the kinetic energy of the ball just before it hits the ground. [1 mark]

b) The ball strikes the ground and rebounds to a height of 6.5 m.
Calculate how much energy is transferred to heat and sound during the impact with the ground. [2 marks]

Q3 A 70.0 kg woman is bouncing on a trampoline and reaches a constant maximum height.
When the woman is at the bottom of her bounce and the trampoline is fully stretched, it has gained 2750 J of elastic strain energy. Calculate her speed when she is at half the maximum height of a bounce. [3 marks]

Energy is never lost — it just sometimes prefers the scenic route...

Make sure you can recall the equations for kinetic and gravitational potential energy in a flash. They'll most likely be needed in a few questions. Remember to check your answers if you've got time — I always forget to multiply by the ½.

Radioactivity and Exponential Decay

Making models in physics is nothing to do with squeezy bottles and sticky-back plastic, I'm afraid. But models are designed to make life easier — they simplify things and show links between topics you might not think are connected.

Models Use Assumptions to Simplify Problems

1) A **model** is a **set of assumptions** that **simplifies** and **idealises** a particular situation.

2) The assumptions mean you can write **equations** that describe what's going on, allowing you to make **calculations** and **predictions**. Without the assumptions, there would be **too many factors** to consider.

3) The topics in this section may appear to be **unconnected**, but they're all based on **models** that use **differential equations** (see below) to describe the **rate of change** of something.

4) This is another **benefit** of models — once you have a model that describes one process you can often **extend it**, or **change it slightly**, to describe **another**, **unrelated process** without having to start all over again — compare the models for **radioactive decay** (p.104) and **capacitor discharge** (p.107) and you'll see what I mean.

Unstable Nuclei are Radioactive

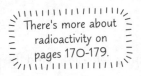
There's more about radioactivity on pages 170-179.

This radio was pretty active...

1) If a nucleus has **too many neutrons**, **not enough neutrons**, **too many nucleons** in total, or **too much energy**, it may be **unstable**.

2) Unstable nuclei **break down** by **releasing energy** and/or **particles**, until they reach a **stable form** — this process is called **radioactive decay**.

3) Radioactive decay is a **random** process — you **can't** tell when any **one nucleus** will **decay**, or **which nucleus** in a sample will be the **next** to decay.

Radioactivity can be Modelled by Exponential Decay

1) Although you can't predict when a nucleus will decay, you can still make predictions about the behaviour of a radioactive source using a **model** — **exponential decay** — based on a **very large number** of undecayed nuclei.

2) If you take a **large** enough **sample** of **unstable nuclei**, the **overall behaviour** shows a **pattern**. This means you can predict **how many nuclei** will decay in a **given time** (even though you can't predict which ones).

3) If you plot a graph showing the **number** of unstable nuclei that **decay each second** against **time**, you always get an **exponential decay curve**, like the one on page 103 — so this can be used as a **model** for radioactive decay.

The Rate of Decay is Measured by the Decay Constant

The **number** of unstable nuclei that **decay each second** is called the **activity** of the sample. The **activity** of a sample is **proportional** to its size — as **nuclei decay**, the **sample** size gets **smaller**, so the **activity falls**. If you plot a graph of **activity** against time, you'll see that the **gradient** gets **shallower and shallower**. This kind of graph, where the rate of change decreases as the quantity gets smaller, is called an **exponential decay** curve.

The **decay constant** (λ) measures how **quickly** an isotope will **decay** — it's the **probability** of a given nucleus **decaying** in a certain **time**. The **bigger** the value of λ, the **more likely** a decay is, so the **faster** the rate of decay. Its unit is **s^{-1}**. For a given isotope, λ is a **fixed** probability (it doesn't change at all).

> **activity = decay constant × number of undecayed nuclei**

In symbols: $A = \lambda N$

Don't get λ confused with wavelength.

Activity is measured in **becquerels** (Bq). An activity of 1 Bq means that 1 nucleus decays every second.

If you plot a graph of the **number of undecayed nuclei** remaining in a sample (**N**) against time (see next page), the **gradient** of the graph is **negative**. The gradient is the change in the number of radioactive nuclei remaining in a given time (the rate of decay), which must also be **negative**.

$$\frac{dN}{dt} = -\lambda N$$

Equations like $\frac{dN}{dt} = -\lambda N$ are a type of **differential equation**. They're used to describe the **rate of change** of something, and are really helpful for modelling situations where the rate of change of a quantity **is proportional to the value** of that quantity (like exponential decay). In the case of radioactive decay, the rate of decay is proportional to the number of undecayed nuclei remaining. Equations like this have the general form: $\frac{dx}{dt} = -kx$, where k is a constant.

You can model the charge remaining on a discharging capacitor in the same way (p.107).

Radioactivity and Exponential Decay

You can *Find* the *Half-Life* of an *Isotope* from a *Graph*

The **half-life** ($T_{1/2}$) of an **isotope** is the **average time** it takes for the **number of undecayed nuclei** to **halve**.

The **longer** the **half-life** of an isotope, the **longer** a sample of a given initial size will remain **radioactive**.
You can find the **half-life** of an isotope from a graph of the number of **undecayed nuclei** remaining against **time**:

1) Read off the original number of undecayed nuclei (when $t = 0$), N_0.
2) Go to **half** the original value of N.
3) Draw a **horizontal line** to the **curve**, then a **vertical line** down to the *x*-axis.
4) The **half-life** is where this line meets the *x*-axis.
5) It's always a good idea to **check** your answer. Repeat steps 1-3 for a **quarter** of the original value of N, and divide the time where the line meets the *x*-axis by **two**. That will also give you the half-life. You can do the same for an eighth of the original value (divide the time by 3), and a sixteenth of the original value (divide the time by 4). Check that you get the **same answer** each time.

If you're not sure what an isotope is, see p.170.

The half-life stays the same. It takes the same amount of time for half of the nuclei to decay regardless of the number of nuclei you start with.

The number of undecayed nuclei approaches zero.

In practice, half-life isn't measured by counting undecayed nuclei (which can be very tricky), but by measuring the **time it takes** for the **activity** (or the count rate) to **halve**. The method is **exactly the same**, you just plot activity (or count rate) against time rather than the number of undecayed nuclei.

Activity is the number of decays per second. Count rate is the number of decays detected per second. As detectors generally only detect radiation that's emitted in one direction, but sources emit radiation in all directions, the count rate will be proportional to, but less than, the source's activity.

You can Generate a *Count-Rate* Decay Graph *Experimentally*

You're most likely to do this using the isotope **protactinium-234**.
Protactinium-234 is formed when **uranium** decays (via another isotope).
You can measure protactinium-234's decay rate using a **protactinium generator** — a bottle containing a uranium salt, the decay products of uranium (including protactinium-234) and two solvents, which separate out into layers, like this:

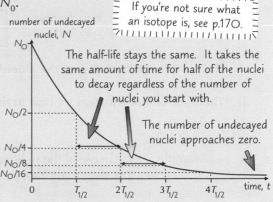

layer containing protactinium-234
layer containing uranium salt

1) **Shake the bottle** to mix the solvents together, then add it to the equipment shown on the right.
2) Wait for the liquids to **separate**. The protactinium-234 will be in solution in the top layer, and the uranium salt will stay in the bottom layer. Then you can point the Geiger-Müller tube at the top layer to measure the activity of the protactinium-234.
3) As soon as the liquids separate, record the count rate. Re-measure the count rate at sensible intervals (e.g. every 30 seconds).
4) Once you've collected your data, leave the bottle to stand for at least ten minutes (this should be long enough for all the protactinium in the top layer to decay), then take the count rate again. This is the **background count rate** corresponding to background radiation — the low level radiation that you get everywhere. (You could also do this at the beginning of the experiment, before shaking the bottle).
5) **Subtract this value** from your measured count rates, then plot a graph of count rate against time. It should look like the graph on the right. You can use this graph to find the **half-life** in exactly the same way as above. In this case the half-life is the time taken for the count rate to halve.

Geiger counter
point the Geiger-Müller tube at the top layer in the generator
Clamp and clamp stand
Protactinium generator
Geiger-Müller tube

count rate
time, t

You could also connect the Geiger-Müller tube to a data logger and a computer to record this data automatically, then use the computer to generate the graph (you'll still need to remove the background count rate though).

Radioactivity and Exponential Decay

You Need to Know the Equations for Half-Life and Decay

1) The **half-life** can be **calculated** using the equation:

$$T_{1/2} = \frac{\ln 2}{\lambda}$$

where $T_{1/2}$ is the half-life (in s), ln is the natural log (see page 182) and λ is the decay constant (in s^{-1})

2) The **number of undecayed nuclei** remaining, N, depends on the **number originally** present, N_0. The **number remaining** can be calculated using the equation:

Here t = time, measured in seconds.

$$N = N_0 e^{-\lambda t}$$

This is the equation of the curve on the graph at the top of page 103.

This is the **exact solution** of the differential equation $\frac{dN}{dt} = -\lambda N$.

3) There's a similar equation for how **activity** changes with time:

$$A = A_0 e^{-\lambda t}$$

where A is the activity (in Bq) and A_0 is the initial activity

Example: A sample of the radioactive isotope ^{13}N contains 5.0×10^6 undecayed nuclei. The decay constant for this isotope is 1.16×10^{-3} s^{-1}.

a) What is the half-life for this isotope?

$$T_{1/2} = \frac{\ln 2}{\lambda} = \frac{\ln 2}{1.16 \times 10^{-3}} = 597.54... = \textbf{598 s (to 3 s.f.)}$$

b) How many undecayed ^{13}N nuclei will remain after 810 seconds?

$$N = N_0 e^{-\lambda t} = (5.0 \times 10^6) \times e^{-(1.16 \times 10^{-3} \times 810)} = 1.953... \times 10^6$$
$$= \textbf{2.0} \times \textbf{10}^6 \textbf{ nuclei (to 2 s.f.)}$$

Practice Questions

Q1 What is meant by the statement 'radioactive decay is a random process'?

Q2 What does the decay constant of a radioactive isotope correspond to?

Q3 Define radioactive activity. What units is it measured in?

Q4 What is the general form of an equation where the rate of change of a quantity is proportional to the value of that quantity?

Q5 What is meant by the term 'half-life'?

Q6 Sketch a typical radioactive decay graph showing the number of undecayed nuclei against time.

Q7 Describe how you could find the half-life of a radioactive isotope from a graph of activity against time.

Q8 Describe an experiment to measure the half-life of protactinium-234.

Exam Question

Q1 A pure radioactive source initially contains 51 000 undecayed nuclei. The decay constant for the sample is $\lambda = 0.014$ s^{-1}.

a) Calculate the initial activity of this sample. [1 mark]

b) Calculate the half-life of this sample. [1 mark]

c) Estimate how many nuclei of the radioactive source there will be after 300 seconds. [1 mark]

d) Exponential decay is used to model radioactive decay. Give one reason why models are useful in science. [1 mark]

Radioactivity is a random process — just like revision shouldn't be...

Remember the shape of that graph — whether it's count rate, activity or number of nuclei plotted against time, the shape's always the same. The maths is a bit of a pain, but I think the experiment's pretty good.

Capacitors

You might not have guessed that a page on radioactive decay would be followed by a page on capacitors, but by the time you get to pages 106-109 it'll make perfect sense. Anyway, first you need to learn about capacitors...

Capacitance is Defined as the Amount of Charge Stored per Volt

Capacitors are made up of two metal plates separated by an air gap or an insulator (so no charge can flow between them). These plates **store electrical charge** — a bit like a charge bucket. **Capacitance**, **C**, is a measure of **how much charge** a capacitor can hold — it's defined as the **amount of charge stored per volt**.

$$C = \frac{Q}{V}$$

Q is the charge in coulombs and V is the potential difference in volts

Capacitance is measured in **farads** (F). **1 farad = 1 C V⁻¹** (i.e. one coulomb per volt).

A farad is a **huge** unit, so you'll usually see capacitances expressed in terms of:

μF — microfarads ($\times 10^{-6}$), **nF** — nanofarads ($\times 10^{-9}$), **pF** — picofarads ($\times 10^{-12}$)

Remember the link between **current**, *I*, **charge**, *Q*, and **time**, *t*, too — you'll often need **both equations** for capacitor questions.

$$I = \frac{\Delta Q}{\Delta t}$$

Capacitors Also Store Energy

1) In the circuit on the right, when the switch is flicked to the **left**, **charge** builds up on the plates of the **capacitor**. Energy provided by the battery is **stored** by the capacitor, in the form of **electrical potential energy**.

2) If the switch is flicked to the **right**, the energy stored on the plates will **discharge** through the **bulb**, converting electrical potential energy into light and heat.

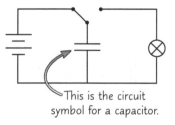
This is the circuit symbol for a capacitor.

3) Whilst the capacitor is charging, **work** is done **removing charge** from **one plate** and depositing **charge** onto the other one. The energy for this must come from the **energy** stored in the **battery**, and is given by **charge × average p.d.**

4) You can find the **energy stored** by the capacitor from the **area** under a **graph** of **p.d.** against **charge stored** on the capacitor. The p.d. across the capacitor is **proportional** to the charge stored on it, so the graph is a **straight line** through the origin. The **energy stored** is given by the **yellow triangle**.

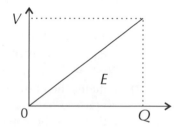

5) **Area of triangle = ½ × base × height**, so the energy stored by the capacitor is: $E = \frac{1}{2}QV$

6) You can rearrange $C = \frac{Q}{V}$ to get $Q = CV$.

If you substitute this into the equation for the area under the graph you get **another equation** for the energy stored on a capacitor: $E = \frac{1}{2}QV = \frac{1}{2}(CV)V$ so $E = \frac{1}{2}CV^2$

You may get given, or be asked to draw, a graph of charge stored against potential difference (i.e. a graph with the axes swapped). The energy stored is still the area under the graph, which will still be ½QV.

Practice Questions

Q1 Define capacitance.

Q2 How would you find the energy stored on a capacitor from a graph of potential difference against charge stored?

Exam Question

Q1 A 0.50 F capacitor is fully charged up from a 12 V supply.

a) What is the total energy stored by the capacitor:
A: 36 J　　B: 36 kJ　　C: 74 J　　D: 74 kJ 　　[1 mark]

b) Calculate the charge stored by the capacitor. 　　[1 mark]

Capacitance — fun, it's not...
Capacitors are really useful in the real world. Pick an appliance, any appliance, and it'll probably have a capacitor or several. If I'm being honest though, the only saving grace of this page for me is that it's not especially hard...

Charging and Discharging

You know, I've got the weirdest feeling I've seen some of these graphs before...

You can **Investigate** What Happens When you **Charge** a **Capacitor**

1) Set up the test circuit shown in the circuit diagram on the right.

2) Close the switch to connect the **uncharged** capacitor to the power supply.

3) Let the capacitor **charge** whilst the **data logger** records both the **potential difference** (from the voltmeter) and the **current** (from the ammeter) over time.

4) When the current through the ammeter is **zero**, the capacitor is fully charged (this won't take very long).

5) You should be able to plot the following graphs from the data collected from this experiment:

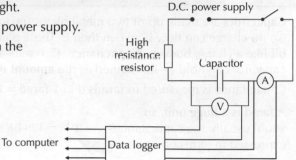
D.C. power supply
High resistance resistor
Capacitor
A
V
To computer
Data logger

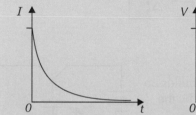 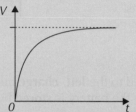 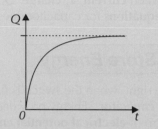 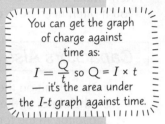

> You can get the graph of charge against time as:
> $I = \dfrac{Q}{t}$ so $Q = I \times t$
> — it's the area under the I-t graph against time.

1) As soon as the switch closes, current starts to flow. The electrons flow onto the plate connected to the **negative terminal** of the power supply, so a **negative charge** builds up.

2) This build-up of negative charge **repels** electrons off the plate connected to the **positive terminal** of the power supply, making that plate positive. These electrons are attracted to the positive terminal of the power supply.

3) An **equal** but **opposite** charge builds up on each plate, causing a **potential difference** between the plates. Remember that **no charge** can flow **between** the plates because they're **separated** by an **insulator** (e.g. a vacuum or air gap).

4) Initially, the current through the circuit is high. But, as **charge** builds up on the plates, **electrostatic repulsion** makes it **harder** and **harder** for more electrons to be deposited. When the p.d. across the **capacitor** is equal to the p.d. across the **power supply**, the **current** falls to **zero**.

To **Discharge** a Capacitor, **Disconnect** the **Power** and **Close** the **Switch**

1) **Disconnect** the power from the test circuit and close the **switch** to let the capacitor **discharge** whilst the data logger records **potential difference** and **current** over time.

> Connect the wires from the two terminals of the power supply together, so the circuit is complete when the switch is closed.

2) When the **current** through the ammeter and the **potential difference** across the plates are zero, the capacitor is fully discharged.

3) You can then plot graphs of current, potential difference and charge against time once more.

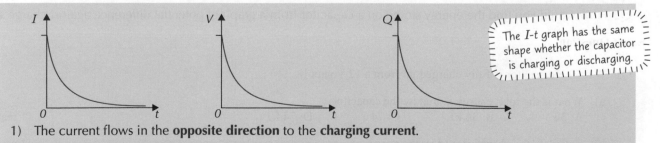

> The I-t graph has the same shape whether the capacitor is charging or discharging.

1) The current flows in the **opposite direction** to the **charging current**.

2) As the **potential difference** decreases, the **current** decreases as well.

3) When a capacitor is **discharging**, the amount of **charge** on and **potential difference** between the plates falls **exponentially** with time. That means it always takes the **same length** of time for the charge or potential difference to **halve**, no matter what value it starts at — like radioactive decay (see p.103).

4) The same is true for the amount of **current flowing** around the circuit.

Charging and Discharging

The *Time Taken* to *Charge* or *Discharge* Depends on *Two Factors*

The **time** it takes to charge or discharge a capacitor depends on:

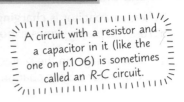

A circuit with a resistor and a capacitor in it (like the one on p.106) is sometimes called an R-C circuit.

> 1) The **capacitance** of the capacitor (**C**). This affects the amount of **charge** that can be transferred for a given **potential difference**.
>
> 2) The **resistance** of the circuit (**R**). This affects the **current** in the circuit.

Discharge Rate is Proportional to the Charge Remaining

1) As you can see, the graph of **charge remaining** against **time** for a discharging capacitor has the same shape as the graph for radioactive decay (p.103). The amount of charge **initially falls quickly**, but the rate **slows** as the amount of **charge decreases** — the **rate of discharge** is **proportional** to the **charge remaining**.

2) You can show this **relationship** by drawing a **graph** of the rate of discharge (dQ/dt) against the charge remaining (Q) — you get a lovely straight line through the origin. This means that $dQ/dt \propto Q$.

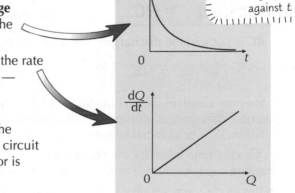

dQ/dt is the gradient of the graph of Q against t.

3) The rate of discharge of a capacitor also depends on the **capacitance** of the capacitor and the **resistance** of the circuit (see above). In fact, the rate of discharge of a capacitor is given by the **differential equation**:

$$\frac{dQ}{dt} = -\frac{Q}{RC}$$

where Q is the charge remaining (C), R is the resistance of the circuit (Ω) and C is the capacitance of the capacitor (F)

4) The relationship between charge remaining and time for a discharging capacitor is an example of **exponential decay**. This means you can **model** the charge remaining on a discharging capacitor **in the same way** as you'd model radioactive decay.

You can Calculate *Charge*, *P.d.* and *Current* as a Capacitor *Discharges*

1) The **charge left** on the plates at a given time after a capacitor begins discharging from being fully charged is given by the equation:

$$Q = Q_0 e^{\frac{-t}{RC}}$$

where Q_0 = the initial charge on the plates of the capacitor (C) and t = the time since the capacitor began discharging (s)

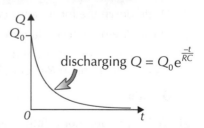

discharging $Q = Q_0 e^{\frac{-t}{RC}}$

This is the **exact solution** of the differential equation $\frac{dQ}{dt} = -\frac{Q}{RC}$.

2) The **proportion** of charge that is transferred from a discharging capacitor in a given time interval is **constant** (so the same proportion of the remaining charge will be transferred in the first second as in the second second). This is called the **constant ratio property**, and is true for all exponential relationships.

In radioactive decay, the number of undecayed nuclei remaining halves in each half-life (p.104). This is also an example of the constant ratio property.

3) As the **potential difference** and **current** also decrease **exponentially** as a capacitor discharges, the formulas for calculating the current or potential difference at a certain time are similar:

$$I = I_0 e^{\frac{-t}{RC}}$$

$$V = V_0 e^{\frac{-t}{RC}}$$

where I_0 = the initial current as the capacitor begins discharging, and V_0 = the initial potential difference across the capacitor

As these are also **exponential decay** relationships, the time taken for the **current** to **halve** and the time taken for the **potential difference** to **halve** are also **constant** for a **given capacitor** in a **given circuit**.

Charging and Discharging

You can do the Same for a Charging Capacitor

When a capacitor is **charging**, the **growth rate** of the amount of **charge on** and **potential difference across** the plates shows **exponential decay** (so over time they increase more and more slowly).

1) The **charge** on the plates at a given time after a capacitor begins charging is given by the equation:

$$Q = Q_0(1 - e^{\frac{-t}{RC}})$$

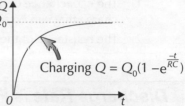

2) Similarly, the **potential difference** across the plates at a given time is given by the equation:

$$V = V_0(1 - e^{\frac{-t}{RC}})$$

Charging $Q = Q_0(1 - e^{\frac{-t}{RC}})$

3) The **charging current** is different — it **decreases exponentially**. The formula to calculate the charging current at a given time is the same as for when it's discharging:

$$I = I_0 e^{\frac{-t}{RC}}$$

Time Constant $\tau = RC$ τ is the Greek letter 'tau'

If $t = \tau = RC$ is put into the **discharging** equations on p.107, then $Q = Q_0 e^{-1}$, $V = V_0 e^{-1}$ and $I = I_0 e^{-1}$.

So when $t = \tau$: $\frac{Q}{Q_0} = \frac{1}{e} = \frac{1}{2.718...} \approx 0.37$.

The units of τ are seconds, s.

1) τ, the **time constant**, is the time taken for the charge, potential difference or current of a discharging capacitor to **fall** to **37%** of its initial value.

2) It's also the time taken for the charge or potential difference of a charging capacitor to **rise** to **63%** of its value when fully charged.

3) So the **larger** the **resistance** in series with the capacitor, the **longer** the capacitor takes to charge or discharge.

4) In practice, the time taken for a capacitor to charge or discharge **fully** is taken to be about $5RC$.

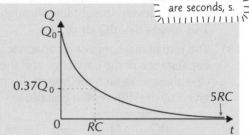

Practice Questions

Q1 Describe an experiment to investigate how potential difference, current, and charge vary with time as a capacitor charges and discharges. Sketch graphs of the results you would expect to get.

Q2 What two factors affect how quickly a capacitor charges?

Q3 Write down the formula for calculating charge at a given time for a discharging capacitor.

Q4 Write down the formula for calculating potential difference at a given time for a charging capacitor.

Q5 What is the time constant of a discharging capacitor? How is it calculated? Describe how you could find the time constant of an R-C circuit from a graph of current against time for a charging capacitor.

Exam Questions

Q1 A 250 µF capacitor is fully charged from a 6.0 V battery and then discharged through a 1.0 kΩ resistor.

a) Calculate the potential difference across the capacitor 0.25 s after it begins charging. [2 marks]

b) Calculate the percentage of the total charge remaining on the capacitor 0.7 s after it begins discharging. [2 marks]

Q2 A fully charged 320 µF capacitor is discharged through a 1.6 kΩ resistor.

a) Calculate the time taken for the charge on the capacitor to fall to 37% of its fully charged value after it begins discharging. [2 marks]

b) Calculate the rate of change of the charge on the capacitor when the charge remaining is 5.5 mC. [1 mark]

I don't like capacitor circuits — they're so RC...

You'll be given the equation for how the charge on a discharging capacitor changes with time in the exam, but you won't be given any of the other exponential equations on the last three pages (*gulp*), so make sure you learn them.

Modelling Decay

Who'd have thought that capacitors and radioactive isotopes could have so much in common? Read on...

Capacitors and Radioactive Isotopes Have Similar Decay Equations

Radioactive isotopes (p.102-104) might seem very different from capacitors in R-C circuits (p.106-108), but the decay models for them are very similar. This table shows the similarities and differences between the models.

	DISCHARGING CAPACITORS	RADIOACTIVE ISOTOPES
1)	Decay equation is $Q = Q_0 e^{-t/RC}$.	Decay equation is $N = N_0 e^{-\lambda t}$.
2)	The **quantity** that decays is Q, the amount of charge left on the plates of the capacitor.	The **quantity** that decays is N, the number of undecayed nuclei remaining.
3)	**Initially**, the charge on the plates is Q_0.	**Initially**, the number of undecayed nuclei is N_0.
4)	It takes RC seconds for the amount of charge remaining to fall to **37% of its initial value**.	The time taken for the number of undecayed nuclei to decay by half (the **half-life**) is $T_{1/2} = \ln 2 / \lambda$.

You Can Use a Logarithmic Graph to Find the Decay Constant and Half-life

1) If you plot a **graph** of the **number of undecayed nuclei**, N, in a radioactive sample against **time**, t, you get an **exponential curve** like the one on page 103.

2) But, if you plot the **natural log** (ln) of the number of **undecayed nuclei** against **time**, you get a **straight line**. To find the **natural log** of a number, just use the **ln button** on your calculator.

3) You get a straight line because the **decay equation**, $N = N_0 e^{-\lambda t}$, can be **rearranged**, via the mystical wonder of **logs**, to the **general form** of a **straight line** — $y = mx + c$.

$$N = N_0 e^{-\lambda t} \implies \ln(N) = -\lambda t + \ln(N_0)$$
$$\phantom{N = N_0 e^{-\lambda t} \implies} y = mx + c$$

4) The **gradient** of the line is $-\lambda$ (the **decay constant**). From this you can **calculate** the half-life, $T_{1/2}$, of the sample.

5) This works for graphs of **activity** against **time** too — $A = A_0 e^{-\lambda t}$ becomes $\ln(A) = -\lambda t + \ln(A_0)$. But remember to **subtract** the **background activity** from any measurements first.

If you're not sure about logs, take a look at the stuff on page 182 to see where this comes from.

Example: The graphs below show how the number of undecayed nuclei of a radioactive isotope decreases over time. Use each graph to calculate the half-life of the isotope.

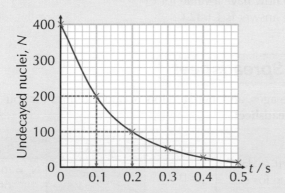

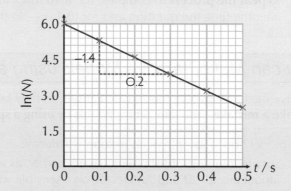

The first graph shows that it takes 0.1 s for the number of undecayed nuclei to fall from 400 to 200 (i.e. to halve). So, the **half-life** is **0.1 s (to 1 s.f.)**.

The **gradient** of this graph is $-1.4 \div 0.2 = -7$, so the **decay constant**, $\lambda = 7$. Substitute this into the equation for half-life: $T_{1/2} = \ln(2) \div 7 = 0.099... = $ **0.1 s (to 1 s.f.)**.

You can use the **same method** with $Q = Q_0 e^{\frac{-t}{RC}}$ to find the **time constant** for an R-C circuit — the gradient of a graph of $\ln Q$ against t is $-\frac{1}{RC}$.

Modelling Decay

You Can Solve Differential Equations Using Iterative Methods

1) $\dfrac{dQ}{dt} = -\dfrac{Q}{RC}$ is a **differential equation** with an **exact solution**: $Q = Q_0 e^{\frac{-t}{RC}}$ (see p.107).

2) Many differential equations **don't have** exact solutions, so scientists use **iterative numerical methods** to solve them. Iterative methods work for **every type** of differential equation. However, the answers are only **approximate**.

3) Iterative methods work by breaking up the time period you're modelling over into **short intervals**, and calculating the value of the variable you're interested in at the end of each interval.

4) You can use the method below for **capacitor decay**, **radioactive decay** or **any** other model where the **rate of change** is **related** to the quantity that's changing — just substitute the **relevant equation**.

Before you start:

- Rearrange your equation to get dQ on its own: $dQ = -(Q/RC)dt$. You'll be dealing with average changes in Q rather than instantaneous ones, so you can rewrite this as $\Delta Q = -(Q/RC)\Delta t$ (see p.111).

- Pick a **time interval**, Δt, that the steps in your model will be separated by (the smaller the interval, the more accurate your answer will be, but the more iterations you'll need to do).

Then you're ready to go:

1) Start at time = 0, with the **initial value of Q**, (call this Q_0).

2) Increase the time by your time interval, Δt. **Substitute** your value of Q into the equation $\Delta Q = -(Q/RC)\Delta t$ to find ΔQ — the change in Q over this time interval.

3) **Add** this value of ΔQ to your current value of Q to find the value of Q after Δt (Q will get smaller, as ΔQ is negative). Call this new value Q_1. Then go back to step 2 and **repeat the process**.

It's easiest to do this using a table — you'll need columns for time (t), charge (Q) and change in charge (ΔQ).

Example: A 150 µF capacitor storing 1.8 C of charge is discharged through a resistance of 40 kΩ. Using an iterative method and a time interval of 0.2 s, find the charge remaining on the capacitor after 0.4 s.

Just follow the method above:

1) Draw your table, and enter your **initial values** of Q (Q_0 = 1.8 C) and t (0 s).

2) **Add Δt** (0.2 s) to the initial time, and write this in the **second row** of the table.

3) Substitute the starting value of Q into the equation: $\Delta Q = -(Q/RC)\Delta t$ to find ΔQ over the first 0.2 seconds. Write this in the second row of the table.

4) **Add ΔQ** to the **initial value** of Q to find the value of Q at t = 0.2 s.

5) **Repeat the process** to complete the third row. You now have a value for Q after the time the question asks for (0.4 s) — so the answer is **1.682 C**.

$-1.8 \div ((40 \times 10^3) \times (150 \times 10^{-6})) \times 0.2$

$1.8 + (-0.06)$

t / s	ΔQ / C	Q / C
0		1.8
0.2	−0.06	1.74
0.4	−0.058	1.682

leave this cell blank

You can Make Iterative Models using a Spreadsheet

Iterative methods involve lots of calculations, so they take ages, and there are lots of opportunities for you to make a **mistake**. You can get round this by using a **spreadsheet**.

To model how a sample of an isotope will decay:

1) Set up columns for **total time (t)**, ΔN and N, as well as data input cells for Δt and λ. Decide on a sensible value for Δt.

2) Rearrange $\dfrac{dN}{dt} = -\lambda N$ (p.102) to get $dN = -\lambda N dt$.
As you're calculating **average rates of change** in N (ΔN) over fixed time intervals, Δt, write this as: $\Delta N = -\lambda N \Delta t$.

3) **Enter formulas** into the spreadsheet to calculate the number of undecayed nuclei left in the sample after each time interval. If you write these properly, the spreadsheet can **automatically** fill them in for as many rows (iterations) as you want.

t / s	ΔN	N
$t_0 = 0$		N_0 = initial no. of nuclei
$t_1 = t_0 + \Delta t$	$(\Delta N)_1 = -\lambda N_0 \Delta t$	$N_1 = N_0 + (\Delta N)_1$
$t_2 = t_1 + \Delta t$	$(\Delta N)_2 = -\lambda N_1 \Delta t$	$N_2 = N_1 + (\Delta N)_2$
$t_3 = ...$	$(\Delta N)_3 = ...$	$N_3 = ...$

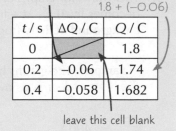

λ (s^{-1}) = e.g. 1×10^{-4}
Δt (s) = e.g. 1000

Make sure the references to these cells don't change when you autofill new rows.

Modelling Decay

Iterative Methods Only Give You **Approximate Answers**

1) Whether you use a spreadsheet or do your calculations by hand, using an iterative method to model a relationship in the form **dx/dt = kx** only gives **approximate** answers.

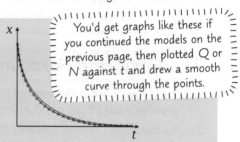

Your model gives you an estimate of how much x changes by (Δx) over each time interval, Δt. You can use this to estimate the average rate of change of x over t, called $\Delta x / \Delta t$. As Δt gets smaller, $\Delta Q / \Delta t$ gets closer to dQ/dt.

2) This is because iterative methods assume that dx/dt **doesn't change** over the time interval you're using. In fact, dx/dt is changing **all the time** (you can tell this from the fact that relationships like this give you graphs that are smooth curves — remember dx/dt is the **gradient** of an x-t graph). dx/dt is called the **instantaneous rate of change**.

3) The **smaller** the value of Δt you use, the **more accurate** your model will be. But using smaller values of t means you need to do **more iterations**.

4) This is why making iterative models using **spreadsheets** that can carry out a very **large number** of iterations very **quickly** is really useful — it lets you make Δt as small as you need it to be.

'That's iteration sorted. Now, does this thing have solitaire?'

You'd get graphs like these if you continued the models on the previous page, then plotted Q or N against t and drew a smooth curve through the points.

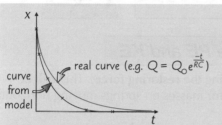

Big Δt — model is **quite different** to the real curve.

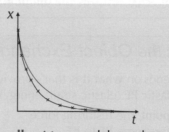

Smaller Δt — model matches the real curve a **bit better**.

Really small Δt — model **matches** the real curve pretty well.

Practice Question

Q1 Use a spreadsheet to model the radioactive decay of a sample initially containing 200 000 undecayed nuclei with a decay constant of 0.002 s^{-1}. If you don't have access to a computer, draw a table and do the first five iterations using a calculator.

Exam Questions

Q1 The graph on the right shows how the natural log of the activity of a sample of a radioactive isotope changes with time. The background activity has been subtracted from the graph.

a) Calculate the decay constant of the isotope. [1 mark]

b) Calculate the initial activity of the sample. [1 mark]

Q2 A teacher set up an R-C circuit to model the radioactive decay of an isotope of radon gas. The values of R and C were chosen so that the charge and resistance were related to the decay constant of the radon by $RC = \lambda^{-1}$. The capacitance of the capacitor was 520 µF and the resistance of the circuit was 144 kΩ. Calculate the decay constant of the radon. [2 marks]

Q3 A 10.0 µF capacitor is discharged through a resistance of 0.20 MΩ. The capacitor initially stores 5.0×10^{-2} C. Using an iterative method estimate the charge after 1.0 s. Use a time interval of 0.50 s for each iteration. [2 marks]

Modelling decay — when the train set in the back garden starts to rust...

Iteration is a bit of a pain, but it's really powerful — especially if you can get a computer to do all the tedious bits for you. This is the end of the capacitors and radioactive decay stuff (although radiation is coming up again later, you'll be pleased to know), so now's a good time to flick back over the last few pages to check it all makes sense...

Simple Harmonic Motion

Radioactive decay to capacitors to... simple harmonic motion? Well, of course — they're all examples of modelling.

SHM is Defined in Terms of Acceleration and Displacement

The **motion** of some **oscillating systems**, e.g. a **pendulum**, can be **modelled** by **simple harmonic motion** (SHM).

1) An object moving with **simple harmonic motion** **oscillates** to and fro, either side of a **midpoint**.

2) The distance of the object from the midpoint is called its **displacement**.

3) There is always a **restoring force** pulling or pushing the object back **towards** the **midpoint**.

4) The **size** of the **restoring force** depends on the **displacement**, and the force makes the object **accelerate** towards the midpoint:

Midpoint

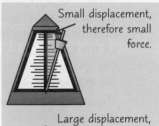
Small displacement, therefore small force.

Large displacement, therefore large force.

> **SHM:** an oscillation in which the **restoring force** on an object (and hence the **acceleration** of the object) is **directly proportional** to its **displacement** from the **midpoint**, and is directed **towards the midpoint**.

The Restoring Force makes the Object Exchange PE and KE

1) The **type** of **potential energy** (PE) depends on **what it is** that's providing the **restoring force**. This will be **gravitational PE** for pendulums and **elastic PE** (elastic strain energy) for masses on springs moving horizontally.

2) As the object moves **towards the midpoint**, the restoring force **does work** on the object and so **transfers** some PE to **KE**. When the object is moving **away from the midpoint**, all that KE is transferred **back to PE** again.

3) At the **midpoint**, the object's **PE** is **zero** and its **KE** is **maximum**.

4) At the **maximum displacement** (the **amplitude**) on both sides of the midpoint, the object's **KE** is **zero** and its **PE** is **maximum**.

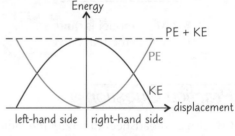
Energy / PE + KE / PE / KE / displacement
left-hand side | right-hand side

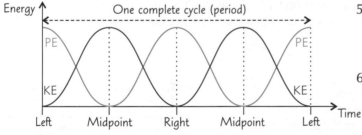
Energy / One complete cycle (period) / PE / KE / PE / KE / Time
Left | Midpoint | Right | Midpoint | Left

5) The **sum** of the **potential** and **kinetic** energy is called the **mechanical energy** and **stays constant** (as long as the motion isn't damped — see p.118-119).

6) The **energy transfer** for one complete cycle of oscillation (see graph) is: PE to KE to PE to KE to PE ... and then the process repeats... This is an example of the **conservation of energy**.

You can Draw Graphs to Show Displacement, Velocity and Acceleration

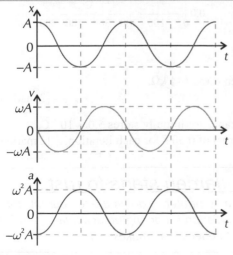

Displacement, x, varies with time, t, as a cosine (or sine) wave with a maximum value, A (the amplitude).

Velocity, v, is the gradient of the **displacement-time** graph. It is a **quarter of a cycle** in front of the **displacement** (a phase difference of $\pi/2$) and has a maximum value of ωA.

Acceleration, a, is the gradient of the **velocity-time** graph. It has a maximum value of $\omega^2 A$, and is in **antiphase** with the **displacement**.

ω is the **angular frequency** of the oscillation (in rad s^{-1}).

$$\omega = 2\pi f \text{ and } \omega = \frac{2\pi}{T}$$

Where T is the time taken for one oscillation and f is the frequency (the number of oscillations per second — see the next page).

There's more on these graphs coming up on page 116.

Simple Harmonic Motion

The **Frequency** and **Period** don't depend on the **Amplitude**

1) From **maximum positive displacement** (e.g. maximum displacement to the right) to **maximum negative displacement** (e.g. maximum displacement to the left) and **back again** is called a **cycle** of oscillation.

2) The **frequency**, *f*, of the SHM is the number of cycles per second (measured in Hz).

3) The **period**, *T*, is the **time** taken for a complete cycle (in seconds).

4) The relationship between **frequency** and **period** is given by the equation: ⟹ $f = \frac{1}{T}$
In other words, they're **inversely proportional** to each other.

> Don't get confused between *f*, the frequency of oscillations, and *ω*, the angular frequency.

> In SHM, the **frequency** and **period** are independent of the **amplitude** (i.e. constant for a given oscillation). So a pendulum clock will keep ticking in regular time intervals even if its swing becomes very small.

Learn the SHM Equations

1) According to the definition of SHM, the **acceleration**, d^2x/dt^2, is directly proportional to the **displacement**, *x*.

2) The **constant of proportionality** depends on the **frequency**, and the acceleration is always in the **opposite direction** to the displacement (so there's a minus sign in the equation).

$$\frac{d^2x}{dt^2} = a = -\omega^2 x$$

This is another differential equation. d^2x/dt^2 is the rate of change of dx/dt (ie the rate of change of the velocity — the acceleration).

3) The **velocity** is **positive** when the object's moving in one direction, and **negative** when it's moving in the opposite direction. For example, a **pendulum's velocity** is **positive** when it's moving from **left to right** and **negative** when it's moving from **right to left**.

4) The **displacement** varies with time according to one of two equations, depending on **where** the object was when the timing was started — they're really similar so you shouldn't have too much trouble learning both.

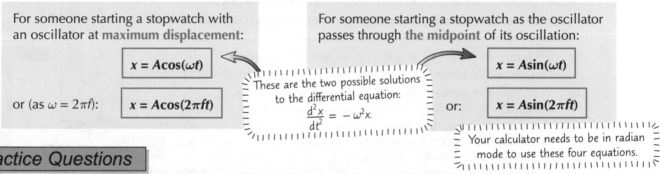

For someone starting a stopwatch with an oscillator at **maximum displacement**:

$$x = A\cos(\omega t)$$

or (as $\omega = 2\pi f$): $\quad x = A\cos(2\pi f t)$

These are the two possible solutions to the differential equation: $\frac{d^2x}{dt^2} = -\omega^2 x$.

For someone starting a stopwatch as the oscillator passes through **the midpoint** of its oscillation:

$$x = A\sin(\omega t)$$

or: $\quad x = A\sin(2\pi f t)$

Your calculator needs to be in radian mode to use these four equations.

Practice Questions

Q1 What is the relationship between the acceleration and the displacement in SHM?

Q2 Sketch a graph of how the velocity of an object oscillating with SHM varies with time.

Q3 Describe how energy is transferred between kinetic and potential energy for a mass-spring system oscillating horizontally with SHM.

Q4 State the equation linking frequency and period.

Q5 Give two equations for the displacement of a simple harmonic oscillator, in terms of *ω*. When does each apply?

Exam Questions

Q1 a) Define simple harmonic motion. [2 marks]

b) Explain why the motion of a ball bouncing off the ground is not SHM. [1 mark]

Q2 A pendulum is pulled 0.050 m to the left and released. It oscillates with SHM with a frequency of 1.5 Hz.

a) What is the maximum velocity of the pendulum?
A: 0.24 ms⁻¹   B: 9.4 ms⁻¹   C: 0.15 ms⁻¹   D: 0.47 ms⁻¹ [1 mark]

b) Calculate its displacement 0.10 s after it is released. [2 marks]

"Simple" harmonic motion — hmmm, I'm not convinced...

The basic concept of SHM is simple enough (no pun intended). Make sure you can remember the shapes of all the graphs on page 112 and the equations from this page, then just get as much practice at using the equations as you can.

Investigating Simple Harmonic Motion

You can investigate simple harmonic motion in a few different ways — make sure you've read pages 112-113 before you tackle this lot, or it won't make much sense.

A Mass on a Spring is a Simple Harmonic Oscillator (SHO)

1) When the mass is **pushed to the left** or **pulled to the right** of the **equilibrium position**, there's a **force** exerted on it. The size of this force is:

$$F = kx$$

where k is the spring constant (stiffness) of the spring in Nm^{-1} and x is the displacement in m (see p.40)

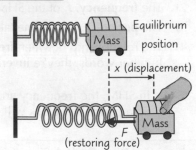

Equilibrium position

Mass

x (displacement)

Mass

F
(restoring force)

2) After a bit of jiggery-pokery involving Newton's second law ($F = ma$) and some of the ideas on the previous page, you get the **formula for the period of a mass oscillating on a spring**:

$$T = 2\pi \sqrt{\frac{m}{k}}$$

where T = period of oscillation in seconds, m = mass in kg
k = spring constant in Nm^{-1}

You can check this result **experimentally**:

1) Set up the equipment as shown in the diagram.

2) **Pull** the masses down a set amount — this displacement will be your initial **amplitude**. Let the masses go.

3) The masses will now oscillate with **simple harmonic motion**.

4) The **position sensor** will measure the **displacement** of the mass over **time**.

5) Connect the position sensor to a computer and create a **displacement-time** graph. Read off the period T from the graph.

6) You can measure the effects of changing the **mass**, the **spring constant** and the **amplitude**. Remember, you should only change **one factor at a time**.

   a) To change the **mass**, m — add extra masses to the spring (be careful not to stretch the spring past its limit of proportionality, p.40).

   b) To change the **spring stiffness**, k — use **different springs**, or **combinations of springs**. You can measure the stiffness of a spring by hanging a mass, m, from it and measuring how much it extends by, then using the equation $F = kx$, where $F = mg$ (see p.90). If you use a **combination** of springs, you can **combine** their stiffnesses like this:

   c) To change the **amplitude**, A — pull the mass down by **different amounts** (again, be careful about how far you stretch the spring). Place a ruler behind the spring and line your eye up with the mass to make sure you measure the distance correctly (you could use a set-square to check that your eye is lined up with the ruler).

7) For each condition, you should take **repeated measurements**, and don't change any of the equipment halfway through the experiment.

8) You should get the following results:

   a) $T \propto \sqrt{m}$ so $T^2 \propto m$ b) $T \propto \sqrt{\frac{1}{k}}$ so $T^2 \propto \frac{1}{k}$ c) T doesn't depend on amplitude, A.

string — Clamp and clamp stand

spring

Ruler

workbench

mass

position sensor

to computer

k $2k$ $3k$

$\frac{1}{2}k$

$\frac{1}{3}k$

Compressing or Stretching a Spring Stores Elastic Strain Energy

When the mass is **displaced** from the **equilibrium point**, the spring is **compressed** or **stretched**, so it stores **elastic strain energy**. You can work out the energy stored using:

$$E = \frac{1}{2}kx^2$$

For a mass oscillating horizontally, this accounts for all of the potential energy in the system. For a mass oscillating vertically, you also need to take gravitational potential energy into account.

You can also find the energy stored from a force-extension graph — the area under the graph is the elastic strain energy (see page 42).

MODULE 5: SECTION 1 — CREATING MODELS

Investigating Simple Harmonic Motion

The *Simple Pendulum* is the *Classic Example* of an *SHO*

A **pendulum** will also move with simple harmonic motion, provided you don't displace it too far.

Here's a method for investigating the simple harmonic motion of a pendulum without using a computer:

1) Set up the equipment shown on the right (you'll also need a **stopwatch**). Measure the **mass**, *m*, of the bob, and use a ruler to find the **length**, *L*, of the string.

2) Pull the bob to the side (as shown) and measure the **angle**, *A*, between the string and the vertical (it should be less than 10°).

3) Position your eye **level** with the **reference mark** (its called a fiduciary marker) then let the bob go. Start the stopwatch when the bob passes in front of the mark, then record the times when the bob passes in front of the mark again, travelling from the **same direction** (e.g. from left to right). The length of time that elapses between each time the bob passes in front of the mark from the same direction is the **time period**, *T*, of the oscillator.

4) *T* might be **too short** to measure accurately from one swing. If so, measure the total time for a number of complete oscillations **combined** (say 5 or 10) and **divide** this time by the number of oscillations to find the time period.

5) You can then vary the **mass**, *m*, of the bob, the **length**, *L*, of the string, and the **angle**, *A*, that you release the string from, keeping it less than 10° (changing this angle varies the amplitude of the oscillations). You should find that:

   a) $T \propto \sqrt{L}$, so $T^2 \propto L$ b) *T* does not depend on *m*   c) *T* does not depend on *A*

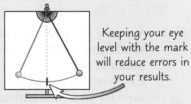

Keeping your eye level with the mark will reduce errors in your results.

You could also do this experiment with an angle sensor and a data logger, which would give you more precise data.

In fact, for small angles of oscillation (up to about 10°), the **period of a pendulum** is:

$$T = 2\pi\sqrt{\frac{L}{g}}$$

where *T* is the period of oscillation in s, *L* is the length of the pendulum in m, and *g* is the gravitational field strength in Nkg⁻¹

Practice Questions

Q1 Write down the formulas for the period of a mass on a spring and the period of a pendulum.

Q2 Describe a method you could use to measure the period of: a) a mass-spring system,   b) a pendulum.

Q3 For a mass-spring system, what graphs could you plot to find out how the period depends on:
a) the mass,   b) the spring constant,   c) the amplitude?
What would they look like?

Exam Questions

Q1 A spring of original length 0.100 m is suspended from a stand and clamp.
A mass of 0.10 kg is attached to the bottom and the spring extends to a total length of 0.200 m.

   a) Calculate the spring constant of the spring in Nm⁻¹. ($g = 9.81$ Nkg⁻¹) [2 marks]

   b) The mass is pulled down a further 0.020 m and then released.
   The spring oscillates with simple harmonic motion, with a period of 0.63 s.
   i) Calculate the elastic strain energy stored in the spring
   when the mass is at the lowest point of its oscillation. [1 mark]

   ii) Calculate the mass that would be needed to make the period of oscillation twice as long. [2 marks]

Q2 Two pendulums of different lengths were released from rest at the top of their swing.
It took exactly the same time for the shorter pendulum to make five complete oscillations
as it took the longer pendulum to make three complete oscillations.
The shorter pendulum had a length of 0.20 m. Show that the length of the longer one was 0.56 m. [3 marks]

Go on — SHO the examiners what you're made of...

The most important things to remember on these pages are those two period equations. You'll be given them in your exam, but you need to know what they mean and be happy using them.

Modelling Simple Harmonic Motion

Just when you thought the modelling was all over...

You Can Model Simple Harmonic Motion **Graphically**

1) If you carry out an **experiment** to investigate the simple harmonic motion of a mass-spring system using a **position sensor** and a computer (see page 114), you'll get data on how displacement changes with time, which you can get the computer to plot as a **graph**.

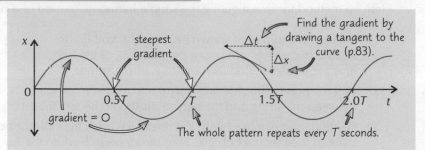

2) **Velocity** is the **rate of change** of **displacement** (dx/dt), so velocity is the **gradient** of an x-t graph. This means you can **generate** a graph of velocity against time for your data **without measuring velocity directly**. You'd need to find the gradient of the x-t graph at many points and plot these values against time. In practice you'd normally get the **computer** to calculate the velocity for you, but you can do this by **hand** if you need to.

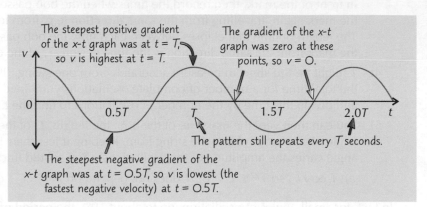

3) **Acceleration** is the **rate of change** of **velocity** (d^2x/dt^2). This means you can generate a graph of acceleration against time from a v-t graph by measuring the gradient of the v-t graph at many points and plotting these values against time.
The **shape** of the a-t graph is the **same** as the x-t graph, but a is **negative** when x is **positive** and vice versa. So $a \propto -x$ (which you know from page 113).

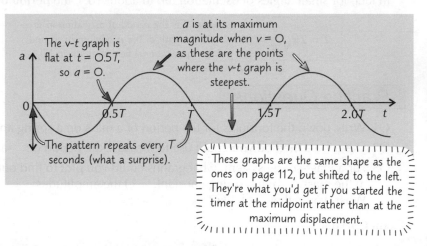

These graphs are the same shape as the ones on page 112, but shifted to the left. They're what you'd get if you started the timer at the midpoint rather than at the maximum displacement.

The Force on a SHO is **Proportional** to its **Displacement**

1) From the **definition** of **simple harmonic motion** (p.112) you know that the **restoring force** on a SHO is **proportional** to its **displacement**. You can express this in an equation as $F = -kx$. For a **mass on a spring**, k is the **spring constant**. For a **pendulum**, it's a bit more **complicated**. Just think of it as a constant.

2) Because $F = ma$ (p.90), this means the **acceleration** of an SHO is **also proportional** to its **displacement**, as you can see in the graphs above.

3) Put all this together and you get:

$$F = ma = m\frac{d^2x}{dt^2} \quad \text{and} \quad F = -kx \quad \text{so:} \quad \boxed{\frac{d^2x}{dt^2} = -\frac{k}{m}x}$$

The minus sign in the equation $F = -kx$ means the force always acts to pull (or push) the oscillator back to the midpoint — it acts in the opposite direction to the oscillator's displacement.

4) This is a **differential equation** that you can use to model SHM. It's a bit like the ones for **radioactive decay** and **discharging capacitors** on p.102 and p.107, but it's $\frac{d^2x}{dt^2}$ rather than $\frac{dx}{dt}$. This is because it's an equation for the **rate of change of the rate of change** of x (i.e. the acceleration), rather than just the rate of change of x.

Modelling Simple Harmonic Motion

You Can **Model** SHM Using **Iteration**

1) You can use the differential equation $\dfrac{d^2x}{dt^2} = -\dfrac{k}{m}x$ to **estimate** the **displacement** (or velocity) of an object moving with simple harmonic motion after a certain time.

2) You need to use an **iterative method** (like the one for capacitors and radioactive decay on page 110). As this equation is for the rate of change of the rate of change, your model will need a few **extra steps** — you'll need to model how the **velocity** of the oscillator changes over time to work out what happens to the **displacement**.

Personally, I prefer modelling hats.

> **Example**   A 0.50 kg mass is attached to a spring with a spring constant of 10.0 Nm⁻¹. The mass is displaced by 0.050 m, then released and allowed to oscillate freely. Use an iterative method to find the displacement of the mass 0.2 s after its release. Use a time interval of 0.1 s for each iteration.

Before you start, you'll need to do some algebra:

- Remember, acceleration is the rate of change of velocity (v). So you can rewrite $\dfrac{d^2x}{dt^2} = -\dfrac{k}{m}x$ as $\dfrac{dv}{dt} = -\dfrac{k}{m}x$.

- As you're considering changes over a fixed time interval, change this to $\dfrac{\Delta v}{\Delta t} = -\dfrac{k}{m}x$ (p.111). Rearrange this to get Δv on its own:

  | **Equation 1: $\Delta v = -(k/m)x\Delta t$** |

- Velocity is change in displacement over time, $\dfrac{dx}{dt}$.
  So, over a fixed time interval, Δt, $v = \Delta x/\Delta t$. Rearrange this to get Δx on its own:

  | **Equation 2: $\Delta x = v\Delta t$** |

Now you can get going:

1) Draw a **table** like the one on the right and fill in the **time column** and the initial values of x and v. The initial velocity is **0 ms⁻¹** because the mass is held at a fixed displacement before being released.

2) Calculate Δv over the first time interval, using equation 1 above. Add this to the initial velocity to find **v**.

3) Calculate Δx using equation 2 above and this value of v. Add this to the initial displacement to find **x** after 0.1 s.

4) **Repeat the process** to complete the third row of the table. You now have a value for x after the time the question asks for (0.2 s) — so the answer is **0.022 m**.

$(-10.0 \div 0.50) \times 0.050 \times 0.1$

$0.050 + (-0.010)$

$0 + (-0.10)$ -0.10×0.1

t / s	Δv / ms⁻¹	v / ms⁻¹	Δx / m	x / m
0		0		0.050
0.1	−0.10	−0.10	−0.010	0.040
0.2	−0.080	−0.18	−0.018	0.022

The acceleration at each iteration is just $\Delta v / \Delta t$.

As on page 110, you can make this kind of model using a spreadsheet. If you plotted the results of this model against time, you'd get sin and cos graphs like the ones on page 112. You could use these to read off the values of displacement or velocity at a given time.

Practice Questions

Q1 Explain how the graphs of displacement, velocity, and acceleration for simple harmonic motion are related to each other.

Q2 State the differential equation relating the acceleration of an SHO to its mass and displacement.

Exam Question

Q1 A 25 g pendulum bob is pulled 2.4 cm to the right and released. It swings with simple harmonic motion.

a) Using an iterative method, calculate the displacement of the bob after 0.15 s. Use a time interval of 0.05 s for each iteration (for this pendulum, $k = 0.82$ Nm⁻¹). [3 marks]

b) Calculate the maximum acceleration of the pendulum bob ($k = 0.82$ Nm⁻¹). [2 marks]

Iteration — it just seems to come up again and again...

The graph stuff here can be a bit painful, but getting your head round it will really help you to understand how displacement, velocity and acceleration are related to each other in simple harmonic motion. So if you're feeling a bit uncertain about what's going on, go back to the top of page 112 and have another look.

Free and Forced Vibrations

Resonance... tricky little beast. The Millennium Bridge was supposed to be a feat of British engineering, but it suffered from a severe case of the wobbles caused by resonance. How was it sorted out? By damping, of course — read on...

Free Vibrations — No Transfer of Energy to or from the Surroundings

1) If you stretch and release a mass on a spring, it oscillates at its **natural frequency**.

2) If **no energy's transferred** to or from the surroundings, it will **keep** oscillating with the **same amplitude forever**.

3) In practice this **never happens**, but a spring vibrating in air is called a **free vibration** anyway.

4) You need to know this formula for the **total energy** of a freely oscillating mass on a spring: $\Rightarrow$

5) When x is at its maximum ($x = A$), all the energy is potential energy, so $E_{total} = \frac{1}{2}kA^2$.

$$E_{total} = \frac{1}{2}mv^2 + \frac{1}{2}kx^2$$

or total energy = KE + PE

This is true for a mass oscillating horizontally. You'd need to include gravitational potential energy (p.123) if it was moving vertically (as in the example below).

Resonance Happens when Driving Frequency = Natural Frequency

1) A system can be **forced** to vibrate by a periodic **external force**.

2) The vibrations this produces are called **forced vibrations**.

3) The frequency of this force is called the **driving frequency**.

Free and forced vibrations are also called free and forced oscillations.

4) When the **driving frequency** approaches the **natural frequency**, the system gains more and more energy from the driving force and so vibrates with a **rapidly increasing amplitude**. When this happens the system is **resonating**.

Example: You can investigate how amplitude varies with driving frequency using a system like the one below.

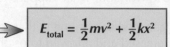

Mass oscillates with very large amplitude at the resonant frequency

Mass

Signal Generator

Frequency

Sets driving frequency

Vibration Generator

If you vary the driving frequency using the signal generator, and plot amplitude against driving frequency, you get a graph like this:

amplitude

natural frequency

driving frequency

Here are some examples of resonance:

a) organ pipe
The column of air resonates, driven by the motion of air at the base.

c) glass smashing
A glass resonates when driven by a sound wave of the right frequency. This can make the glass break.

b) swing
A swing resonates if it's driven by someone pushing it at its natural frequency.

Armies deliberately march 'out of step' when they cross a bridge. This reduces the risk of the bridge resonating and breaking apart.

d) radio
A radio is tuned so the electric circuit resonates at the same frequency as the radio station you want to listen to.

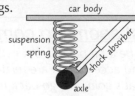

Damping Happens when Energy is Lost to the Surroundings

1) In practice, **any** oscillating system **loses energy** to its surroundings.

2) This is usually down to **frictional forces** like air resistance.

3) These are called **damping forces**.

4) Systems are often **deliberately damped** to **stop** them oscillating or to **minimise** the effect of **resonance**.

car body

suspension spring

shock absorber

axle

Shock absorbers in a car suspension provide a damping force by squashing oil through a hole when compressed.

MODULE 5: SECTION 1 — CREATING MODELS

Free and Forced Vibrations

Different Amounts of Damping have Different Effects

1) The **degree** of damping can vary from **light** damping (where the damping force is small) to **overdamping**.

2) Damping **reduces** the **amplitude** of the oscillation over time. The **heavier** the damping, the **quicker** the amplitude is reduced to zero.

3) **Critical damping** reduces the amplitude (i.e. stops the system oscillating) in the **shortest possible time**.

4) Car **suspension systems** and moving coil **meters** (which control the arm in analogue voltmeters and ammeters) are critically damped so that they **don't oscillate** but return to equilibrium as quickly as possible.

5) Systems with **even heavier damping** are **overdamped**. They take **longer** to return to equilibrium than a critically damped system.

6) **Plastic deformation** of ductile materials **reduces** the **amplitude** of oscillations in the same way as damping. As the material changes shape, it **absorbs energy**, so the oscillation will become smaller.

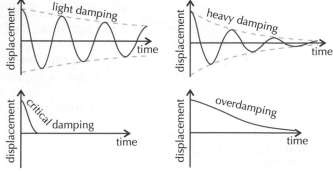

Damping Affects Resonance too

1) **Lightly damped** systems have a **very sharp** resonance peak. Their amplitude only increases dramatically when the **driving frequency** is **very close** to the **natural frequency**.

> Structures are damped to avoid being damaged by resonance. Loudspeakers are also made to have as flat a response as possible so that they don't 'colour' the sound.

2) **Heavily damped** systems have a **flatter response**. Their amplitude doesn't increase very much near the natural frequency and they aren't as **sensitive** to the driving frequency.

Example: You can show how damping affects resonance using the experiment on the previous page.

Here's how increasing the damping affects resonance in this system:

The mass oscillates at a smaller amplitude at the resonant frequency than a free oscillator.

Adding a disc increases air resistance.

Signal Generator
Frequency

amplitude

sharp
increasing degree of damping

flat

natural frequency → driving frequency

> In general, the more damped a system is, the flatter the graph of amplitude of oscillation against driving frequency.

You could also investigate damping using a horizontal mass-spring system (top of p.114) by altering the surface (and hence the friction) below the trolley, or using a pendulum — damping will increase with the surface area of the bob.

Practice Questions

Q1 What is the equation for the total energy of a freely vibrating mass on a spring?

Q2 What is a free vibration? What is a forced vibration?

Q3 Define resonance and give an example of where it occurs.

Exam Questions

Q1 a) Draw a diagram to show how the amplitude of a lightly damped system varies with driving frequency.   [2 marks]

   b) On the same diagram, show how the amplitude of the system varies with driving frequency when it is heavily damped.   [1 mark]

Q2 Define critical damping and state a situation where it is used.   [2 marks]

Physics — it can really put a damper on your social life...

Resonance can be really useful (radios, organ pipes, swings — yay) or very, very bad...

Circular Motion

*It's probably worth putting a bookmark in here — this stuff is needed **all over** the place.*

Angles can be Expressed in Radians

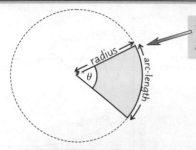

The angle in **radians**, θ, is defined as the **arc-length** divided by the **radius** of the circle, r.

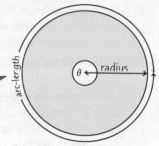

For a **complete circle** (360°), the arc-length is just the circumference of the circle ($2\pi r$). Dividing this by the radius (r) gives 2π. So there are **2π radians** in a **complete circle**.

Some common angles

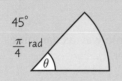

45°

$\frac{\pi}{4}$ rad

90°

$\frac{\pi}{2}$ rad

180°

π rad

To convert from degrees to radians, multiply by $\frac{\pi}{180}$. To convert from radians to degrees, multiply by $\frac{180}{\pi}$. 1 radian ≈ 57°.

The Angular Velocity is the Angle an Object Rotates Through per Second

1) Just as **linear velocity**, v, is defined as displacement ÷ time, the **angular velocity**, ω, is defined as **angle ÷ time**. The unit is rad s⁻¹ — radians per second.

$$\omega = \frac{\theta}{t}$$

ω = angular velocity (rad s⁻¹)
θ = angle (rad) turned through in time t
t = time (s)

2) The **linear velocity**, v, and **angular velocity**, ω, of a rotating object are linked by the equation:

$$v = r\omega$$

v = linear velocity (ms⁻¹)
r = radius of the circle (m)

The symbol for angular velocity is the little Greek 'omega', not a w.

Example: In a cyclotron, a beam of particles spirals outwards from a central point. The angular velocity of the particles remains constant. The beam of particles in the cyclotron rotates through 360° in 35 μs.

FAST

$v = ?$

SLOW

$r = 1.5$ m

a) Explain why the linear velocity of the particles increases as they spiral outwards, even though their angular velocity is constant.

Linear velocity depends on r, the radius of the circle being turned, as well as ω. So as r increases, so does v, even though ω remains constant.

b) Calculate the linear velocity of a particle at a point 1.5 m from the centre of rotation.

First, calculate the angular velocity:

$$\omega = \frac{\theta}{t} = \frac{2\pi}{35 \times 10^{-6}} = 1.7951... \times 10^5 \, \text{rad s}^{-1}$$

Then substitute ω into $v = r\omega$:

$$v = r\omega = 1.5 \times 1.7951... \times 10^5$$
$$= 2.6927... \times 10^5 \, \text{ms}^{-1}$$
$$= 2.7 \times 10^5 \, \text{ms}^{-1} \, \text{(to 2 s.f.)}$$

You can find out more about cyclotrons on p.166.

Circular Motion has a Frequency and Period

1) The frequency, f, is the number of complete **revolutions per second** (rev s⁻¹ or hertz, Hz).

2) The period, T, is the **time taken** for a complete revolution (in seconds). Frequency and period are **linked** by the equation:

$$f = \frac{1}{T}$$

f = frequency in rev s⁻¹ or Hz
T = period in s
ω = angular speed in rad s⁻¹

3) For a complete circle, an object turns through **2π radians** in a time T, so frequency and period are related to ω by:

$$\omega = \frac{2\pi}{T} = 2\pi f$$

You should remember this second equation from p.112.

Circular Motion

An Object Travelling in a Circle is *Accelerating* since its *Velocity is Changing*

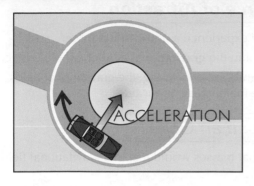

1) Even if the car shown is going at a **constant speed**, its **velocity** is changing since its **direction** is changing.

2) Since acceleration is defined as the **rate of change of velocity**, the car is accelerating even though it isn't going any faster.

3) This acceleration is called the **centripetal acceleration** and is always directed towards the **centre of the circle**.

There are two formulas for centripetal acceleration:

$$a = \frac{v^2}{r} \quad \text{and} \quad a = \omega^2 r$$

a = centripetal acceleration in ms^{-2},
v = linear velocity in ms^{-1},
ω = angular velocity in rad s^{-1}, r = radius in m.

The *Centripetal Acceleration* is produced by a *Centripetal Force*

From Newton's laws, if there's a **centripetal acceleration**, there must be a **centripetal force** acting towards the **centre of the circle**.

Since $F = ma$, the centripetal force must be:

$$F = \frac{mv^2}{r} \quad \text{and} \quad F = m\omega^2 r$$

F = centripetal force in N
m = mass in kg

The centripetal force is what keeps the object moving in a circle — remove the force and the object would fly off at a tangent.

Men cowered from the force of the centipede.

Practice Questions

Q1 How many radians are there in a complete circle?

Q2 How is angular velocity defined? What is the relationship between angular velocity and linear velocity?

Q3 Define the period and frequency of circular motion. What is the relationship between period and angular velocity?

Q4 Write equations for centripetal acceleration, a, and centripetal force, F, for an object of mass m, travelling at a linear velocity v, in a circular path with a radius r.

Q5 In which direction does the centripetal force act? What happens when this force is removed?

Exam Questions

Q1 The Earth orbits the Sun with an angular velocity of 2.0×10^{-7} rad s^{-1} at a radius of 1.5×10^{11} m. The Earth has a mass of 6.0×10^{24} kg.

a) Calculate the Earth's linear velocity. [2 marks]

b) i) Calculate the centripetal force needed to keep the Earth in its orbit. [2 marks]

ii) State what provides this centripetal force. [1 mark]

Q2 A car is driving in a circle around a roundabout with linear velocity 15 ms^{-1}. The radius of the car's circular motion is 12 m.

a) Calculate the centripetal acceleration of the car. [1 mark]

b) Calculate the time taken for the car to drive once around the roundabout. [2 marks]

My head is spinning after all that...

"Centripetal" just means "centre-seeking". The centripetal force is what actually causes circular motion. What you feel when you're spinning, though, is the reaction (centrifugal) force. Don't get the two mixed up.

Gravitational Fields

*Gravity's all about masses **attracting** each other. If the Earth didn't have a **gravitational field**, you'd be drifting around...*

Masses in a *Gravitational Field* Experience a *Force of Attraction*

1) A **gravitational field** is a force field — a **region** where an object will experience a **non-contact force**.
2) Any object with mass will **experience an attractive force** if you put it in the **gravitational field** of another object.
3) Only objects with a **large** mass, such as stars and planets, have a significant effect. E.g. the gravitational fields of the **Moon** and the **Sun** are noticeable here on Earth — they're the main cause of our **tides**.

You can Draw *Field Lines* to Show the *Field* Around an Object

Gravitational field lines are **arrows** showing the **direction of the force** that masses would feel in a gravitational field. The closer together the field lines are, the stronger the gravitational field.

1) A **uniform field** is a field that is **the same** everywhere. This is shown by the field lines being **equally spaced** and going in the **same direction**.

2) Point masses have a **radial field**. **Spherical** objects — like the **Earth** — can be **modelled** as point masses, as they act as if all of their mass is concentrated at their **centre**:

   1) The Earth's gravitational field is radial — the lines of force meet at its centre.
   2) If you put a small mass, *m*, anywhere in the Earth's gravitational field, it will always be attracted **towards** the Earth. If you move mass *m* further away from the Earth — where the **lines of force** are **further apart** — the **force** it experiences **decreases**.
   3) The small mass, *m*, has a gravitational field of its own. This doesn't have a noticeable effect on the Earth though, because the Earth is so much **more massive**.
   4) Close to the Earth's surface, the gravitational field is (almost) uniform — so the **field lines** are (almost) **parallel** and **equally spaced**. You can usually **assume** that the field is perfectly uniform.

You can *Calculate Forces* Using *Newton's Law of Gravitation*

The **force** experienced by an object in a gravitational field is always **attractive**. It's a **vector** which depends on the **masses** involved and the **distance** between them. It's easy to work this out for **point masses** using this equation:

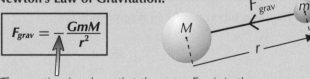

Newton's Law of Gravitation:

$$F_{grav} = -\frac{GmM}{r^2}$$

The negative sign shows that the vector F_{grav} is in the opposite direction to *r* (displacement of *m* from *M*).

The diagram shows the force acting **on *m* due to *M***. (The force on *M* due to *m* is equal but in the opposite direction.) *M* and *m* behave as point masses. Both *M* and *m* are in kg. $G = 6.67 \times 10^{-11}$ Nm²kg⁻² is the **gravitational force constant**. *r* is the displacement (in metres) of *m* from *M*.

It doesn't matter what you call the masses: M and m, m_1 and m_2, Paul and Larry...

The law of gravitation is an **inverse square law** $\left(F_{grav} \propto \frac{1}{r^2} \right)$ so:

1) If the distance *r* between the masses **increases** then the force F_{grav} will **decrease**.
2) If the **distance doubles** then the **force** will be one **quarter** the strength of the original force.

The *Field Strength* is the *Force per Unit Mass*

Gravitational field strength, *g*, is the **force per unit mass**. Its value depends on **where you are** in the field. There's a really simple equation for working it out:

$$g = \frac{F_{grav}}{m}$$

g has units of newtons per kilogram (Nkg⁻¹)

1) F_{grav} is the force experienced by a mass *m* when it's placed in the gravitational field at a given *r*. Divide F_{grav} by *m* and you get the **force per unit mass**.
2) *g* is a **vector** quantity, always pointing towards the centre of the mass whose field you're describing (because the gravitational force acts in that direction). This means *g* is often defined to be **negative**.
3) Since the gravitational field is almost uniform at the Earth's surface, you can assume *g* is a constant if you don't go too high.

   The **value** of *g* at the **Earth's surface** is approximately **9.81** Nkg⁻¹ (or 9.81 ms⁻²).

4) *g* is just the **acceleration** of a mass in a gravitational field. It's often called the **acceleration due to gravity**.

Gravitational Fields

A *Mass* in a *Uniform Gravitational Field* Experiences a *Constant Force*

The **force** on an object with mass **m** in a gravitational field is given by **mg**.
In a **uniform gravitational field** (like near the Earth's surface) the value of **g** is
the **same** at all locations. This means that the **force** experienced by a mass
due to gravity will also be the **same** everywhere within the field.

A uniform field:
field strength = g
force = mg

Potential Energy is *Proportional* to *Height* in a *Uniform Gravitational Field*

The change in **gravitational potential energy** of an object with mass **m** in a gravitational field is given by **mgh**,
where **h** is the change in distance from a certain point — e.g. the **Earth's surface**.
In a uniform field, the value of **mg** is constant whatever the value of **h**, so:

1) **Increasing** the height of a mass, **m**, by a value of **h** changes the
potential energy by the **same amount** wherever the mass is placed
in the field. You can write this relationship as an **equation**:

$$\Delta E_{grav} = mgh$$

You're only looking at the change in E_{grav} so you don't need to worry about the sign of g.

2) ΔE_{grav} is **positive** when the **height increases**, and **negative** when the **height decreases**.

Energy is Never *Destroyed*

The **Principle of Conservation of Energy**: Energy **cannot be created** or **destroyed**. Energy **can be transferred** from one form to another but the total amount of energy in a closed system will not change.

Conservation of energy can be used to explain the changes in gravitational potential energy, **mgh**,
and kinetic energy, $\frac{1}{2}mv^2$ when objects **move** in a **gravitational field**.

Example: A pomegranate of mass m is catapulted vertically with an initial velocity of 13 ms⁻¹ from a height of 1.00 m above the Earth's surface. Calculate the height reached by the pomegranate, ignoring friction.

The kinetic energy given to the pomegranate is transferred into gravitational potential energy as the
pomegranate gains height. The pomegranate will stop gaining height when all of the kinetic energy
has been converted into gravitational potential energy: $\frac{1}{2}mv^2 = mgh$ so $h = \frac{v^2}{2g} = \frac{13^2}{2 \times 9.81} = 8.613...$ m

So the pomegranate reaches 8.613... + 1.00 = **9.6 m (to 2 s.f.)** above the Earth's surface.

Practice Questions

Q1 Describe and draw diagrams showing the Earth's gravitational field:
    a) extending far from the Earth's surface,   b) close to the Earth's surface.

Q2 Write down Newton's law of gravitation for two spherical masses, stating the assumption made about their fields.

Q3 What is meant by gravitational field strength?

Q4 What is the equation for a change in gravitational potential energy with a change in height *h* in a uniform field?

Exam Question

Q1 The Moon has a mass of 7.35×10^{22} kg and a radius of 1740 km.
    ($G = 6.67 \times 10^{-11} Nm^2kg^{-2}$)

   a) Use Newton's law of gravitation to calculate the force on a 25 kg mass at the Moon's surface. [2 marks]

   b) i) On the Moon, $g = -1.62$ Nkg⁻¹. A rock of 0.5 kg is fired vertically from the Moon's surface
         and reaches a maximum height of 4.5 m above the surface.
         Assuming g is constant, calculate the initial velocity of the rock. [2 marks]

      ii) Describe and explain the changes in gravitational potential and kinetic energy as the rock rises,
          changes direction and falls back to the surface. [3 marks]

If you're really stuck, put 'Inverse Square Law'...

Clever chap, Newton, but famously tetchy. He got into fights with other physicists, mainly over planetary motion and calculus... the usual playground squabbles. Then he spent the rest of his life trying to turn scrap metal into gold. Weird.

Gravitational Potential and Orbits

Gravity's a tricky little thing, don't you think? You know there must be a force pulling you to Earth (or whatever planet you're on), but you can't see it or feel it... or maybe you can, you just don't realise it because you've always felt it, hmm.

In a **Radial Field**, *g* is **Inversely Proportional** to *r²*

Point masses have **radial** gravitational fields (see the diagram on page 122). The strength of the gravitational field, **g**, **decreases** the **further away** you are from the centre of the mass, as shown on the graph below.

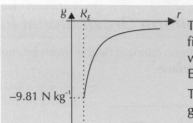

The graph shows how the gravitational field strength of the Earth, *g*, varies with the distance from the centre of the Earth, *r*. R_E is the Earth's radius.

The **area** under this curve gives you gravitational potential, *V* — see below.

You can estimate the area under a curve by counting squares (if the graph is on squared paper), or by splitting the curve up into trapeziums and calculating the area of each one with the formula $A = \frac{1}{2}(a + b)h$ (see page 85).

You can see from the graph that the relationship between **g** and **r** isn't linear. In fact it's another **inverse square law** — make sure you know how to use it.

$$g = -\frac{GM}{r^2}$$

Remember, *g* has units N kg⁻¹.

You Gain **Gravitational Potential Energy** *if you Move Away from the Earth*

The **gravitational potential energy** of a mass at a certain point in a gravitational field, E_{grav}, is the **work** that would need to be done to move it from infinity to that point. Since gravitational fields are attractive, E_{grav} is always negative.

You can express the gravitational potential energy of a mass *m* in terms of its distance *r* from a large point mass *M* by combining the equation $E_{grav} = mgh$ (see previous page), where *h* is equal to *r*, with the one for **g**, above.

$$E_{grav} = -\frac{GmM}{r}$$

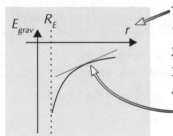

The graph shows how gravitational potential energy varies with distance from the Earth.

1) A mass on the Earth's surface (at R_E) has **negative** gravitational potential energy.

2) As you move a mass away from the Earth, it **gains potential energy**.

3) Potential energy is **zero** at an **infinite** distance from the Earth.

4) The gradient of a **tangent** to the graph gives the value of the gravitational **force** at that point — the force is **greatest** at the **Earth's surface** where the graph is **steepest**.

When you **move** a mass, *m*, between two different distances from the centre of a radial gravitational field, its gravitational potential energy will **change**. This is because **work is done** against the force of **gravity**. The work done depends on the **force** and the **distance moved**:

$$\Delta E_{grav} = F_{grav}\Delta s$$

ΔE_{grav} can be found from a graph of F_{grav} **against** *r*.
$\Delta E_{grav} = F_{grav}\Delta s =$ the **area** under the curve between the two distances.
If the mass *m* is moved but the distance from the mass *M* is kept **the same** (i.e. the mass is moved along an equipotential — see next page), no **work** is done against gravity ($\Delta s = 0$).

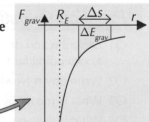

Gravitational Potential is Potential Energy per Unit Mass

The **gravitational potential** at a point, V_{grav}, is the **potential energy per unit mass**: $V_{grav} = \frac{E_{grav}}{m}$

In a **radial field**, the equation is: $V_{grav} = -\frac{GM}{r}$

The units of V_{grav} are either J kg⁻¹ or N m kg⁻¹.

The graph of **gravitational potential** against distance has the **same shape** as the graph of **gravitational potential energy** against distance. Gravitational potential, V_{grav}, increases with distance, *r*, from the mass, and is **zero** at **infinity**.
The **gradient of a tangent** to the graph gives the value of **g** at that point.

Gravitational Potential and Orbits

Equipotentials Show All the Points in a Field Which Have the Same Potential

1) If you travel along a line of equipotential you **don't lose or gain energy** (**no** work is done).

2) For a uniform spherical mass (you can usually assume the Earth's one) the equipotentials are spherical surfaces.

3) **Equipotentials** and **field lines** are **perpendicular**.

4) At the Earth's surface, $V = -63$ MJ kg^{-1}.

Equipotentials of −60, −50, −40 and −30 MJ kg^{-1} around Earth. Equipotentials at regular intervals aren't equally spaced — they get further and further apart (O MJ kg^{-1} is at infinity)

Gravitational Fields Cause Planetary Orbits

1) A **satellite** is just any **smaller mass** that **orbits** a **much larger mass**.

2) For example, the **Moon** is a satellite of the Earth, the **planets** are satellites of the Sun and **man-made satellites** orbit the Earth (e.g. broadcasting TV signals).

3) In our Solar System, the planets have **nearly circular orbits**, so you can use the **equations of circular motion** to describe their motion — go back and have a look at pages 120-121 if you've forgotten them already.

1) Earth feels a force due to the gravitational 'pull' of the **Sun**. This force is given by Newton's law of gravitation:

$$F = -\frac{GmM}{r^2}$$ (see p.122)

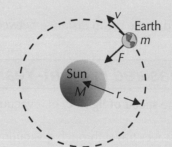

2) The Earth has velocity v. Its linear speed is constant but its **direction** is not — so it's accelerating. The **centripetal force** causing this acceleration is:

$$F = \frac{mv^2}{r}$$

3) The **centripetal force** on the Earth must be a result of the **gravitational force** due to the Sun, and so these forces must be **equal**...

$$\frac{mv^2}{r} = \frac{GmM}{r^2}$$ and rearranging... $$v = \sqrt{\frac{GM}{r}}$$

Practice Questions

Q1 Sketch graphs to show how the values of g and F_{grav} vary with distance from the Earth's surface.

Q2 What does the area under each graph you drew in Q1 represent?

Q3 What is the difference between gravitational potential and gravitational potential energy? Draw graphs of both quantities against distance for a radial field and state the quantity represented by the gradient of each graph.

Q4 Write down an equation for ΔE_{grav} in terms of F_{grav}.

Q5 Explain the meaning of equipotentials in terms of work done. What shape are the Earth's equipotentials?

Exam Question

(Use $G = 6.67 \times 10^{-11}$ Nm^{2}kg^{-2}, mass of Earth = 5.98×10^{24} kg, radius of Earth = 6400 km)

Q1 A satellite with a mass of 3015 kg orbits 200 km above the Earth's surface.

a) Calculate the gravitational field strength at this distance from Earth. [2 marks]

b) Calculate the gravitational potential at this distance from Earth. [2 marks]

c) Calculate the satellite's gravitational potential energy. [1 mark]

d) Calculate the linear velocity of the satellite. [2 marks]

Increase your potential — stand on a chair...

It was a charming fellow called Johannes Kepler who showed that the planets' orbits are nearly circular. He's also been proclaimed as the first science fiction writer — busy chap. He wrote a tale about a fantastic trip to the Moon, where the book narrator's mum asks a demon the secret of space travel, to boldly go where — oh wait, different story.

Using Astronomical Scales

Space is big. I mean really, really big...

Our **Solar System** Contains the **Sun**, the **Planets** and Other Objects

1) The **universe** is **everything** that exists — from **stars** and **galaxies** to **microwave radiation** (page 131).

2) **Galaxies**, like our **Milky Way galaxy**, are clusters of **stars** and **planets** that are held together by gravity.

3) Our **Solar System** consists of the **Sun** and all of the objects that **orbit** it:

> The planets (in order): **Mercury**, **Venus**, **Earth**, **Mars**, **Jupiter**, **Saturn**, **Uranus** and **Neptune** (as well as the asteroid belt between Mars and Jupiter) all have nearly **circular** orbits. **Pluto** is a dwarf planet beyond Neptune.

Remember — planets, moons and comets don't emit light, they just reflect it.

4) As well as planets, there are **moons**, **asteroids**, **comets**, **satellites** and lots of **dust** and **gas**.

Distances in the Solar System can be Measured in **Astronomical Units (AU)**

From the **16th century**, astronomers were able to work out the **distance** the **planets** are from the Sun **relative** to the Earth, using **astronomical units** (AU). But they could not work out the **actual distances** — it wasn't until 1769 that the size of the AU was accurately measured.

1 AU is about 150 million km.

> One **astronomical unit** (AU) is defined as the **mean distance** between the **Earth** and the **Sun**.

Bigger Distances can be Measured in **Light-Years (ly)**

1) All **electromagnetic waves** travel at the **speed of light**, *c*, in a vacuum ($c = 3.00 \times 10^8$ ms^{-1}).

> The **distance** that electromagnetic waves travel through a vacuum in **one year** is called a **light-year** (**ly**).

2) You need to know that 1 ly is around **10^{16} m**.

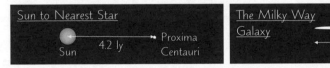

Just as a comparison, 1 ly is equivalent to about 63 000 AU.

3) If we see the light from a star that is, say, **10 light-years away** then we are actually seeing it as it was **10 years ago**. The further away an object is, the further **back in time** we are actually seeing it.

4) So when we look at the stars we're looking **back in time**, but since the universe has a **finite** age, we can only see as far back as the **beginning of the universe**. Since light has a finite **speed**, the **size** of the **observable universe** (the universe we can see) is limited (p.130).

Logarithmic Scales of Magnitude are used for **Large Ranges**

1) Quantities in astronomy can vary over huge ranges. For example, the distance to the Sun's **nearest star** is **hundreds of thousands** of times further than the Earth-Sun distance. And the distance to the furthest galaxy discovered so far is nearly **1 thousand trillion** times more than the Earth-Sun distance...

2) **Linear scales** (that go up in equal amounts) aren't much good for dealing with such huge ranges — **logarithmic scales** (p.11) are often needed instead.

3) Logarithmic scales are **non-linear**. **Instead** of going up by equal amounts, each step on the scale is 'so many **times**' bigger than the last (e.g. **10 times**).

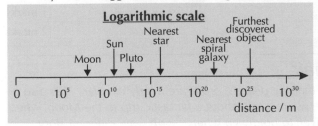

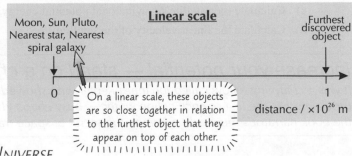

Using Astronomical Scales

There Are Loads of Examples of **Logarithmic Scales** in Astronomy

1) The brightness of stars is often measured with a logarithmic scale, called apparent magnitude.

2) Images of astronomical objects are often displayed using a logarithmic scale of brightness, so that the difference between the brightest and dimmest parts of the image is less intense.

3) The Hertzsprung-Russell (H-R) diagram is a plot of luminosity (power output) against temperature for stars. It has logarithmic scales on both axes.

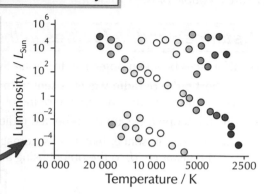

The **H-R Diagram** Can Be Used to Find the **Ages** of Stars

Finding the **age** of objects in astronomy is a tricky process. For an **individual star**, it is impossible to tell how **old** it is, even if you **know** properties like its distance and brightness.

Instead, astronomers need to study **clusters** — groups of stars that are assumed to have formed at the **same time**. They plot them on the **Hertzsprung-Russell (H-R) diagram** to work out what stages of their lives they're at:

1) Stars spend the **majority** of their lives fusing hydrogen into helium to produce energy (p.179). This is known as the **main sequence** stage. The **position** of a star on the H-R diagram main sequence depends on its **mass**.

2) At the **end** of this stage, the stars **move** off the main sequence to the **top-right** of the H-R diagram.

3) The **time spent** on the main sequence depends on the **mass** of the star — **more massive** stars use their fuel **more quickly** and spend **less time** in this stage. This means that the more **massive** stars at the top-left of the main sequence **leave** the main sequence **first**.

4) When astronomers plot the stars in a **cluster** on a **H-R diagram**, they can identify the **most massive** star left on the main sequence. They **assume** that it's about to **leave** the main sequence, and work out how old a star of that **mass** would be when it **uses up** all of its hydrogen fuel. This gives an estimate of the **age** of the star, and therefore the **age of the cluster**.

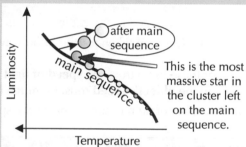

Practice Questions

Q1 What is the definition of an astronomical unit?

Q2 What is the difference between a linear scale and a logarithmic scale?

Q3 What assumption is made about a star cluster when determining the ages of the stars within it?

Exam Questions

Q1 The apparent magnitude, m, of a star is how bright it appears to be from Earth. It depends on the intensity of radiation received on Earth, I, and is defined using a logarithmic scale, where $m = -2.5 \log_{10} I +$ constant.

    a) Show that the intensity of a magnitude 1 star ($m = 1$) is $10^{\frac{2}{5}}$ greater than that of a magnitude 2 star.   **[3 marks]**

    b) State how many times greater is the intensity of a magnitude 1 star than that of a magnitude 6 star.   **[1 mark]**

Q2 a) State the definition of a light-year.   **[1 mark]**

    b) Light travels at 3.00×10^8 ms^{-1} in a vacuum. Calculate the distance of a light-year in metres.   **[2 marks]**

    c) Explain why the size of the observable universe is limited by the speed of light.   **[2 marks]**

So — using a ruler's out of the question then...

Good luck getting your head round these distances — they're pretty tricky to imagine. That's why astronomers often need to use logarithmic scales — imagine the Hertzsprung-Russell diagram on a linear scale and it should become clear.

Astronomical Distances and Velocities

There are loads of ways of measuring distances in space. Which one you use depends on how far away the object is. Here are a couple of ways to do it...

Distances and Velocities in the Solar System can be Measured using Radar

1) **Distances** between objects in the **Solar System** are enormous — one way to measure them is using **radar**.

2) A **short pulse** of **radio waves** is sent from a **radio telescope** towards a distant object, e.g. a planet or asteroid. When the pulse hits the surface of the object, it's **reflected** back to Earth.

3) The telescope picks up the reflected radio waves and records the **time**, *t*, taken for them to return.

4) Radio waves in space, like all electromagnetic waves, travel at the **speed of light**, *c*, so you can work out the **distance**, *d*, to the object using a variation of the formula **speed = distance ÷ time**:

$$2d = ct$$

It's 2*d*, not just *d*, because the pulse travels twice the distance to the object — there and back again.

5) **Space-time worldlines** can also be used to find the distance to an object from the time interval between **sending** and **receiving** a radar pulse. On a grid of time (in seconds) against distance (in **light-seconds**), **start** the line showing the radar pulse at *t* = 0. The **gradient** of the line should be **1** (as light travels **1 light-second** in **1 second**). The radar pulse **changes direction** half way between leaving and arriving back, so the line should too. The point at which it changes direction is the **distance** of the object that reflected it.

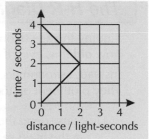

6) You can also use radar to find the **average velocity** of an object **relative** to the Earth. You send **two pulses** separated by a certain **time interval**, to give two separate measurements of the object's **distance**. The difference between the distances shows **how far** the object has moved relative to Earth in the time interval — and **speed = distance ÷ time**.

7) Like most things in physics, this method is based on a couple of **assumptions**:

> 1) The **speed** of the **radio waves** is the **same** on the way **to the object** and the **way back** to the telescope.
>
> 2) The **time** taken for the **radio waves** to **reach the object** is the **same** as the **time** taken to **return**.

For these to be true, the **speed of light** must be **constant**, even though the observer and object are both **moving**, and the **object's speed** must be **much less** than the **speed of light**, so that there are no **relativistic effects** (p.129).

8) More accurate measurements of the speed of distant objects can be made using **Doppler shifts**.

The Doppler Effect — the Motion of a Wave's Source Affects its Wavelength

1) Imagine an ambulance driving past you. As it moves **towards you** its siren sounds **higher-pitched**, but as it **moves away**, its pitch is **lower**. This change in **frequency** and **wavelength** is called the **Doppler shift**.

2) The frequency and the wavelength **change** because the waves **bunch together** in **front** of the source and **stretch out behind** it.

> The **amount** of stretching or bunching together depends on the **velocity** of the **source**.

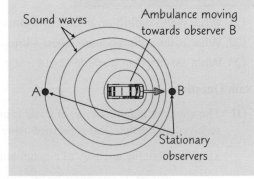

3) This happens with light too — when a **light source** moves **away** from us, the wavelengths become **longer** and the frequencies become lower. This shifts the light towards the **red** end of the spectrum and is called **red shift**.

4) When a light source moves **towards** us, the **opposite** happens and the light undergoes **blue shift**.

5) The amount of red shift or blue shift is determined by the following formula:

$$\frac{\Delta\lambda}{\lambda} = \frac{v}{c} \quad \text{if } v \ll c$$

$\Delta\lambda$ is the difference between the observed and emitted wavelengths, λ is the emitted wavelength, *v* is the velocity of the source in the direction of the observer and *c* is the speed of light.

v << *c* means "*v* is much less than *c*" (see the next page for why this is important).

Astronomical Distances and Velocities

Stars Produce Absorption Spectra

1) Radiation is emitted from a **very hot** region of a star (called the **photosphere**) in a **continuous spectrum**.

2) **Atoms** in the atmosphere of the star **absorb** certain **wavelengths** of the radiation, producing dark **absorption lines** within the spectrum.

3) Different atoms absorb different parts of the spectrum, resulting in a **characteristic pattern** for each atom. By looking at the absorption lines from a star, and comparing them with known spectra in the lab, the **composition** of the **stellar atmosphere** can be worked out. ⟶

4) Once you've worked out which **atoms** make up the **pattern of absorption lines**, you can compare the **position** of the **absorption lines** for **each atom** in the star's **spectrum** with the **same spectrum** recorded in the **lab**.

Stellar spectrum (containing H, He and Na)

Hydrogen
Helium } (Lab spectra)
Sodium

5) This shows **how much** the **spectrum** has been **shifted** by the movement of the star.

> **Example:** The spectrum from this star is **shifted** towards the **red end** of the spectrum, showing that it is **moving away** from Earth.
>
> Stellar spectrum
>
> Lab spectrum

Time Dilation Happens Close to the Speed of Light

1) A big **assumption** of the methods on these two pages is that the **speed** of the object being studied is **much less** than the **speed of light**, c.

2) This matters because **time** runs at **different speeds** for two objects **moving relative** to each other — but it's only really noticeable **close to** the **speed of light** (which is why you can **ignore** it as long as the object isn't travelling too fast).

3) This effect is called **relativistic time dilation**.

It's not just time that starts doing weird things at high speeds, mass and energy do too (see page 167).

A **stationary** observer measures the time interval between two events as t_0, the **proper time**.

An observer moving at a **constant velocity**, v, will measure a **longer** interval, t, between the two events. t is given by the equation:

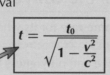

$$t = \frac{t_0}{\sqrt{1 - \frac{v^2}{c^2}}}$$

$\frac{1}{\sqrt{1 - \frac{v^2}{c^2}}}$ is called the **relativistic factor**, γ.

When v << c, $\gamma \approx 1$, so the time measured by both observers is almost the same, $t = t_0$ (which is why you can ignore relativistic effects at low speeds).

Practice Questions

Q1 How do we measure the distance to objects in the Solar System using radar?

Q2 What is the Doppler effect? Explain how it can be used to work out the speed of a distant object.

Exam Questions

Q1 A pulse of radio waves is transmitted from a telescope on Earth towards Venus. The telescope detects the radio waves returning after 4.6 minutes.

a) Show that the distance from Earth to Venus at this time is approximately 4.1×10^{10} m. [3 marks]

b) State two assumptions that your calculation in part a) is based on. [2 marks]

Q2 A spacecraft is travelling through the Solar System, away from Earth. Radar is being used to track its position. Radar pulses are sent to the spacecraft every second and a receiver detects how long they take to return.

a) Two consecutive pulses take 2.8 s and 3.8 s to return. Estimate the relative velocity of the spacecraft. [3 marks]

b) The estimate won't be accurate as the spacecraft is travelling close to the speed of light. Calculate the time interval measured between the two pulses by an observer on the spacecraft. [2 marks]

Time dilation occurs close to the speed of light — and in history lessons...

Luckily it only happens close to the speed of light, so as long as 'v << c' is true it's pretty safe to ignore it.

The Hot Big Bang Theory

Right, we're moving on to the BIG picture now — we all like a bit of cosmology...

Hubble Realised that Recessional Velocity is Proportional to Distance

1) The **spectra** from **galaxies** (apart from a few very close ones) all show **red shift** (see page 128).
   The amount of **red shift** gives the **recessional velocity** — how fast the galaxy is moving away from Earth.

2) When **Hubble** plotted the **recessional velocity** of galaxies against their **distance** from Earth he found that they
   were **proportional**. This gave rise to **Hubble's law**:

$$v = H_0 d$$

where v = recessional velocity in $km\,s^{-1}$, d = distance in Mpc
and H_0 = Hubble's constant in $km\,s^{-1}\,Mpc^{-1}$.

A megaparsec (Mpc) is just a unit
of distance used in astronomy.
$1\ Mpc = 3.09 \times 10^{22}$ m

3) Since distance is very difficult to measure, astronomers used to **disagree** greatly on the value of H_0, with
   measurements ranging from 50 to 100 $km\,s^{-1}\,Mpc^{-1}$. It's now generally accepted that H_0 lies **between 65 and
   80 $km\,s^{-1}\,Mpc^{-1}$** and most agree it's around the **mid to low 70s**. You'll be given a value to use in the exam.

The Universe is Expanding

1) By showing that objects in the universe are **moving away** from each other, Hubble's work is strong evidence that
   the **universe is expanding**. The rate of expansion depends on the value of H_0, Hubble's constant.

2) The way cosmologists tend to look at this, the galaxies aren't actually moving **through space** away from us.
   Instead, **space itself** is expanding and the light waves are being **stretched** along with it. This is called
   cosmological red shift to distinguish it from **red shift** produced by sources that **are** moving through space.
   Don't worry though — you can use the **formula** on page 128 for **both kinds** of red shift.

3) Since the universe is **expanding uniformly** away from **us** it seems as though we're at the **centre** of the universe,
   but this is an **illusion**. You would observe the **same thing** at **any point** in the universe.

The Age and Observable Size of the Universe Depend on H_0

1) If the universe has been **expanding** at the **same rate** for its whole life, the **age** of the universe is $t = 1/H_0$
   (time = distance/speed). This is only an estimate since the universe probably hasn't always been expanding at the same rate.

2) Since no one knows the **exact value** of H_0 we can only guess the universe's age.
   If $H_0 = 75\ km\,s^{-1}\,Mpc^{-1} = 2.4 \times 10^{-18}\ s^{-1}$, then the age of the universe $\approx 1 \div (2.4 \times 10^{-18}\ s^{-1})$
   $= 4.1 \times 10^{17}$ s, which is approximately **13 billion years**.

3) The **absolute size** of the universe is **unknown** (and changing) but there is a limit on the
   size of the **observable universe**. This is simply a **sphere** (with the Earth at its centre)
   with a **radius** equal to the **maximum distance** that **light** can travel during its **age**. So if
   $H_0 = 75\ km\,s^{-1}\,Mpc^{-1}$ then this sphere will have a radius of **13 billion light years**. Taking
   into account the **expansion** of the universe, it is thought to be more like 46-47 billion
   light years.

NB — 13 billion candles
is too many to put on a
birthday cake.

The Red Shift of Galaxies is Strong Evidence for the HBB

1) If the universe is **expanding**, then further back in time it must have been much **smaller**. In fact, if you trace
   time back **far enough**, and assume that the **expansion** has always been happening, then the entire universe
   must once have been contained in a **single point** — this is the basis of the **hot big bang (HBB) theory**. The
   HBB theory is currently the **best explanation** we've got for the state of the universe and is widely **accepted**.

> **THE HOT BIG BANG THEORY (HBB):** the universe started off **very hot** and **very dense**
> (perhaps as an **infinitely hot, infinitely dense** singularity) and has been **expanding** ever since.

2) Since Hubble published his findings, the **red shifts** of other, more distant objects in the **universe** have been
   measured — and they **continue** to fit the **pattern** he predicted, providing more **evidence** for the **HBB theory**.
   And it doesn't stop there — there's even more evidence for the HBB theory on the next page.

The Hot Big Bang Theory

Cosmic Microwave Background Radiation — More Evidence for the HBB

1) The hot big bang model predicts that loads of **electromagnetic radiation** was produced in the **very early universe**. This radiation should **still** be observed today (it hasn't had anywhere else to go).

2) Because the universe has **expanded**, the wavelengths of this cosmic background radiation have been **stretched** and are now in the **microwave** region.

3) This radiation was **accidentally** detected by Penzias and Wilson in the 1960s.

Properties of the Cosmic Microwave Background Radiation (CMBR)

1) In the late 1980s a satellite called the **Cosmic Background Explorer** (**COBE**) was sent up to have a **detailed look** at the radiation.

It's sometimes called 'cosmological microwave background'.

2) It found a **continuous spectrum** corresponding to a **temperature** of **2.73 K**.

3) The radiation is largely **isotropic** (the same in all directions) and **homogeneous** (the same everywhere) — it's about the **same intensity** whichever direction you look.

4) There are **very tiny fluctuations** in temperature, which were at the limit of COBE's resolution. These are due to tiny energy-density variations in the early universe, and are needed for the initial '**seeding**' of galaxy formation.

5) The background radiation also shows a **Doppler shift**, indicating the Earth's motion through space. It turns out that our galaxy is rushing towards an unknown mass (the **Great Attractor**) at over a **million miles an hour**.

Practice Questions

Q1 What is cosmological red shift? How is it different from ordinary red shift?

Q2 Outline the hot big bang theory.

Q3 Explain why cosmological red shift of light from other galaxies provides evidence for the hot big bang theory for the origin of the universe.

Q4 What is the cosmic microwave background radiation?

Exam Questions

Q1 a) Describe what Hubble's law suggests about the nature of the universe. [2 marks]

b) Using the value $H_0 = 75$ km s^{-1} Mpc^{-1}: *(1 year $\approx 3.16 \times 10^7$ s, 1 Mpc = 3.09×10^{22} m)*

   i) Calculate H_0 in SI base units. [2 marks]

   ii) The age of the universe is approximately equal to H_0^{-1}. Calculate an estimate of the age of the universe in years, and hence the radius of the observable universe, ignoring expansion. [3 marks]

Q2 a) An astronomer observes that the spectral line corresponding to a wavelength of 650 nm has been shifted to 890 nm in the spectrum from a distant galaxy. Estimate the speed at which the galaxy is moving, giving a direction. [2 marks]

b) Use Hubble's law to estimate the distance (in light years) that the galaxy is from us. (Use $H_0 = 2.4 \times 10^{-18}$ s^{-1}, 1 ly = 9.5×10^{15} m) [2 marks]

c) Explain why the speed of the galaxy means that your answers to a) and b) are only estimates. [1 mark]

Q3 The cosmic microwave background is a continuous spectrum at a temperature of about 3 K. Explain why its discovery was considered strong evidence for the hot big bang theory for the origin of the universe. [2 marks]

So it's not just about socially awkward physicists trying to get a date then...

The hot big bang model doesn't actually work — not quite, anyway. There are loads of little things that don't quite add up. Modern cosmologists are trying to improve the model using a period of very rapid expansion called inflation.

Temperature and Specific Thermal Capacity

You'd have thought degrees Celsius was a good enough system for anyone — 0 °C = frosty, 25 °C = t-shirts and ice-cream. Apparently not though, as physicists felt the need to invent another one. Physicists, eh...

There's an **Absolute Scale** of Temperature

1) There is a **lowest possible temperature** called **absolute zero***. Absolute zero is given a value of **zero kelvins**, written **0 K**, on the absolute temperature scale.

2) At **0 K** all particles have the **minimum** possible **kinetic energy** — everything theoretically stops. At higher temperatures, particles have more energy. In fact, with the **Kelvin scale** (named after Lord Kelvin, who first suggested it), a particle's **energy** is **proportional** to its **temperature** (see page 139).

3) A change of **1 K** equals a change of **1 °C**.

4) To change from degrees Celsius into kelvins you **add 273** (or 273.15 to be really specific).

$$K = C + 273$$

5) **Equations** in **thermal physics** use temperatures measured in **kelvins**. (Unless you're dealing with a change in temperature, in which case you can use either kelvins or degrees Celsius — since a change of 1 K equals a change of 1 °C.)

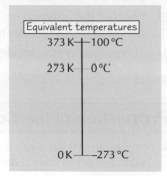

Equivalent temperatures

373 K — 100 °C

273 K — 0 °C

0 K — −273 °C

*It's true. −273.15 °C is the lowest temperature theoretically possible. Weird, huh. You'd kinda think there wouldn't be a minimum, but there is.

A **Change in Temperature** Shows **Thermal Energy** has been **Transferred**

Thermal energy is **always** transferred from regions of **higher temperature** to regions of **lower temperature**.

1) Suppose A and B are identical metal blocks. A has been in a **warm oven** and B has come from a **refrigerator**.

2) There is a **net transfer** of **thermal energy** from A to B. As this thermal energy flows out of A, its temperature **decreases**, and as the thermal energy flows into block B, its temperature **increases**. This is because:

A B

Some energy will also be transferred in the other direction, but overall *there'll be a net transfer from hot to cold.*

A net **transfer** of **thermal energy** causes a **change** in **temperature**.

3) Once the two blocks reach the **same temperature**, there is no longer a net transfer of thermal energy. We say that the two blocks are in **thermal equilibrium**.

Specific Thermal Capacity is how much **Energy** it Takes to **Heat** Something

When you heat something, its particles get more **kinetic energy** and its **temperature** rises.

The **specific thermal capacity** (c) of a substance is the amount of **energy** needed to **raise** the **temperature** of **1 kg** of the substance by **1 K** (or 1°C).

So: **energy change = mass × specific thermal capacity × change in temperature**

Or in symbols: $\Delta E = mc\Delta\theta$ *Q is sometimes used instead of E for the change in thermal energy.*

Where ΔE is the energy change in J, m is the mass in kg and $\Delta\theta$ is the temperature change in K or °C.

Remember, Δ means 'change in'.

Specific thermal capacity is measured in J kg^{-1} K^{-1} or J kg^{-1} °C^{-1}.

Temperature and Specific Thermal Capacity

You can **Measure** Specific Thermal Capacity in the **Laboratory**

The **method** is the same for **solids** and **liquids**, but the **set-up** is a little bit different:

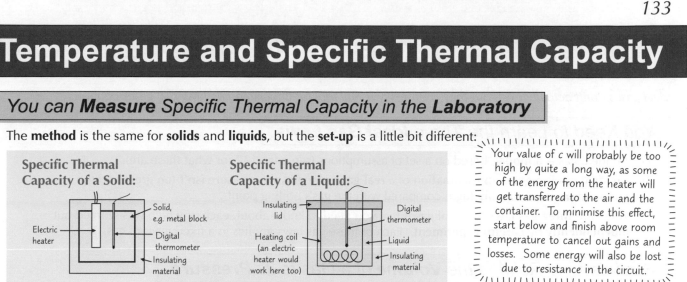

Your value of c will probably be too high by quite a long way, as some of the energy from the heater will get transferred to the air and the container. To minimise this effect, start below and finish above room temperature to cancel out gains and losses. Some energy will also be lost due to resistance in the circuit.

1) **Heat** the substance with the heater so that its temperature increases by about **10 K**.

2) Attach an ammeter and voltmeter to your **electric heater**. You can then calculate the work done by the heater, W, using $W = VIt$ (V is the heater voltage, I is the current and t is the time taken to heat the substance in seconds, see p.29).

3) If you assume all of the **work done** by the heater is transferred into **thermal energy** in the solid or liquid (so $W = E$), you can then plug your data into: $E = mc\Delta\theta$ to calculate c.

Remember — work is also equal to power × time.

Example: An electric immersion heater is used to heat 0.250 kg of water from 12.1 °C to 22.9 °C. The heater has a voltage of 11.2 V and a current of 5.30 A, and is switched on for 205 s. Calculate the specific thermal capacity of water.

$E = VIt = 11.2 \times 5.30 \times 205 = 12\,168.8$ J $\Delta\theta = 22.9 - 12.1 = 10.8$ °C

$E = mc\Delta\theta$ so $c = \dfrac{E}{m\Delta\theta} = \dfrac{12168.8}{0.250 \times 10.8} = 4506.9...$

$= 4510$ J kg^{-1}°C^{-1} (or 4510 J kg^{-1}K^{-1}) **(to 3 s.f.)**

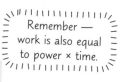

Gary's specific thermal capacity was pretty high...

Practice Questions

Q1 What is meant by absolute zero? Give the value of absolute zero in kelvins and degrees Celsius.

Q2 What is meant by the specific thermal capacity of a substance?

Q3 Briefly describe an experiment to measure the specific thermal capacity of a liquid.

Exam Questions

Q1 a) A stone that has been stored in a freezer is placed in a glass of water at room temperature. Describe how the stone cools the water, in terms of energy transfer. [1 mark]

b) Water has a specific thermal capacity of 4180 J kg^{-1} K^{-1}. Show that the energy change needed to decrease the temperature of 25 g of water from 15°C to 12°C is –310 J. [1 mark]

Q2 A block of tin of mass 0.93 kg is placed in an insulating container then heated by an electric heater. The specific thermal capacity of tin is 210 J kg^{-1} K^{-1}. The heater is connected to a 32 V supply and a current of 5.0 A flows through it when it is switched on.

a) Estimate how long it will take for the temperature of the block of tin to increase from 18.5 °C to 34.2 °C. [2 marks]

b) State how the real time taken for the temperature of the block of tin to increase is likely to differ from your estimate, and explain why. [2 marks]

Specific thermal capacity — it's hot stuff...

You've probably come across a lot of this stuff before, so hopefully it won't be too confusing. You'll be given the equation for specific thermal capacity in the exam, so just make sure you know how to use it.

Ideal Gases

Ideal gases don't actually exist, but they are a really useful tool for understanding how real gases behave.

You Need to Learn the Three *Ideal Gas Laws*

1) An ideal gas is a **model**, based on a set of assumptions (see page 137 for what these are).

2) An ideal gas is a **good approximation** of a **real gas** as long as the **pressure isn't too great** and the **temperature** is **reasonably high** (compared with the gas's boiling point).

3) There are **three gas laws** for ideal gases that you need to know about, each of which was worked out **independently** by **careful experiment**. Each of these gas laws applies to a fixed mass of gas.

Boyle's Law Relates the *Volume* of a Gas to its *Pressure*

Boyle's law states:

> At a **constant temperature**, the **pressure p** and **volume V** of a gas are **inversely proportional**.

So: | pV = **constant** |

An **ideal gas** obeys Boyle's law at all temperatures.

If you plot pressure against volume for an ideal gas at different temperatures, you'll get a graph like this:

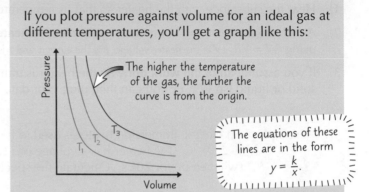

The higher the temperature of the gas, the further the curve is from the origin.

The equations of these lines are in the form $y = \frac{k}{x}$.

You Can *Test Boyle's Law* Using a *Pump* and a *Pressure Gauge*

1) You can investigate the effect of **pressure** on **volume** by setting up the experiment shown on the right.

2) The **oil** confines a parcel of air in a sealed **tube** with **fixed dimensions**. A **tyre pump** is used to **increase** the pressure in the tube and the **Bourdon gauge** records the **pressure**. As the pressure increases the air will **compress** and the volume occupied by air in the tube will **reduce**.

3) Measure the volume of air when the system is at **atmospheric pressure**, then gradually increase the pressure, noting down **both** the pressure and the volume of air. Multiplying them together at any point should give a **constant**.

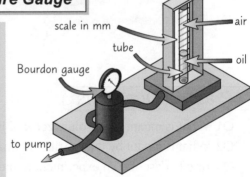

scale in mm
air
tube
oil
Bourdon gauge
to pump

You could also use an electronic pressure sensor, (e.g. a differential pressure monitor) attached to a data logger to record your results automatically.

Charles' Law Relates the *Temperature* of a Gas to its *Volume*

Charles' law states:

> At constant **pressure**, the **volume V** of a gas is **directly proportional** to its **absolute temperature T**.

| V/T = **constant** |

Ideal gases also obey Charles' law.

If you plot volume against temperature for an ideal gas at a given pressure, you'll get a graph like this:

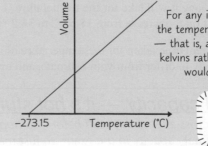

For any ideal gas, the line meets the temperature axis at −273.15 °C — that is, absolute zero. If you used kelvins rather than Celsius, the line would stop at the origin.

Remember, temperature in kelvins is sometimes called absolute temperature.

Ideal Gases

You Can **Test Charles' Law** Using a **Capillary Tube**

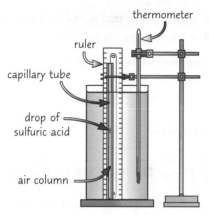

1) Set up the experiment shown on the left. You'll need a **capillary tube** containing a drop of **concentrated sulfuric acid** halfway up the tube. The tube should be **sealed** at the bottom, so that a **column of air** is trapped between the bottom of the tube and the acid drop.

2) Fill the beaker with **near-boiling water**. Measure the **length** of the column of air trapped between the bottom of the tube and the drop of acid.

3) As the water cools, regularly record the **temperature** of the water and the **length** of the air column. The length of the trapped air column will **decrease** as the water temperature decreases.

4) **Repeat** with fresh near-boiling water twice more, letting the capillary tube adjust to the new temperature between each repeat. Record the length at the **same temperatures** each time and take an **average** of the three results.

5) Plot your **average results** on a graph of **length** against **temperature** and draw a line of best fit — you should get a **straight line**. This shows that the length of the air column is **proportional** to the temperature.

6) The volume of the column of air is equal to the volume of a cylinder, which is proportional to its length ($V = \pi r^2 l$), so the **volume** is also proportional to the temperature. This agrees with **Charles' law**.

You can use this experiment to estimate the value of absolute zero by continuing (extrapolating) your straight line graph down to where it meets the temperature axis.

The Pressure Law Relates the Temperature of a Gas to its Pressure

The Pressure law states:

At constant **volume**, the **pressure** p of a gas is **directly proportional** to its **absolute temperature** T.

$$p/T = \text{constant}$$

Unsurprisingly, this is another law that **ideal gases** obey.

If you plot pressure against temperature for an ideal gas at a given volume, you'll get a graph like this:

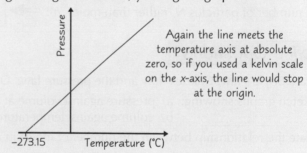

Again the line meets the temperature axis at absolute zero, so if you used a kelvin scale on the x-axis, the line would stop at the origin.

You Can Investigate the Pressure Law Experimentally Too

If the markings on your measuring equipment are quite far apart, you can often interpolate between them (e.g. if the temperature is halfway between the markings for 24 °C and 25 °C you could record it as 24.5 °C). But it's better to use something with a finer scale if you can.

1) Immerse a stoppered flask of air in a beaker of water so that as much as possible of the flask is submerged. Connect the flask to a Bourdon gauge using a short length of tube — the volume of the tubing must be much smaller than the volume of the flask. Record the temperature of the water and the pressure on the gauge.

2) Heat the water for a few minutes then remove the heat source, stir the water to ensure it is at a uniform temperature and allow some time for the heat to be transferred from the water to the air. Record the pressure on the gauge and the temperature, then heat the water again and repeat until the water boils.

3) Repeat your experiment twice more with fresh cool water, taking pressure measurements at the same set of temperatures each time.

4) Plot your results on a graph of pressure against temperature. Draw a line of best fit — you'll see it looks like the graph above.

5) This experiment also allows you to estimate the value of absolute zero, again by extrapolating your line of best fit until it reaches the x-axis.

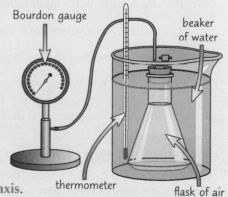

Ideal Gases

If you **Combine** All Three Laws you get the **Ideal Gas Equation**

Combining all three gas laws gives the equation: **pV/T = constant**.
1) The constant depends on the amount of gas used. The amount of **gas** can be **measured** in **moles**, **n** (see below).
2) The constant is equal to **nR**, where **R** is called the **gas constant**. Plugging this into the equation gives:

$$\frac{pV}{T} = nR$$ or rearranging, $$pV = nRT$$ — the ideal gas equation

The value of R is **8.31 J mol⁻¹ K⁻¹**. This equation works well (i.e., a real gas approximates to an ideal gas) for gases at **low pressure** and fairly **high temperatures**.

The **Boltzmann Constant** k is like a **Gas Constant** for **One Particle** of Gas

One mole of **any** material contains the same **number of particles**, no matter what the material is. This number is called the **Avogadro constant** and has the symbol N_A. The value of N_A is **6.02 × 10²³ mol⁻¹**.

1) The **number of particles**, **N**, in an amount of gas is given by the **number of moles**, **n**, multiplied by the **Avogadro constant**, N_A.

$$N = nN_A$$

The molar mass is the mass of one mole of a substance.

2) The **Boltzmann constant**, **k**, is given by $k = \frac{R}{N_A}$. You can think of the Boltzmann constant as the **gas constant** for **one gas particle**, while **R** is the gas constant for **one mole of gas**.

3) The value of the Boltzmann constant is **1.38 × 10⁻²³ J K⁻¹**.

4) If you combine $N = nN_A$ and $k = \frac{R}{N_A}$ you'll see that:

$$Nk = nR$$

5) This can be substituted into the ideal gas equation to give this **alternative form** (in terms of number of particles N, rather than moles, n):

$$pV = NkT$$

This means that the pressure of a gas is proportional to both the number of particles and the temperature of the gas, and is inversely proportional to its volume.

Practice Questions

Q1 State Boyle's law, Charles' law and the pressure law. Describe how you could test each law experimentally.
Q2 Sketch graphs showing: a) pressure against volume at a constant temperature for an ideal gas.
b) volume against temperature at constant pressure for an ideal gas.
Q3 State the relationship between the number of moles in a gas, n, and the number of particles in a gas, N.
Q4 What is the relationship between the Boltzmann constant, k, and the gas constant, R?
Q5 Write the ideal gas equation in terms of the number of particles in a gas.

Exam Questions

Q1 State the relationship between the pressure and absolute temperature of a gas at a constant volume, and describe two features of a graph of pressure against absolute temperature that show this relation. [3 marks]

Q2 The mass of one mole of nitrogen gas is 0.028 kg.

a) A flask holds 0.014 kg of nitrogen gas. Calculate how many particles of nitrogen gas are in the flask. [2 marks]

b) The flask has a volume of 0.010 m³ and is at a temperature of 27 °C. Calculate the pressure inside it. [2 marks]

c) Describe how the pressure inside the flask would change if the number of molecules inside was halved. [1 mark]

Q3 A large helium balloon has a volume of 10.0 m³ at ground level. The temperature of the gas in the balloon is 293 K and the pressure is 1.0 × 10⁵ Pa. The balloon is released and rises to a height where its volume is 25 m³ and its temperature is 260 K. Calculate the pressure inside the balloon at its new height. [2 marks]

Ideal revision equation: marks = (pages read × questions answered)...

All this might sound a bit theoretical, but most gases you'll meet in the everyday world come fairly close to being 'ideal'. They only stop obeying these laws when the pressure's too high or they're getting close to their boiling point.

Kinetic Theory and Internal Energy

*Kinetic theory tries to **explain** the **gas laws**. It basically models a gas as a series of hard balls that obey Newton's laws. It's a pretty powerful model, and more importantly it's in your exams, so make sure you know about it...*

Lots of **Simplifying Assumptions** are Used in **Kinetic Theory**

In **kinetic theory**, physicists picture gas particles moving at **high speed** in **random directions**. To get **equations** like the ones on the last few pages, some **simplifying assumptions** are needed. These are the assumptions that you **need to know**:

1) Particles occupy a **negligible volume** compared with the volume of the container.

2) **Collisions** between particles themselves or at the walls of a container are **perfectly elastic** (so no energy is lost, see p.92).

3) There are **negligible forces** between particles (except for when they collide).

Kinetic theory also assumes that the gas contains a **large number of particles** that **move rapidly** and **randomly** and that the motion of the particles obeys **Newton's laws** (see below).

A **gas obeying** these **assumptions** is called an **ideal** gas (see p.134-136). Remember — real gases behave like ideal gases as long as the **pressure isn't too big** and the **temperature** is **reasonably high** (compared with their boiling points).

Each Particle in a Gas Goes on a **Random Walk**

1) There's no way you can **record** the **random motion** of all the particles in a **gas** (without going cross-eyed in the process, of course). Instead you can **model** the movement of the particles by a **random walk**.

2) A **random walk** assumes that each **particle** starts in one place, **moves N steps** in random directions, and ends up **somewhere else**.

3) Here's the path taken by one particle in a box filled with air. The particle **changes direction** each time it **collides** with another particle in the box.

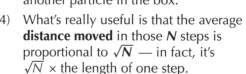

starting point of particle

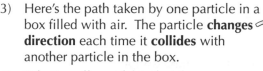

3 steps | 10 steps | 100 steps

4) What's really useful is that the average **distance moved** in those N steps is proportional to $\sqrt{N}$ — in fact, it's $\sqrt{N}$ × the length of one step.

5) The distance a particle can travel between collisions is usually around 10^{-7} m. So to travel 1 m from its starting point, a particle will have had to take 10 000 000 steps. That's quite a few, so it's no wonder that diffusion is a **slow process**, even if the particles are travelling at high speeds.

Diffusion is the net movement of particles from an area of higher concentration to an area of lower concentration.

Kinetic Theory Assumes Particles Obey **Newton's Second Law**

1) Kinetic theory assumes that particles in a gas obey Newton's laws.

2) According to Newton's Second Law (p.90), the force exerted by a particle in a collision is equal to the rate of change of momentum of the particle, so: $F = \dfrac{\Delta (mv)}{\Delta t} = \dfrac{\Delta p}{\Delta t}$

Remember, $mv = p$, or momentum (p.92).

3) This means that if a particle collides with a wall of the container, the faster it is travelling, the more force it exerts on the wall:

A graph of force against time shows how the force acting on (or exerted by) an object changes during an interaction, e.g.:

You know: $F = \dfrac{\Delta p}{\Delta t}$

so: $F\Delta t = \Delta p$

This means the **area under a force-time graph**, $F\Delta t$, is equal to Δp — the **change in momentum**, or the **impulse** of the interaction (see page 93).

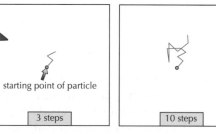
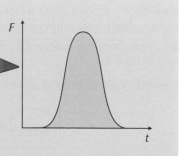

Kinetic Theory and Internal Energy

The **Root Mean Square** Speed **is a Measure of Average Speed**

Before you can combine all of this to make a model of ideal gases,
you need to know about the **root mean square speed**:

1) As the particles in a gas are all moving in **different directions**, if you averaged their velocities you'd get **zero**.

2) Instead, you take the average of their **squared velocities**.
   This quantity is called the **mean square speed** and is written $\overline{c^2}$. Its units are m^2s^{-2}.

3) The square root of this number gives you the speed of a typical particle, the **root mean square speed (r.m.s.)**, $\sqrt{\overline{c^2}}$.

To **Understand** an Ideal Gas, Think About **Gas Particles** in a **Box**

Imagine a cubic box with sides of length **l** containing one particle, Q, of mass **m**.

Say particle Q **moves horizontally** towards **wall A** with velocity **u**,
so its **momentum** is **mu**. It strikes wall **A**, exerting a **force** on the wall,
and heads back in the opposite direction.

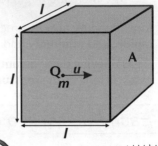

1) Particle Velocity is Proportional to the Pressure

The **faster** the particle, the **larger** its **momentum**, so the **greater the impulse**
of the collision and the **larger** the **force** on the wall. The **particle** will also
take **less time** to travel across the box and back again, and so will hit the walls
more often. And as **pressure = force ÷ area**, the **pressure** will be **greater** too.

Remember: $F\Delta t = \Delta p$, impulse equals change in momentum.

2) The Number of Particles, N, is Proportional to the Pressure

Instead of just one particle, imagine you've got a whole stream of them hitting wall A.
Each particle exerts a force on the wall as it hits it, so the **total force** on the wall will be
proportional to the number of particles. And you've guessed it, as **pressure = force ÷ area**,
the **pressure** is proportional to the number of particles too.

3) The Volume of the Box is Inversely Proportional to the Pressure

Now imagine you shrink the box. The particles have **less**
distance to travel before they hit a wall, so you've **increased**
the number of times the particles hit the walls of the box per
second, which increases the total force on the wall.
Because the box is now smaller, the **area** of the walls is **smaller**.
So there's a greater force on a smaller area,
meaning the **pressure is greater**.

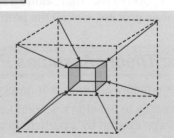

4) Particles Travel in Random Directions at Different Velocities

Obviously gas particles don't all neatly go in the same direction — you can estimate that **a third** of
all the particles are travelling in one dimension at any time (as there are three dimensions, x, y, z).

To take account of the different particle velocities, you use the **mean square speed**, $\overline{c^2}$ (see above).

If you do the maths, it all whittles down to give you this amazing **equation**:

$$pV = \frac{1}{3}Nm\overline{c^2}$$

Where *p* is pressure (Pa or Nm^{-2}), *V* is volume (m^3), *N* is the number
of particles in the gas, *m* is the mass of a particle (kg), and $\overline{c^2}$ is the
mean square speed (m^2s^{-2}).

Kinetic Theory and Internal Energy

Internal Energy is Proportional to Temperature for an Ideal Gas

1) All things (solids, liquids, gases) contain **energy**. The amount of **energy** contained in a system is called its **internal energy**:

> **Internal energy** is the **sum** of the **kinetic** and **potential energy** of the **particles** within a system.

2) All the **internal energy** of an **ideal gas** is due to the **kinetic energy** of its **particles** (there's no potential energy).

3) You can get an expression for the **average kinetic energy of a particle** in an ideal gas in terms of temperature by combining the **ideal gas equation** ($pV = NkT$, page 136), and the equation on p.138 ($pV = \frac{1}{3}Nm\overline{c^2}$):

- $\frac{1}{2}m\overline{c^2}$ is the **average kinetic energy** of an **individual particle** (because $KE = \frac{1}{2}mv^2$).

- If you **equate** the equations in point 3) above, and rearrange a little, you get: (To get the **internal energy** of a whole gas, just multiply this equation by N, the **number of particles** it contains).

> **average energy per particle** $= \frac{1}{2}m\overline{c^2} = \frac{3}{2}kT$
>
> k is the Boltzmann constant (1.38×10^{-23} JK^{-1}), T is the temperature (in K)

You can rearrange this equation to find the r.m.s. speed from the temperature, T.

- You can approximate this to:

> **average energy per particle** $\approx kT$

4) This means the **internal energy** of an ideal gas is **proportional** to its **absolute temperature** (or vice-versa — the temperature of a gas is proportional to the average energy per particle). So...

> A **rise** in **absolute temperature** increases the **kinetic energy** of each particle, causing a rise in **internal energy**.

Practice Questions

Q1 State the three main assumptions required by the kinetic theory of ideal gases.

Q2 A gas particle takes a random walk of 10 000 steps, each of length x. How far does it travel from its starting point?

Q3 Explain how can you calculate the impulse of an interaction from a force-time graph.

Q4 Why should you estimate the average speed of particles in a gas using the root mean square speed?

Q5 What is internal energy? What would cause a rise in the internal energy of an ideal gas?

Q6 What is the average energy per particle in an ideal gas approximately equal to?

Exam Questions

Q1 Some helium gas is contained in a flask of volume 7.0×10^{-5} m^3. Each helium atom has a mass of 6.6×10^{-27} kg, and there are 2.0×10^{22} atoms present. The pressure of the gas is 1.0×10^5 Pa.

a) Calculate the root mean square speed of the atoms. [2 marks]

b) The absolute temperature of the gas is doubled. Use ideas about particle velocity, impulse and momentum to explain why the pressure of the gas will have increased. [4 marks]

Q2 Some air freshener is sprayed at one end of a room. The room is 8.0 m long and the temperature is 22 °C.

a) The average freshener molecule moves at 410 ms^{-1}. Calculate how long would it take for a particle to travel a distance equal to the length of the room. [1 mark]

b) The perfume from the air freshener only slowly diffuses from one end of the room to the other. Explain why this takes much longer than suggested by your answer to part a). [2 marks]

c) Calculate the average energy per air freshener particle. [1 mark]

Matter very simple — my foot...

Kinetic theory basically allows you to treat molecules of gas as little ping-pong balls whizzing about, and (hopefully) it means the ideal gas laws make a bit more sense. If you didn't follow the box stuff on page 138, give it another read, and have a go at sketching diagrams for each point to figure out what's going on.

Activation Energy

Welcome to the big bad world of statistical physics — Ludwig Boltzmann's got a lot to answer for...

The Average Thermal **Energy** of a Particle is Proportional to the **Temperature**

1) Any particle above absolute zero has some **thermal energy**.

> The **average thermal energy per particle** is (very roughly) **kT**.

k is the <u>Boltzmann constant</u>, $k = 1.38 \times 10^{-23}$ J K^{-1}. T is the temperature in kelvins. See page 139 for more.

2) This table gives you an idea of the magnitude of the thermal energy at various temperatures:

Temperature / K	Average thermal energy (approx.) — kT		
	J (per particle)	J mol^{-1}	eV (per particle)
1	1×10^{-23}	8	9×10^{-5}
300 (room temp.)	4×10^{-21}	2000	0.03
6000 (Sun's surface)	8×10^{-20}	5×10^4	0.5

To convert kT in J to J mol^{-1}, multiply by the Avogadro constant (6.02×10^{23} mol^{-1}).

To convert kT to eV (electronvolts), divide by the magnitude of the charge on the electron (1.60×10^{-19} C). (See p.62 for more on electronvolts.)

3) Particles in matter are **held together** by **bonds**. The **energy** needed to break these bonds in a given substance is the **activation energy**, E_A.

4) The ratio E_A/kT is really important. When kT is **big enough** compared with E_A, the bonds are broken and the matter comes apart.

Activation Energy is the Energy Needed to Make Something Happen

1) For a process like a change of state to happen, particles need to 'climb' an **energy barrier**.

2) The **activation energy**, E_A, is the **energy needed** to climb that barrier.

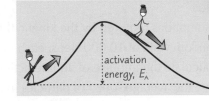

activation energy, E_A

Before you can ski down a mountain, you need to climb to the top of it. So skiing is an activation process.

Lots of Processes have an Activation Energy

1) Lots of processes involving **particles** have activation energies — for example:

> a) **A change of state:** the particles need enough energy to break the forces between them.
>
> b) **Thermionic emission:** if you heat up a conductor, electrons are released from the surface. These electrons need enough energy to escape from the attraction of the positive nuclei.
>
> c) **Ionisation in a candle flame:** the molecules in the air need enough energy to split up into individual atoms and ions. This is a similar process to thermionic emission.
>
> d) **Conduction in a semiconductor:** semiconductors will only start to conduct once there are electrons in a high-energy state called the 'conduction band', so electrons need enough energy to jump from the ground state to this higher-energy state.
>
> e) **Viscous flow:** viscous fluids have strong attractive forces between the particles, causing the fluid to 'flow' slowly. As you increase the temperature, you increase the kinetic energy of the particles. This means they have more energy to overcome these forces and so the fluid will be able to flow more easily.
>
> That's why when you've got cold oil in a pan the oil is fairly viscous and doesn't 'run' very easily. As the pan and oil heat up, the oil will flow around the pan much more easily.

2) In each of these examples, the characteristic **activation energy**, E_A, comes from the **random thermal energy** of the particles. You might think, then, that these processes wouldn't happen unless $kT \geq E_A$... but it's not that simple...

Activation Energy

Getting **Extra Energy** is all about **Random Collisions**

1) If the **ratio** between the characteristic activation energy and the average energy of the particles (E_A/kT) is too high, nothing happens.

2) As E_A/kT gets down to somewhere around **15–30**, the process starts to happen at a **fair rate**.

3) So some particles must have energies of **15–30 times** the **average energy**.

4) Every time particles **collide**, there's a **chance** that one of them will gain **extra energy** — above and beyond the average kT. If that happens **several times** in a row, a particle can gain energies **much, much higher** than the average.

5) Say **f** is the fraction of particles with an extra energy **E**. If **E** is reasonably big compared to **kT**, then **f** will be **small**. (So far so good.)

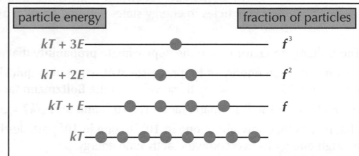

6) Now to get a particle with an extra energy of **2E**, you need a collision between two particles with an **average extra energy** of about **E**.

   So the fraction of particles with an extra energy of **2E** will be: $f \times f = f^2$

7) You can use the same sort of reasoning to find the fraction of particles with any number of times the extra energy **E** above the average particle energy. So the fraction of particles with an extra energy of **3E** is f^3, the fraction of particles with an extra energy of **4E** is f^4, etc.

8) To end up with an energy of **15kT** to **30kT**, a particle would have to get **very lucky**, so there will only be a tiny proportion of particles with this energy.

9) Because there are normally **huge numbers** of particles colliding billions of times each second, this small fraction still adds up to a large number of particles.

Edmond's activation energy was 3 cups of coffee and a whiskey chaser.

Practice Questions

Q1 Give an expression for the approximate thermal energy per particle at a given temperature.

Q2 What is activation energy?

Q3 Write down three processes that involve activation energies.

Q4 At what range of values of the ratio E_A/kT does a process begin to occur at a reasonable speed?

Q5 A fraction f of particles have an extra thermal energy E due to collisions with other particles. What fraction of particles have an extra energy equal to 7E?

Exam Question

Q1 A sample of oil is at 290 K. It is poured into a pan and heated to a temperature of 360 K. *(The Boltzmann constant, k = 1.38 × 10⁻²³ JK⁻¹.)*

    a) Estimate the average thermal energy in joules of an oil molecule at:

       i)   290 K   [1 mark]

       ii) 360 K   [1 mark]

    b) Explain in terms of activation energies why the oil is less viscous at 360 K than at 290 K.   [3 marks]

Billions of collisions? You'd think they'd look where they're going...

It's like the particle version of Goldilocks — if the ratio between the activation energy and the average energy is too high, nothing happens. You need it just right... or bears will mock you for not knowing about activation energies.

The Boltzmann Factor

I know what you're thinking — if only there was some way to work out the ratio of particles in different energy states. Well, today's your lucky day...

The **Boltzmann Factor** tells you the **Ratio** of Particles in two Energy States

1) You can say particles with different energies are in different quantum **energy states**. A particle with an energy of $kT + E$ is in a higher energy state than a particle with an energy of kT.

2) You can find the ratio of particles in two different energy states:

> The **Boltzmann factor**, $e^{-\frac{E}{kT}}$, gives the **ratio** of the **numbers of particles** in energy states E joules apart, at a temperature T in kelvins.

3) The Boltzmann factor is also the **approximate probability** that a particle has an energy of at least E.

4) For an activation energy of E_A, processes start happening **quickly** when E_A/kT is between 15 and 30, so try these values in the **Boltzmann factor**.

5) For $E_A/kT = 15$ the Boltzmann factor is $\sim 10^{-7}$, and for $E_A/kT = 30$ it's only $\sim 10^{-13}$.

6) That means that only about **one in 10^{13}** to **one in 10^7** particles have **enough energy** to overcome the activation energy.

7) But think about a reaction between two gases: gas particles collide about **10^9 times every second**. Every time there's a collision, there's an 'attempt' at the reaction, so even with **so few** particles having enough energy, the reaction can happen in a matter of **seconds**.

Bob and Rodger were both enjoying being in a low energy state.

The **Boltzmann Factor** varies with **Temperature**

For any particular **reaction**, the values of E_A (activation energy) and k (the Boltzmann constant) are **fixed**. This means that the **only** thing that will change the **Boltzmann factor** is the **temperature**.

If you plot a **graph** of the **Boltzmann factor** against **temperature** you get an s-shaped curve like the ones below.

> A graph of the Boltzmann factor against the average thermal energy of the particles would have the same shape, since thermal energy $\propto T$.

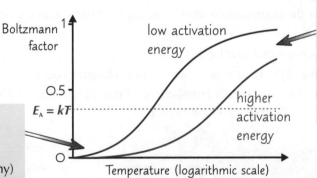

At **high temperatures**, the **Boltzmann factor** approaches 1, so nearly **all the particles** will have enough **energy** to **react** and the **reaction** will be really fast.

This **shape** shows that at **low temperatures**, the **Boltzmann factor** is also very **low**, so **very few** (if any) particles will have sufficient **energy** to **react** and the reaction will be really **slow**.

In between, the Boltzmann factor **increases rapidly** with **temperature**. So a **small increase** in **temperature** can make a **big difference** to the rate.

The Boltzmann factor and **rate** of a reaction both vary with **temperature**, and it is a **reasonable approximation** to say:

> The **rate** of a reaction with **activation energy** E_A is proportional to the **Boltzmann factor**, $e^{-\frac{E_A}{kT}}$.

The Boltzmann Factor

You can use the Boltzmann Factor to Describe the **Rate of a Reaction**

So, now you can use all that lovely knowledge to answer **exam questions** about the rate of a reaction, just like this one.

Example:

Ben has a flask filled with liquid X. The energy, E_A, binding one molecule in liquid X is 0.40 eV.

a) Estimate the average energy of the liquid molecules at 75 K. ($k = 1.38 \times 10^{-23}$ J K^{-1})

Approx. average energy $= kT = 1.38 \times 10^{-23} \times 75 = 1.035 \times 10^{-21} = \mathbf{1.0 \times 10^{-21}}$ **J (to 2 s.f.)**

b) Calculate the ratio E_A/kT for one molecule escaping the liquid at a temperature of 75 K.

$E_A = 0.40$ eV and $kT = 1.38 \times 10^{-23} \times 75 = 1.035 \times 10^{-21}$ J
Convert this energy from J into eV: $(1.035 \times 10^{-21}) \div (1.60 \times 10^{-19}) = 6.468... \times 10^{-3}$ eV
So $E_A/kT = 0.40 \div (6.468... \times 10^{-3}) = 61.835... = \mathbf{62}$ **(to 2 s.f.)**

c) Calculate the Boltzmann factor for the liquid molecules at this temperature.

$e^{-\frac{E_A}{kT}} = e^{-61.835...} = 1.396... \times 10^{-27} = \mathbf{1.4 \times 10^{-27}}$ **(to 2 s.f.)**

d) Ben says, 'The ratio of E_A/kT is very high at 75 K, so there will be a rapid rate of evaporation of the liquid X at 75 K.'
Do you agree? Use your answers to parts b) and c) to explain your answer.

I disagree. A high ratio of activation energy to average particle energy means the activation energy is a lot higher than the average energy of the liquid molecules. For a good rate of reaction the E_A/kT ratio should be lower (around 15-30). Also, the Boltzmann factor at 75 K is extremely small. The rate of evaporation will be approximately proportional to the Boltzmann factor, so the rate of evaporation of the liquid will be extremely slow.

Practice Questions

Q1 What is the Boltzmann factor?

Q2 Two energy states are separated by an energy of $E = 7.8 \times 10^{-20}$ J.
Show that, at a temperature of 295 K, the ratio of the number of particles in the higher energy state to the number of particles in the lower energy state is approximately 5×10^{-9}.

Q3 Sketch a graph to show the relationship between the Boltzmann factor and temperature for a reaction.

Q4 How is the rate of a reaction related to the Boltzmann factor?
Describe the rate of reaction if the Boltzmann factor is almost 1.

Exam Question

Q1 Two liquids, A and B, are mixed together at a temperature of 298 K, and begin reacting with one another.
($k = 1.38 \times 10^{-23}$ J K^{-1})

a) Calculate the approximate average energy of one of the molecules in the mixture at this temperature. [1 mark]

b) For a reaction to occur between a molecule of A and a molecule of B, each molecule needs 9.4×10^{-20} J.
Estimate the proportion of molecules that have sufficient energy to react when the mixture is at 298 K. [2 marks]

c) A Bunsen burner is used to increase the temperature of the mixture to 313 K.
Using your answer to part b), estimate the factor by which the rate of reaction increases. [3 marks]

The Boltzmann Factor — not as much fun as the X Factor...

You can think of the Boltzmann factor as a tool in finding the probability of a particle having a certain energy, or the fraction of particles that have that energy. Or you could think of it as a big pair of pants with pink polka dots — up to you.

Magnetic Fields

Magnetic fields — making pretty patterns with iron filings before spending an age trying to pick them off the magnet.

A **Magnetic Field** is a **Region** Where a **Force** is Exerted on **Magnetic Materials**

Magnetic fields can be represented by **flux lines** (also called **field lines**). Flux lines go from **north to south poles**.
The **strength** of a magnetic field is represented
by how **tightly packed** the lines are — the **closer**
together the lines, the **stronger** the field.

Each **flux line** always **joins up** the north and
south **poles** in one **continuous** line.

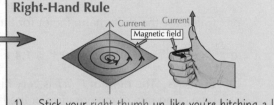

At a <u>neutral point</u>,
magnetic fields
<u>cancel out</u>.

The **flux lines** around a **bar magnet**, or between a pair of magnets, have characteristic shapes.

If the flux lines are **equally spaced** and **in the same direction** the field is **uniform** (i.e. the same everywhere).

There is a **Magnetic Field** Around a **Wire** Carrying **Electric Current**

When **current** flows in a **wire** or any other long straight conductor, a **magnetic field** is induced around the wire.

1)   The **field lines** are **concentric circles** centred on the wire.

2)   The **direction** of a magnetic **field** around a current-carrying
wire can be worked out with the **right-hand rule**.

3)   For a **loop** of wire, the field is **doughnut-shaped**, while a **coil**
(lots of loops) with **length** forms a **field** like a **bar magnet**.

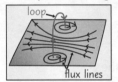 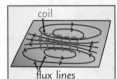

Right-Hand Rule

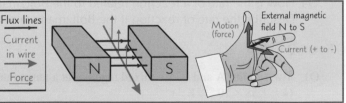

1)   Stick your <u>right thumb</u> up, like you're hitching a lift.
2)   Your <u>thumb</u> points in the direction
of <u>conventional current</u>...
3)   ...your curled <u>fingers</u> point in the direction of the <u>field</u>.

A **Wire** Carrying a **Current** in a **Magnetic Field** will **Experience** a **Force**

1)   If you put a **current-carrying wire** into an **external** magnetic field (e.g. between
two magnets), the field around the wire and the field from the magnets **are**
added together. The shape of the **resultant flux lines** is a combination of the
two fields — here the resultant flux lines are **stretched** around the wire.

2)   Flux lines have a tendency to **contract** (get shorter) and **straighten**,
which causes an **electromagnetic force** that **pushes** on the wire.

3)   If the current is **parallel** to the flux lines, **no force** acts because
the fields are **perpendicular**, so they don't affect each other.

4)   The **direction** of the force is always **perpendicular** to both the
current and the **magnetic field** — given by Fleming's left-hand rule:

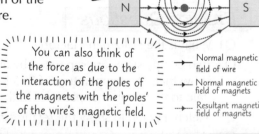

You can also think of
the force as due to the
interaction of the poles of
the magnets with the 'poles'
of the wire's magnetic field.

→   Normal magnetic
field of wire
⇢   Normal magnetic
field of magnets
⇾   Resultant magnetic
field of magnets

Fleming's Left-Hand Rule

The First finger points in the direction of the external uniform
magnetic Field, the seCond finger points in the direction
of the conventional Current. Then your thuMb points in
the direction of the force (in which Motion takes place).

Flux lines
Current
in wire
Force

Motion
(force)

External magnetic
field N to S

Current (+ to -)

The **Force** on a Wire is **Proportional** to the **Flux Density**

1)   The size of the **force**, *F*, on a current-carrying wire at **right-angles** to a uniform magnetic field is
proportional to the **current**, *I*, the **length of wire** in the field, *L*, and **magnetic flux density**, *B*.

$$F = ILB$$

2)   **Magnetic flux density**, *B*, is a measure of the
strength of the magnetic field. It is defined as:
You might see magnetic fields called **B-fields** as a result.

The **force on one metre** of wire carrying a **current**
of **one amp** at **right angles** to the **magnetic field**.

3)   Magnetic flux density is a **vector**
quantity with both a **direction** and
magnitude. It's measured in **teslas, T**.

$$1\,\text{tesla} = \frac{\text{Wb}}{\text{m}^2}$$

It helps to think of flux density as the number of <u>flux</u>
<u>lines</u> (measured in webers (Wb), see p.146) per unit area.

Magnetic Fields

Use a *Digital Balance* to *Investigate* Flux Density

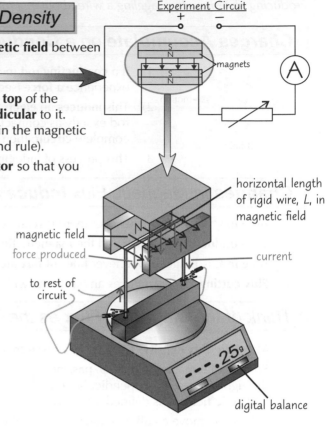

Experiment Circuit

magnets

horizontal length
of rigid wire, L, in
magnetic field

magnetic field

force produced

current

to rest of
circuit

digital balance

You can use the set-up shown to investigate the **uniform magnetic field** between the poles of a magnet and obtain a value for **flux density**, **B**.
You should use magnets with **poles** on their **largest** faces.

1) A **square hoop** of **rigid** metal wire is positioned so that the **top** of the hoop, **length L**, passes through the magnetic field, **perpendicular** to it. When a current flows, this horizontal **length of rigid wire** in the magnetic field will experience a downwards **force** (Fleming's left hand rule).

2) The power supply should be connected to a **variable resistor** so that you can **alter** the **current**. Connect the crocodile clips and zero the digital balance when there is **no** current through the wire. Then turn on the power supply.

3) Note the **mass** showing on the digital balance and the **current**. Then use the variable resistor to **change** the **current**. **Repeat** this until you have tested a large range of currents, then do the whole thing **twice** more and calculate the **mean** mass for each current reading.

4) Convert your mass readings into a **force** using $F = mg$. **Plot** the data on a graph of **force F** against **current I**. Draw a line of best fit.

5) Because $F = ILB$, the **gradient** of your graph is equal to $B \times L$. Measure the gradient, then divide by length L to **get a value for B**.

Practice Questions

Q1 Sketch the lines of magnetic flux around a long straight current-carrying wire and a coil of wire with length. Show the direction of the current and magnetic field on each diagram.

Q2 Write down the equation you would use to find the force on a current-carrying wire at right-angles to a uniform magnetic field.

Q3 A copper bar can roll freely on two copper supports, as shown in the diagram. When current is applied in the direction shown, which way will the bar roll?

Q4 Describe an experiment you could carry out to determine the uniform magnetic flux density between the poles of a magnet.

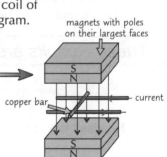

magnets with poles
on their largest faces

copper bar

current

Exam Questions

Q1 a) Explain, in terms of flux lines, why a current-carrying wire at right angles to an external uniform magnetic field will experience a force. [2 marks]

   b) The flux lines are vertical and go from top to bottom. The current flows from right to left. State the direction in which the force will act. [1 mark]

Q2 A 4.00 cm length of wire carrying a current of 3.0 A runs perpendicular to a uniform magnetic field of strength 2.0×10^{-5} T.

   a) Calculate the magnitude of the force on the wire. [2 marks]

   b) The wire is rotated so that it runs parallel to the magnetic field. Give the new force on the wire. Explain your answer. [2 marks]

I revised the right-hand rule by the A69 and ended up in Newcastle...

Fleming's left-hand rule is the key to this section — so make sure you know how to use it and understand what it all means. Remember that the direction of the magnetic field is from N to S, and that the current is from +ve to –ve — this is as important as using the correct hand. You need to get those right or it'll all go to pot...

Electromagnetic Induction

Producing electricity by waggling a wire about in a magnetic field sounds like magic — but it's real physics...

Charges Accumulate on a Conductor Moving Through a Magnetic Field

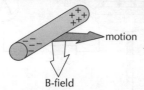

1) If a **conducting rod** moves perpendicular to a magnetic field, the **electrons** in the rod will experience a **force** (see p.144), which causes them to **accumulate** at one end of the rod.

2) This **induces** an **electromotive force (e.m.f.)** across the ends of the rod exactly as connecting a **battery** to it would. If the rod is part of a complete **circuit**, then an induced **current** will **flow** through it too.

3) This process of inducing an e.m.f. is called **electromagnetic induction**.

Changes in Magnetic Flux Induce an Electromotive Force

1) An **e.m.f.** is **induced** whenever there is **relative motion** between a **conductor** and **magnetic flux**.

2) The **conductor** can **move** and the **magnetic field** stay **still** or the **other way round** — you get an e.m.f. either way.

3) An **e.m.f.** is **induced** whenever **lines of flux** are **cut**.

4) **Flux cutting** always induces an e.m.f. but will only **induce** a **current** if the **circuit** is complete.

Think of the Magnetic Flux as the Total Number of Flux Lines in an Area

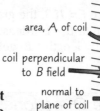

1) **Magnetic flux density, B**, measures the **strength** of the magnetic field **per unit area**.

2) So, the total **magnetic flux, ϕ**, passing through an **area, A**, perpendicular to a **magnetic field, B**, is defined as:

$$\phi = BA$$

(The unit of ϕ is the weber, Wb. 1 tesla = 1 Wb m^{-2}.)

3) When you move a **coil** in a magnetic field, the size of the e.m.f. induced depends on the **magnetic flux** passing through the coil, ϕ, and the **number of turns** on the coil, **N**. The product of these is called the **flux linkage, ϕN**. The **unit** of flux linkage, ϕN, is the **same** as for flux, ϕ — both are measured in **webers, Wb**.

4) The **size of the e.m.f.** also depends on **how quickly** the flux and the conductor move relative to one another — the **faster** you move a coil in a field, the **greater the size** of the e.m.f. induced.

These Results are Summed up by Faraday's Law

FARADAY'S LAW: The **induced e.m.f.** is **directly proportional** to the **rate of change of flux linkage**.

1) **Faraday's law** can be written as:
   (The minus sign comes from Lenz's Law — see the next page.)

$$\text{Induced e.m.f., } \varepsilon = -\frac{\text{flux linkage change}}{\text{time taken}} = -\frac{d(\phi N)}{dt}$$

There's more on differential equations like this on page 102.

2) The **size** of the e.m.f. is shown by the **gradient** of a graph of flux linkage (ϕN) against time.

3) The **area under** the graph of e.m.f. against time gives the **flux linkage change, $\Delta(\phi N)$**.

A graph of induced current against time will give the same shape graph as e.m.f. against time (but the area under the graph won't be equal to ϕN).

Example: A conducting rod of length L moves through a perpendicular uniform magnetic field, B, at a constant velocity, v. Show that the e.m.f. induced in the rod is equal to $-BLv$.

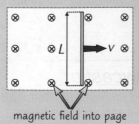

magnetic field into page

Distance travelled, $s = v\Delta t$ (distance = speed × time)

Area of flux it cuts, $A = Lv\Delta t$

Total magnetic flux cut through, $\phi = BA = BLv\Delta t$

Faraday's (and Lenz's) law gives $\varepsilon = -\frac{d(N\phi)}{dt} = -\frac{d\phi}{dt}$ (since N = 1)

So induced e.m.f., $\varepsilon = -\frac{d\phi}{dt} = -\frac{BLvdt}{dt} = -BLv$

You might be asked to find the e.m.f. induced on something more interesting than a rod, e.g. the Earth's magnetic field across the wingspan of a plane. Just think of it as a moving rod and use the equation as usual.

Electromagnetic Induction

The **Direction** of the **Induced E.m.f.** and **Current** are given by **Lenz's Law**

LENZ'S LAW: The induced e.m.f. is always in such a direction as to oppose the change that caused it.

1) The idea that an induced e.m.f. will **oppose** the change that caused it agrees with the principle of the **conservation of energy** — the **energy used** to pull a conductor through a magnetic field, against the **resistance** caused by magnetic **attraction**, is what **produces** the **induced current**.

2) **Lenz's law** can be used to find the **direction** of an **induced e.m.f.** and **current** in a conductor travelling at right angles to a magnetic field:

> 1) **Lenz's law** says that the **induced e.m.f.** will produce a force that **opposes** the motion of the conductor — in other words a **resistance**.
>
> 2) Using **Fleming's left-hand rule** (see p.144), point your thumb in the direction of the force of **resistance** — which is in the **opposite direction** to the motion of the conductor.
>
> 3) Your **second finger** will now give you the direction of the **induced e.m.f.**
>
> 4) If the conductor is **connected** as part of a **circuit**, a current will be induced in the **same direction** as the induced e.m.f.

That's why there's a minus sign in the equation for induced e.m.f. on the previous page.

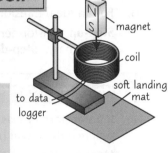

You can **Induce** an **Em.f.** by **Dropping** a **Magnet** Through a **Coil**

You can investigate induced e.m.f. by **dropping** a magnet through a **coil**. An e.m.f. is induced because the conducting coil **cuts** the **flux lines** of the magnet. By connecting a **data logger** or oscilloscope to the coil and recording the e.m.f. in the coil at **very small** time intervals (e.g. 0.002 s), you can plot a graph of induced e.m.f. against time.

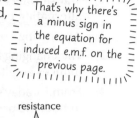

1) Peak e.m.f. occurs when the **change in flux linkage**, $\Delta(\phi N)$, is **greatest**, which is when each **pole** passes through the coil.

2) The **amplitude** of the **second** peak is **greater** because the **speed** of the magnet has increased (so Δt has decreased) and so the rate of change of flux is greater.

3) The **area** under each peak is the **same**, because the **total change** in ϕN must be **zero** (there was no e.m.f. before the magnet was dropped, and there is no e.m.f. after).

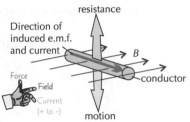

You'll get **different graphs** if you change the magnet or coil that you use.
If you use a **wider** coil, the magnitude of the induced e.m.f. will be **lower** than if you used a **narrow** coil because the coil will cut **fewer** flux lines.
If you use a **long** bar magnet, there will be a **longer period** between the peaks because there is only a change in ϕN when a pole enters or leaves the coil. The **second** peak will have an even **greater magnitude** and a **shorter duration** because the magnet will have been **accelerating** for **more time** when the second pole passes through the coil, and so will be travelling **faster** (so Δt will be even smaller and $d(\phi N)/dt$ will be even larger).

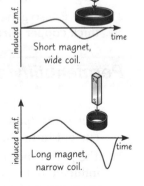

Practice Questions

Q1 What is the difference between magnetic flux density, magnetic flux and magnetic flux linkage?

Q2 Describe and explain the features of a graph of induced e.m.f. against time for a magnet falling through a coil.

Exam Question

Q1 A coil with 150 turns has area 0.23 m² and is placed at right angles to a magnetic field of 2.0×10^{-3} T.
   a) Calculate the magnetic flux passing through the coil and the magnetic flux linkage in the coil. **[2 marks]**
   b) Over a period of 2.5 seconds the magnetic flux is reduced uniformly to 3.5×10^{-4} Wb. Calculate the e.m.f. induced across the ends of the coil during this time. Explain whether this is positive or negative. **[3 marks]**

Beware — physics can induce extreme confusion...

OK... I know that might have seemed a bit scary... but the more you go through it, the more it stops being a big scary monster of doom and just becomes another couple of equations you have to remember.

Transformers and Dynamos

Transformers are like voltage aerobics instructors. They say step up, the voltage goes up. They say step down, the voltage goes down. They say star jump, and the voltage does nothing because neither of them are alive — it's just induction.

Transformers Work by Electromagnetic Induction

1) **Transformers** are devices that make use of electromagnetic induction to **change** the size of the **voltage** for an **alternating current**. They use the principle of flux linking in two coils of wire, wrapped around an iron core.

2) Alternating current flowing in the **primary coil** produces **magnetic flux**.

3) The changing **magnetic field** passes through the **iron core** to the **secondary coil**, where it **induces** an alternating **voltage** (e.m.f.) of the same frequency as the input voltage.

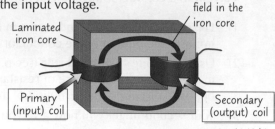

4) From Faraday's and Lenz's laws (p.146-147), the **induced** e.m.f.s in both the **primary** and **secondary** coils can be calculated:

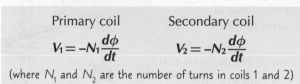

Primary coil
$$V_1 = -N_1 \frac{d\phi}{dt}$$

Secondary coil
$$V_2 = -N_2 \frac{d\phi}{dt}$$

(where N_1 and N_2 are the number of turns in coils 1 and 2)

5) These can be combined to give the equation for an **ideal transformer**: An ideal transformer is one that is **100% efficient**. Unless otherwise specified in a question, you can assume that transformers are ideal.

$$\frac{V_1}{V_2} = \frac{N_1}{N_2}$$

You won't be given these equations in the exam — make sure you learn them.

6) For an ideal transformer, power in = power out. Power is current × voltage, so $I_1V_1 = I_2V_2$, so:

$$\frac{I_2}{I_1} = \frac{N_1}{N_2}$$

7) **Step-up** transformers **increase** the **voltage** by having **more turns** on the **secondary** coil than the primary. **Step-down** transformers **reduce** the voltage by having **fewer** turns on the secondary coil.

Transformers are Not 100% Efficient

1) If a transformer was **100% efficient** the **power in** would **equal** the **power out**. However, in practice there will be **small losses** of **power** from the transformer, mostly in the form of **heat**.

2) **Heat** can be produced by **eddy currents** in the transformer's iron core — currents **induced** by the changing magnetic flux in the core. This effect is reduced by **laminating** the core with layers of **insulation**.

3) Heat is also generated by **resistance** in the coils — to minimise this, **thick copper wire** is used, which has a **low resistance**.

Permeability and Conductivity Affect Transformer Dimensions

1) Magnetic flux lines are always **continuous** and form a **closed loop**, so you can think of the current-carrying coil as the "**power supply**" of a **magnetic circuit** (although nothing actually flows anywhere). The number of **current turns**, NI, is equivalent to the "**e.m.f.**", and the **magnetic flux** is equivalent to the "**current**".

2) The **permeance** of an object is like its 'conductance' (p.30) — it's the **amount of flux induced** in it for a given number of current turns that surround it. The **higher** the **permeance** of an object, the **greater** the **amount of flux** induced.

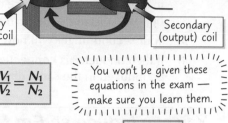

permeance, $\Lambda = \dfrac{\mu A}{L}$

3) Both permeance and conductance are **inversely proportional** to the **length** of the object, and **proportional** to the **cross-sectional area**.

Where A is the cross-sectional area, L is the length and μ is the permeability of the material.

4) When you're **designing** a transformer, you want to make the **permeance** of the core as **high** as possible to get the maximum flux induced in it. Ideally you want the core to be **short** (low L) and **fat** (high A) and made from a **high permeability** material like **iron**.

The permeability of a material, μ, is the permeance per unit cross-section of a unit length of material.

5) Unfortunately, you also want the **conductance** of the **copper coils** used on a transformer to be as **high** as possible — to limit **energy loss**. So you want to make the right **number of turns** with the **shortest** piece of wire possible, i.e. use small-radius (tight) coils. This doesn't really work when you have a fat core to wrap them around, so you have to try to get a **balance** in **dimensions** to get the **best** overall transformer performance.

6) Unlike an electric circuit, a magnetic circuit will still work if there's an **air** (or vacuum) **gap** in it. So in the case of transformers, if there's an air gap in an otherwise iron core, magnetic flux stills 'flows' around the magnetic circuit. But because air has a very **low permeability** compared to iron, the total amount of flux in the magnetic circuit would be **dramatically lower** than without the air gap.

Transformers and Dynamos

You can *Investigate* the *Turns*, *Voltage* and *Current* in a *Transformer*

To investigate the relationship between **number of turns** and the **voltages** across the coils:

1) Set up the equipment as shown. Put two C-cores together and wrap wire around each to make the coils. Begin with 5 turns in the primary coil and 10 in the secondary coil (a **ratio** of 1:2).

2) Turn on the a.c. supply to the primary coil. **Use a low voltage** — remember transformers **increase voltage**, so make sure you keep it at a safe level. Record the voltage across each coil.

3) Keeping V_1 the same so it's a fair test, repeat the experiment with different ratios of turns. Try 1:1 and 2:1. Divide N_2 by N_1 and V_2 by V_1. You should find that for each ratio of turns, $\frac{N_2}{N_1} = \frac{V_2}{V_1}$.

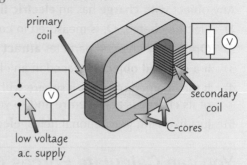

To investigate the relationship between **number of turns**, **voltage** across and **current** of the transformer coils:

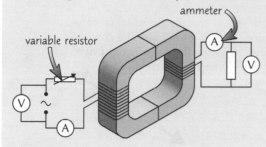

1) Use the same equipment as above, but add a **variable resistor** to the primary coil circuit and an **ammeter** to both circuits.

2) Turn on the power supply and **record** the **current through** and **voltage across** each coil.

3) Leaving the number of turns **constant**, adjust the variable resistor to change the input current. Record the current and voltage for each coil, then **repeat** this process for a **range** of input currents.

4) You should find that for each current, $\frac{N_2}{N_1} = \frac{V_2}{V_1} = \frac{I_1}{I_2}$.

Dynamos Convert *Kinetic Energy* into *Electrical Energy*

1) We've seen that **relative motion** of a **coil** and **flux** results in a change in **flux linkage** and an **e.m.f.** is induced in the coil (p.146).

2) **Dynamos**, or generators, **induce** an electric **current** by **rotating** a **coil** in a magnetic field.

3) The output **voltage** and **current** change direction with every **half rotation** of the coil, producing **alternating current** (**a.c.**).

4) A **split ring commutator** is used to change this **a.c. current** to **direct current** (**d.c.**). This current is carried to an external circuit using **brushes**.

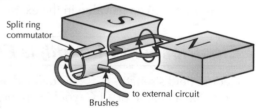

Practice Questions

Q1 Explain, in terms of flux, how a transformer works. How could you reduce losses in the core due to eddy currents?

Q2 What is meant by the permeance of an object? What is it equivalent to in an electrical circuit?

Q3 What is the effect on the permeance of an iron core transformer of making it:
a) fatter, b) shorter, c) have an air gap?

Q4 How could you demonstrate the relationship between the number of turns and the voltages across transformer coils?

Q5 Describe what a dynamo is, and explain how one works.

Exam Question

Q1 An ideal transformer with 150 turns in the primary coil has an input voltage of 9.0 V
a) State what is meant by an 'ideal transformer'. [1 mark]
b) Calculate the number of turns needed in the secondary coil to step up the voltage to 45 V. [2 marks]
c) The input current for the transformer is 1.5 A. Calculate the output current of the transformer. [2 marks]

Breathe a sigh of relief and pat yourself on the back...

...well done, you've reached the end of the section. Don't let all those equations get you down — once you've learnt them and can use them blindfolded, even the trickiest looking exam question will be a walk in the park...

Electric Fields

*Unlike gravitational fields (p.122), electric fields can be attractive or repulsive. It's all to do with **charge**.*

There is an Electric Field around a Charged Object

Any object with **charge** has an **electric field** around it — the region where it can attract or repel other charges.

1) Electric charge, **Q**, is measured in **coulombs** (C) and can be either positive or negative.

2) **Oppositely** charged particles **attract** each other. **Like** charges **repel**.

3) If a **charged object** is placed in an electric field, then it will experience a **force**.

4) If the charged object is a **sphere** with **evenly distributed** charge (**spherically symmetrical**), it will act as if all of its **charge** is at its **centre** and so you can model it as a **point charge** (at distances larger than its radius).

5) Just like with gravitational fields, **electric fields** can be represented by **field lines**.

You can Calculate Forces using Coulomb's Law

You'll need **Coulomb's law** to work out **F** — the force of attraction or repulsion between two point charges (or two objects that behave as point charges).

COULOMB'S LAW:

$$F_{electric} = \frac{kqQ}{r^2} \quad \text{where} \quad k = \frac{1}{4\pi\varepsilon_0}$$

ε_0 = permittivity of free space, equal to $8.85 \times 10^{-12}\ C^2N^{-1}m^{-2}$.
q and Q are the charges (in C)
r is the distance between q and Q (in m)

If the charges are **opposite** then the force is **attractive**. *F* will be **negative**.

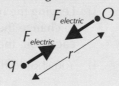

If q and Q are **like** charges then the force is **repulsive**, and *F* will be **positive**.

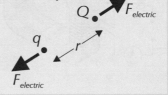

1) The force on q is always **equal** and **opposite** to the force on Q.

2) It's an **inverse square law** (like on p.122). The further apart the charges are, the weaker the force between them.

3) k is called the electric force constant. It's equal to about $9.0 \times 10^9\ Nm^2C^{-2}$. You'll be given its value in the exam, either in the data and formulae booklet, or in the question.

Electric Field Strength is Force per Unit Charge

Electric field strength, $E_{electric}$, is defined as the **force per unit positive charge** — the force that a charge of +1 C would experience if it was placed in the electric field.

$$E_{electric} = \frac{F_{electric}}{q}$$

$F_{electric}$ is the force on a 'test' charge q.

1) $E_{electric}$ is a **vector** pointing in the **direction** that a **positive charge** would **move**.

2) The units of $E_{electric}$ are **newtons per coulomb** (NC^{-1}).

3) Field strength often depends on **where you are** in the field (see below).

4) A **point charge** — or any body that behaves as if all its charge is concentrated at the centre — has a **radial** field.

In a Radial Field, $E_{electric}$ is Inversely Proportional to r^2

1) In a **radial field**, $E_{electric}$ depends on the distance r from the point charge Q (or from the centre of the source of the radial field).

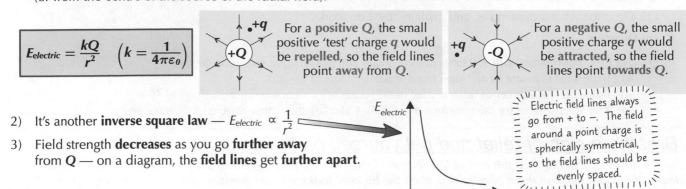

$$E_{electric} = \frac{kQ}{r^2} \quad \left(k = \frac{1}{4\pi\varepsilon_0}\right)$$

For a **positive Q**, the small positive 'test' charge q would be repelled, so the field lines point **away** from Q.

For a **negative Q**, the small positive charge q would be attracted, so the field lines point **towards** Q.

2) It's another **inverse square law** — $E_{electric} \propto \frac{1}{r^2}$

3) Field strength **decreases** as you go **further away** from **Q** — on a diagram, the **field lines** get **further apart**.

Electric field lines always go from + to −. The field around a point charge is spherically symmetrical, so the field lines should be evenly spaced.

Electric Fields

A **Charge** in an Electric Field has **Electric Potential Energy**

The electric potential energy is the **work** that would need to be done to move a small charge **q** from infinity to a distance **r** away from a point charge **Q**.

$$\text{Electric potential energy} = \frac{kQq}{r} \quad \left(k = \frac{1}{4\pi\varepsilon_0}\right)$$

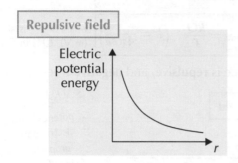

Repulsive field

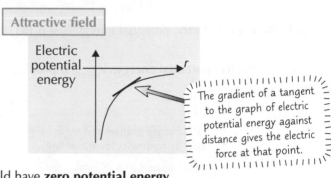

Attractive field

The gradient of a tangent to the graph of electric potential energy against distance gives the electric force at that point.

1) At an **infinite** distance from **Q**, a charged particle **q** would have **zero potential energy**.

2) In a **repulsive** force field (e.g. **Q** and **q** are both positive) you have to **do work** against the repulsion to bring **q** closer to **Q**. The charge **q gains** potential energy as **r decreases**.

3) In an **attractive** field (e.g. **Q** negative and **q** positive) the charge **q gains** potential energy as **r increases**.

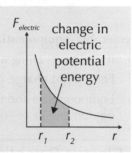

If you **move** a unit charge between two distances, r_1 and r_2, and **change** its **electric potential energy**, you have to apply a **force** and do **work**. The force applied is equal to the electric force. For a point charge **q** (and therefore also for a spherically symmetric charge, see p.150) you can plot the **electric force**, $F_{electric}$, against the **distance**, **r**, from the charge producing the **electric field**, **Q**.

This is an **inverse square law** (p.122) and the **area** under the curve (p.124) between r_1 and r_2 gives the **change** in electric potential energy.

Practice Questions

Q1 Write down Coulomb's law.

Q2 Draw the electric field lines due to a positive charge, and due to a negative charge.

Q3 What is meant by electric field strength? Write down an equation for the electric field strength of any electric field.

Q4 Using your answers to Q2 and Q3, write down a formula for the electric field strength at a distance r away from a point charge Q.

Q5 Draw a graph of $F_{electric}$ against r for the field described by Coulomb's law.
What does the area under the graph between distances r_1 and r_2 represent?

Exam Question

$e = -1.60 \times 10^{-19}$ C, $\varepsilon_0 = 8.85 \times 10^{-12}$ $C^2N^{-1}m^{-2}$ (Fm^{-1}).

Q1 a) Find the electric field strength at a distance of 1.00×10^{-10} m from a proton. [2 marks]

b) A point charge of 6.4×10^{-19} C is placed at a distance of 3.25×10^{-9} m from the proton.
Calculate the electric potential energy of this point charge. [2 marks]

c) Sketch a graph showing how the electric potential energy of the point charge depends on the distance, r, from the proton. [1 mark]

d) State the quantity that is represented by the gradient of this graph at a specific point. [1 mark]

Electric fields — one way to roast beef...
At least you get a choice with electric fields — positive or negative, attractive or repulsive, chocolate or strawberry...

Electric Potential

Electric potential is all to do with how much energy a charge has based on where it is in an electric field.

Electric Potential *is Potential Energy per Unit Charge*

Electric potential, $V_{electric}$, is electric **potential energy** per **unit positive charge**. The electric potential at a point in an electric field is the **work done** to bring a **unit positive charge** from **infinity** to that point. This means that at **infinity**, the **electric potential** will be **zero**.

For a small charge, q, at a distance r away from a point charge, Q, $V_{electric} = \dfrac{\text{electric potential energy}}{q}$.

Substituting for electric potential energy (see p.151) gives: $\boxed{V_{electric} = \dfrac{kQ}{r} \quad \left(k = \dfrac{1}{4\pi\varepsilon_0} \right)}$ where $V_{electric}$ is electric potential (in V), Q is in C and r is in m.

As with **electric potential energy**, $V_{electric}$ is **positive** when the force is **repulsive**, and **negative** when it is **attractive**.

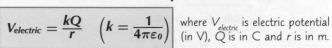

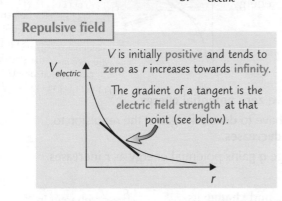

Repulsive field

$V_{electric}$

V is initially positive and tends to zero as r increases towards infinity.

The gradient of a tangent is the electric field strength at that point (see below).

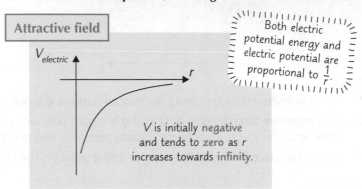

Attractive field

$V_{electric}$

r

V is initially negative and tends to zero as r increases towards infinity.

Both electric potential energy and electric potential are proportional to $\frac{1}{r}$.

Remember, **equipotentials** show all the points in a field which have the same **potential** (p.125).

1) If you travel along a line of **equipotential** you don't lose or gain energy (no work is done).

2) For a **point charge** or **spherically symmetric charge** the equipotentials are spherical surfaces.

3) Equipotentials and field lines are perpendicular. The diagram shows equipotentials of –60, –50, and –40 V around a point charge Q.

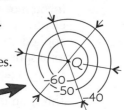

Electric Potential *is Linked to Electric Field Strength*

The **electric field strength**, $E_{electric}$ is equal to the negative of the rate of change of electric potential with distance:

$\boxed{E_{electric} = -\dfrac{dV_{electric}}{dr}}$

There's a minus sign because to increase the charge's potential (and potential energy), you have to do work against the force — i.e. they 'act' in opposite directions.

This means that $E_{electric}$ can also be measured in Vm^{-1} and the **gradient** of a graph of $V_{electric}$ against r is $E_{electric}$, as you've seen above.

You also need to know that the **area** under a graph of $E_{electric}$ against r between two distances gives $\Delta V_{electric}$.

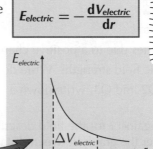

Field Strength *is the Same Everywhere in a Uniform Field*

A **uniform field** can be produced by connecting two **parallel plates** to the opposite poles of a battery.

1) Field strength $E_{electric}$ is the **same** at **all points** between the two plates and is given by:

$\boxed{E_{electric} = \dfrac{V}{d}}$

where V is the **potential difference** between the plates and d is the distance between them.

+ 400 V

+ 300 V

+ 200 V

+ 100 V

0 V

The **field lines** are **parallel** to each other and evenly spaced.

The **equipotential surfaces** are **parallel** to the **plates**, and **perpendicular** to the **field lines**. They're also evenly spaced and symmetric.

2) This formula comes from the equation above for $E_{electric}$, the rate of change of potential is constant for a uniform field.

Electric Potential

There are **Similarities** between **Gravitational** and **Electric Fields**...

If a lot of the stuff on the previous couple of pages sounded strangely familiar it could be because it's very similar to the stuff on gravitational fields (or it could be because you've learnt it before — this is a revision book after all).

Anyway, there are **four** big **similarities** between **electric** and **gravitational fields** that you need to know — read on.

Gravitational field strength, g, is **force** per **unit mass**.	Electric field strength, $E_{electric}$ is **force** per **unit positive charge**.
Newton's law of gravitation for the **force** between two point masses is an **inverse square law**.	Coulomb's law for the electric **force** between two point charges is also an **inverse square law**.
The **field lines** for a point mass (or a spherically symmetric mass)...	The **field lines** for a **negative** point charge (or a spherically symmetric charge)...
Gravitational potential, V_{grav}, is **potential energy** per **unit mass** and is **zero** at **infinity**.	Electric potential, $V_{electric}$ is **potential energy** per **unit positive charge** and is **zero** at **infinity**.

... and **Three Differences** too

Gravitational and electric fields aren't all the same — you need to know the **three main differences**:

1) Gravitational forces are always **attractive**. Electric forces can be either **attractive** or **repulsive**.
2) Objects can be **shielded** from **electric** fields, but not from gravitational fields.
3) The size of an **electric** force depends on the **medium** between the charges, e.g. plastic or air. For gravitational forces, this makes no difference.

> Different materials have different permittivities. If you're not in free space (a vacuum), you'd use the permittivity of the substance, ε, instead of ε_0.

Practice Questions

Q1 What is meant by 'electric potential'?
Q2 State the formula for finding the electric potential in a radial field.
Q3 Sketch the equipotential surfaces around a point charge.
Q4 Write down the formula relating electric potential $V_{electric}$ and electric field strength $E_{electric}$.
Q5 Describe how $E_{electric}$ can be found from a graph of $V_{electric}$ against r, and how the change in $V_{electric}$ can be found from a graph of $E_{electric}$ against r.

Exam Questions

$e = -1.60 \times 10^{-19}$ C, $\varepsilon_0 = 8.85 \times 10^{-12}$ C^{2}N^{-1}m^{-2} (Fm^{-1}).

Q1 Point A is 1.00 mm away from an electron. Calculate the electric potential at point A. [2 marks]

Q2 A spherical conductor with a radius of 3.5×10^{-3} m is charged such that its surface has an electric potential of 500.0 V. By modelling the sphere as a point charge, find its charge. [2 marks]

Q3 a) Two parallel plates are separated by a gap of 4.5 mm and connected to a 1500 V dc supply. What is the electric field strength between the plates? Give the unit and state the direction of the field. [2 marks]

b) The plates are then pulled further apart so that the distance between them is doubled. The voltage is adjusted so that the electric field strength remains the same. State the new voltage between the plates. [1 mark]

Q4 State two similarities and one difference between gravitational and electric fields. [3 marks]

I prefer gravitational fields — electric fields are repulsive...

Revising fields is a bit like a buy-one-get-one-free sale — you learn all about gravitational fields and they throw electric fields in for free. You just have to remember to change m for Q and G for 1/4πε₀... okay, so it's not quite a BOGOF sale. Maybe more like a buy-one-get-one-half-price sale... anyway, you get the point — go learn some stuff.

Millikan's Oil-Drop Experiment

You'll probably know that the fundamental unit of charge, i.e. the size of the charge on an electron, is 1.60 × 10⁻¹⁹ C, and that all other charges are always exact multiples of this value. But at the beginning of the 20th century, many physicists thought that charge was a continuous variable that could take any value at all — Millikan showed this wasn't true.

Millikan's Experiment used Stoke's Law

1) Before you start thinking about Millikan's experiment, you need a bit of **extra theory**.

2) When you drop an object into a fluid, like air, it experiences a **viscous drag** force. This force acts in the **opposite direction** to the velocity of the object, and is due to the **viscosity** of the fluid.

3) You can calculate this viscous force on a spherical object using **Stoke's law**:

$$F = 6\pi\eta rv$$

where η is the viscosity of the fluid, r is the radius of the object and v is the velocity of the object.

Millikan's Experiment — the Basic Set-Up

1) The **atomiser** created a **fine mist** of oil drops that were **charged** by **friction** as they left the atomiser (positively if they lost electrons, negatively if they gained electrons).

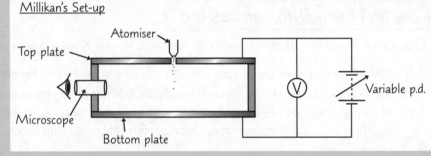

Millikan's Set-up

Atomiser
Top plate
Microscope
Bottom plate
Variable p.d.

2) Some of the drops fell through a **hole** in the top plate and could be viewed through the **microscope**. (The eyepiece carried a **scale** to measure distances — and so **velocities** — accurately.)

3) When he was ready, Millikan could apply a **potential difference** between the two plates, producing a **field** that exerted an upwards **force** on the charged drops. By **adjusting** the p.d., he could vary the strength of the field.

To give you a feel for the **size** of the apparatus, Millikan's plates were circular, with a diameter of about the width of this page. They were separated by about 1.5 cm.

Before the Field is Switched on, there's only Gravity and the Viscous Force

1) With the electric field turned off, the forces acting on each oil drop are:

a) the **weight** of the drop (equal to mg) — acting downwards

b) the **viscous force** from the air — acting upwards

Millikan had to take account of things like upthrust as well, but you don't have to worry about that — keep it simple.

2) The drop will reach **terminal velocity** (i.e. it will stop accelerating) when these two forces are equal. So, from Stoke's law (see above):

$$mg = 6\pi\eta rv$$

It's assumed that the droplets are spherical for this experiment.

3) Since the **mass** of the drop is the **volume** of the drop multiplied by the **density**, ρ, of the oil, this can be rewritten as:

$$\frac{4}{3}\pi r^3 \rho g = 6\pi\eta rv \Rightarrow r^2 = \frac{9\eta v}{2\rho g}$$

Millikan measured η and ρ in separate experiments, so he could now calculate r
— ready to be used when he switched on the electric field...

Millikan's Oil-Drop Experiment

Then he **Turned On** the **Electric Field**...

1) The field introduced a **third major factor** — an **electric force** on each drop.

2) Millikan adjusted the applied p.d. until each drop was **stationary**. Since the **viscous force** is proportional to the **velocity** of the object, once each drop stopped moving, the viscous force **disappeared**.

3) Now the only two forces acting on each oil drop were:

   a) the **weight** of the drop — acting downwards

   b) the force due to the **uniform electric field** — acting upwards

   Only the negatively charged droplets will experience an upwards force due to the electric field. The forces on the positively charged drops both act downwards, so the positively charged drops weren't of interest in this experiment.

4) The **electric force** and the **p.d.** are related to the **electric field strength** by the equations from pages 150 and 152:

   $$E_{electric} = \frac{F_{electric}}{q} \qquad E_{electric} = \frac{V}{d}$$

5) Combining these equations gives: $F_{electric} = \frac{qV}{d}$ where q is the charge on the oil drop, V is the p.d. between the plates and d is the distance between the plates.

6) Since the drop is **stationary**, this electric force must be equal to the weight, so: $\frac{qV}{d} = mg = \frac{4}{3}\pi r^3 \rho g$

   The first part of the experiment gave a value for r, so the **only unknown** in this equation is q.

7) So Millikan could use this equation to find the **charge on the drop**. He repeated the experiment for hundreds of drops — the charge on any drop was always a **whole number multiple** of **1.60×10^{-19} C**.

These Results Suggested that **Charge** was **Quantised**

1) This result was **really significant**. Millikan concluded that charge can **never exist** in **smaller** quantities than 1.60×10^{-19} C. He assumed that this was the size of the **charge** carried by an **electron**.

2) Later experiments confirmed that **both** these things are true.

   Charge is "quantised".
   It exists in discrete "packets" of size **1.60×10^{-19} C** — the **fundamental unit of charge**, e.
   This is the size of the charge carried by **one electron**.

3) The charge on an electron is used to define a **unit of energy** — the **electron volt** (eV). 1eV = **1.60×10^{-19} J** (p.62).

Practice Questions

Q1 List the forces that act on an oil drop in Millikan's experiment:
   a) with the drop falling downwards at terminal velocity but with no applied electrical field,
   b) when the drop is stationary, with an electrical field applied.

Q2 Explain how Millikan's oil drop experiment provided evidence for the quantisation of the charge on an electron.

Exam Question

Q1 An oil drop of mass 1.63×10^{-14} kg is held stationary in the space between two charged plates 3.00 cm apart. The potential difference between the plates is 5000 V. The density of the oil used is 880 kg m^{-3}.

   a) Describe the relative magnitude and direction of the forces acting on the oil drop. [2 marks]

   b) Calculate the charge on the oil drop using $g = 9.81$ Nkg^{-1}.
      Give your answer in terms of e, the size of the charge on an electron. [3 marks]

   The electric field is switched off and the oil drop falls towards the bottom plate.

   c) Explain why the oil drop reaches terminal velocity as it falls. [3 marks]

   d) Calculate the terminal velocity of the oil drop using $\eta = 1.84 \times 10^{-5}$ kg m^{-1}s^{-1}. [3 marks]

So next time you need 1.5×10^{-19} coulombs — tough...

This was a huge leap. Along with the photoelectric effect this experiment marked the beginning of quantum physics.

Charged Particles in Magnetic Fields

Charged particles can be deflected by magnetic fields because the field exerts a force on the particles. This is the same effect that you saw in Module 6: Section 1 where a magnetic field exerted a force on a current-carrying wire.

Forces Act on Charged Particles in Magnetic Fields

Electric current in a wire is caused by the **flow** of negatively **charged** electrons. These charged particles are affected by **magnetic fields** — so a current-carrying wire experiences a **force** in a magnetic field (see page 144).

1) The equation for the **force** exerted on a **current-carrying wire** in a **magnetic field** perpendicular to the current is:

   Equation 1: $\boxed{F = BIl}$ B is the magnetic flux density in teslas (T), I is the current in A, l is the length in m

2) To see how this relates to **charged particles** moving through a wire, you need to know that electric **current**, I, is the flow of **charge**, q, per unit **time**, t. $\longrightarrow$ $\boxed{I = \dfrac{q}{t}}$

3) A charged particle which moves a **distance** l in **time** t has a **velocity**, v:

   $\boxed{v = \dfrac{l}{t} \Rightarrow t = \dfrac{l}{v}}$

   In many exam questions, q is the size of the charge on the electron, which is 1.60×10^{-19} coulombs.

4) Substituting this equation for time into the previous equation for current gives the **current** in terms of the **velocity** of the **charge** flowing through the **wire**:

   Equation 2: $\boxed{I = \dfrac{qv}{l}}$

5) Putting **equation 2** back into **equation 1** gives the **electromagnetic force** on the wire as: $\boxed{F = qvB}$

   B is the magnetic flux density in teslas (T)
   v is the particle velocity in ms^{-1}
   q is the charge on the particle in C.

6) You can use this equation to find the **force** acting on a **single charged particle moving through, and perpendicular to, a magnetic field.**

> **Example:** An electron is travelling perpendicular to a uniform magnetic field of strength 2.0 T. If the electron is travelling at 2.0×10^4 ms^{-1} through the magnetic field, what is the force acting on the electron? (The charge on an electron is -1.60×10^{-19} C.)
>
> $F = qvB$, so $F = (-1.60 \times 10^{-19}) \times (2.0 \times 10^4) \times 2.0 = -6.4 \times 10^{-15}$ N

Charged Particles in a Magnetic Field are Deflected in a Circular Path

1) By **Fleming's left-hand rule** (p.144) the force on a **moving charge** in a magnetic field is always **perpendicular** to its **direction of travel**.

2) Mathematically, that is the condition for **circular** motion (p.120).

3) This effect is found in **particle accelerators** such as **cyclotrons** and **synchrotrons** (see pages 166-167), which use **electric and magnetic fields** to accelerate particles to very **high energies** along circular paths.

4) The **radius of curvature** of the **path** of a charged particle moving through a magnetic field gives you information about the particle's **charge** and **mass** — this means you can **identify different particles** by studying how they're **deflected** (see next page).

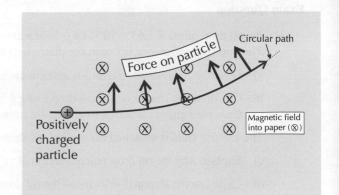

Charged Particles in Magnetic Fields

Centripetal Force Tells Us About a Particle's Path

The centripetal force and the electromagnetic force are equivalent for a charged particle travelling along a circular path.

1) For uniform circular motion **Newton's second law** gives:

$$F = \frac{mv^2}{r}$$

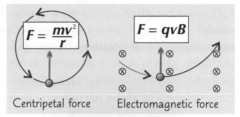

2) So, for a **charged particle** following a **circular** path in a **magnetic field** (where $F = qvB$):

$$qvB = \frac{mv^2}{r}$$

Centripetal force   Electromagnetic force

3) Rearranging gives: $r = \frac{mv}{qB}$ Where: m is the mass of the particle, v is its speed and r is the radius of the circular path.

4) So, different charged particles will have paths with different radii — the higher the ratio of m to q, the larger the radius of the path.

Eric and Phil were *not* lost. They'd just accidentally demonstrated the path of a charge in a magnetic field.

Example: A magnetic field of strength 0.080 T is used to move an electron in a circular path with a radius of 1.8×10^{-4} m at a constant speed. Calculate the speed of the electron.

1) The force on a charged particle moving in a magnetic field, $F = qvB$.

2) The particles move in a circle, so F gives the centripetal force $\Rightarrow qvB = \frac{mv^2}{r}$

3) Rearranging for v gives: $v = \frac{qBr}{m}$ The size of the charge on an electron is 1.60×10^{-19} C (only the magnitude of the charge is used here — we're calculating speed, not velocity).

4) Substitute the values: $v = \frac{(1.60 \times 10^{-19}) \times 0.080 \times (1.8 \times 10^{-4})}{9.11 \times 10^{-31}} = 2.5 \times 10^6$ ms^{-1} (to 2 s.f.)

The mass of an electron is 9.11×10^{-31} kg.

The charge and mass of an electron are given in the data and formulae booklet in the exam.

Practice Questions

Q1 Write down an equation to calculate the force on a charged particle moving in a magnetic field.

Q2 Explain why the force experienced by a moving charge in a magnetic field causes it to move with circular motion.

Q3 Explain how charged particles can be identified as they move through a magnetic field.

Exam Questions

$m_e = 9.11 \times 10^{-31}$ kg, e = magnitude of the charge on an electron = 1.60×10^{-19} C

Q1 a) An electron travels at a velocity of 5.00×10^6 ms^{-1} through a perpendicular magnetic field of 0.770 T. Find the magnitude of the force acting on the electron. [2 marks]

b) An electric field is then applied, which causes the electron to travel in a straight line through the magnetic field. Calculate the electric field strength of the electric field. [2 marks]

Q2 An electron is accelerated to a velocity of 2.3×10^7 ms^{-1} by a particle accelerator. The electron moves in a circular path perpendicular to a magnetic field of 0.6 mT.

a) Use the equations for electromagnetic and centripetal force to show that $qB = \frac{mv}{r}$. [2 marks]

b) Use the relation from part a) to calculate the radius of the electron's path. [1 mark]

Hold on to your hats folks — this is starting to get tricky...

Basically, the main thing you need to know here is that a magnetic field will exert a force on a charged particle, making it follow a circular path. There's even a handy equation to work out the force on a charged particle moving through a magnetic field — it might not impress your friends, but it will impress the examiner, so learn it.

Scattering to Determine Structure

By firing radiation at different materials, you can take a sneaky beaky at their internal structures...

Rutherford's Experiment Disproved the Thomson Model

1) Following his discovery of the electron in the late 19th century, **J.J. Thomson** proposed the **Thomson model** of the atom, also known as the '**plum pudding**' model. This model said that atoms were made up of a globule of **positive charge**, with **negatively charged electrons sprinkled** in it, like fruit in a plum pudding. It was widely accepted at the time, until the **Rutherford scattering experiment** of 1909.

2) In Rutherford's laboratory, **Hans Geiger** and **Ernest Marsden** studied the scattering of **alpha particles** by **thin metal foils**.

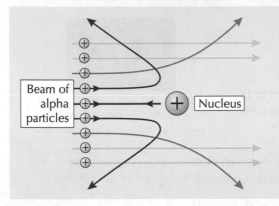

1) A stream of alpha particles from a radioactive source was fired at very thin gold foil.

2) Geiger and Marsden recorded the number of alpha particles scattered at different angles.

3) Geiger and Marsden observed that alpha particles occasionally scatter at angles greater than 90°. This can only be possible if they're striking something more massive than themselves.

Rutherford's Model of the Atom — The Nuclear Model

This experiment led Rutherford to some **important conclusions**:

Alpha particles are made up of two protons and two neutrons, so they have an overall positive charge (see p.170).

1) Most of the fast, charged alpha particles went **straight through** the foil. So the atom is mainly **empty space**.

2) **Some** of the alpha particles were **deflected** through **large angles**, so the **centre** of the atom must have a **large, positive charge** to repel them. Rutherford named this the **nucleus**.

3) Very few particles were deflected by angles greater than **90 degrees**, so the nucleus must be **tiny**.

4) Most of the **mass** must be in the nucleus, since the fast alpha particles (with high momentum) are deflected by the nucleus.

So most of the **mass** and the **positive charge** in an atom must be contained within a **tiny**, **central** nucleus.

When an alpha particle gets close enough to the nucleus, the electrostatic force (see p.150) between the positively charged nucleus and the positively charged alpha particle results in a repulsion between the two. This is what causes some of the alpha particles to scatter.

Atoms are made up of Protons, Neutrons and Electrons

Inside **every atom**, there's a **nucleus** containing **protons** and **neutrons**. **Protons** and **neutrons** are both known as **nucleons**. **Orbiting** this core are the **electrons**. This is the **nuclear model** of the atom.

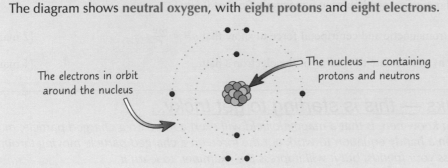

The diagram shows neutral oxygen, with eight protons and eight electrons.

The electrons in orbit around the nucleus

The nucleus — containing protons and neutrons

Forget Rutherford — James reckoned his model would be the best yet.

Scattering to Determine Structure

You can **Estimate** the **Closest Approach** of a **Scattered Particle**

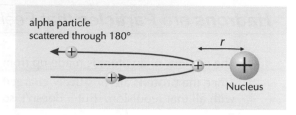

alpha particle scattered through 180°

Nucleus

1) When you fire an alpha particle at a gold nucleus, you can estimate its distance of **closest approach** if you know the alpha particle's **initial kinetic energy**.

2) An alpha particle that 'bounces back' and is deflected through 180° will have momentarily stopped a short distance from the nucleus. It does this at the point where its **electric potential energy** (see p.151) **equals** its **initial kinetic energy**.

3) It's just conservation of energy — and you can use it to find how close the particle can get to the nucleus:

Initial K.E. = electric potential energy $= \dfrac{kq_{alpha}Q_{gold}}{r}$ where $k = \dfrac{1}{4\pi\varepsilon_0}$

You might also see k given as 8.98×10^9 Nm^2C^{-2} (to 3 s.f.)

Q_{gold} is the charge on a gold nucleus in C,
q_{alpha} is the charge on an alpha particle in C,
ε_o is the permittivity of free space, 8.85×10^{-12} Fm^{-1}

4) The **distance of closest approach** is given by r in the equation above.

5) To find the charge of a nucleus, you need to know the atom's **proton number**, **Z** — that tells you how many protons are in the nucleus.

6) A proton has a charge of **+e** (where e is the size of the charge on an electron, 1.60×10^{-19} C), so the charge of a nucleus must be **+Ze**. The charge on an alpha particle is **+2e**.

If you need to calculate the force experienced by the particle as it approaches the nucleus, remember $F_{electric} = \dfrac{kqQ}{r^2}$ (p.150).

Example: An alpha particle with an initial kinetic energy of 6.0 MeV is fired at a gold nucleus ($Z_{gold} = 79$). Calculate the closest approach of the alpha particle to the nucleus.

Initial K.E. = 6.0 MeV = 6.0×10^6 eV

Convert this energy into joules: $6.0 \times 10^6 \times 1.60 \times 10^{-19} = 9.6 \times 10^{-13}$ J

1 eV = 1.60×10^{-19} J.

So, at the distance of closest approach, electric potential energy $= \dfrac{kq_{alpha}Q_{gold}}{r} = \dfrac{q_{alpha}Q_{gold}}{4\pi\varepsilon_0 r} = 9.6 \times 10^{-13}$ J

Rearrange to get $r = \dfrac{q_{alpha}Q_{gold}}{9.6 \times 10^{-13} \times 4\pi\varepsilon_0} = \dfrac{(2 \times 1.60 \times 10^{-19}) \times (79 \times 1.60 \times 10^{-19})}{(9.6 \times 10^{-13}) \times 4\pi \times (8.85 \times 10^{-12})} = 3.788... \times 10^{-14}$

$= 3.8 \times 10^{-14}$ m (to 2 s.f.)

Practice Questions

Q1 Sketch a diagram to show the paths of alpha particles when they are scattered by a nucleus in Rutherford's gold foil experiment.

Q2 Describe the structure of the atom according to the nuclear model.

Q3 Explain how alpha-particle scattering gives evidence for a small massive nucleus.

Exam Questions

Q1 A beam of alpha particles is directed onto a very thin gold film.

a) Explain how alpha particles are scattered by atomic nuclei. [3 marks]

b) Explain why the majority of the alpha particles are not scattered. [1 mark]

Q2 A proton is fired at an aluminium nucleus ($Z_{aluminium} = 13$). It has an initial kinetic energy of 4.0 MeV. Show that the closest approach of the proton to the nucleus is 4.7×10^{-15} m (to 2 s.f.). [4 marks]

Alpha scattering — it's positively repulsive...

The important things to learn from these two pages are the nuclear model for the structure of the atom (i.e. a large mass nucleus surrounded by orbiting electrons) and how Geiger and Marsden's alpha-particle scattering experiment gives evidence that supports this model. Once you know that, take a deep breath — it's about to get a little more confusing.

Particles and Antiparticles

There are loads of different types of particle apart from the ones you get in normal matter (protons, neutrons, etc.).
They only appear in cosmic rays and in particle accelerators, and they often decay very quickly.

Hadrons are Particles that Feel the Strong Interaction (e.g. Protons and Neutrons)

1) The **nucleus** of an atom is made up from **protons** and **neutrons** (this is sounding familiar...).

2) Since the **protons** are **positively charged** you might think that the nucleus would **fly apart**
with all that repulsion. But it doesn't, so there has to be a strong **force** holding the **p's** and **n's** together.

3) That force is called the **strong interaction** (who said physicists lack imagination...).

4) Not all particles can feel the strong interaction — the ones that can are called **hadrons**.

5) Hadrons aren't **fundamental** particles. They're made up of **smaller particles** called **quarks** (see page 164).

6) As well as **protons** and **neutrons**, there are **other hadrons** that you don't get in normal matter,
like **sigmas (Σ)** and **mesons** — luckily you **don't** need to know about them (woohoo!).

The Proton is the Only Stable Hadron

1) Most **hadrons** will eventually **decay** into **other particles**.
The exception is protons — most physicists think that protons don't **decay**.

2) The **neutron** is an **unstable particle** that **decays** into a **proton**.
(But it's much more stable when it's part of a nucleus.) It's really just an
example of β⁻ decay (see p.172), which is caused by the **weak interaction**.
The particle reaction for this decay is:

$$n \rightarrow p + e^- + \bar{\nu}$$

This is an antineutrino
(see p.161).

Some theories predict that protons should decay with a very long half-life (p.103) of about 10³² years — but there's no experimental evidence for it at the moment.

3) Free neutrons (i.e. ones not held in a nucleus) have a half-life of about **15 minutes**.

There's more about representing (nuclear) decay with equations on p.171.

Leptons Don't Feel the Strong Interaction (e.g. Electrons and Neutrinos)

1) **Leptons** are **fundamental particles** that **don't** feel the **strong interaction**. They **interact** with other particles via
the **weak interaction** and **gravity** (and the electromagnetic force if they're charged).

2) There are two types of lepton you need to know about —
electrons (e⁻), which should be familiar to you, and **neutrinos (ν)**.

3) Neutrinos have **zero** (or almost zero) **mass** and **zero**
electric charge — so they don't do much. **Neutrinos** only
take part in **weak interactions** (see p.165). In fact, a neutrino
can **pass right through the Earth** without **anything** happening to it.

4) **Lepton number** is the number of leptons.
Electrons and neutrinos have a lepton number of **+1**.

5) The total lepton number in any particle reaction **never changes**
— **lepton number is conserved**. For example, in the neutron decay reaction above,
n and p have lepton number 0, e⁻ has lepton number 1, and $\bar{\nu}$ has lepton number −1 (see next page).
So $0 \rightarrow 0 + 1 - 1$. There's more on the **properties** of **different particles** on the next page.

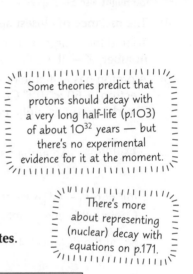

Name	Symbol	Charge (relative to the fundamental charge, e)
electron	e⁻	−1
neutrino	ν	0

ν is the Greek letter "nu".

Antiparticles were Predicted Before they were Discovered

When **Paul Dirac** wrote down an equation obeyed by **electrons**, he found a kind of **mirror image** solution.

1) It predicted the existence of a particle like the **electron** but with **opposite electric charge** — the **positron**.

2) The **positron** turned up later in a cosmic ray experiment.
Positrons have **identical mass** to electrons but they carry a **positive** charge.

Particles and Antiparticles

Every Particle has an Antiparticle

Each particle type has a **corresponding antiparticle** with the **same mass** but with **opposite charge**.
For instance, an **antiproton** is a **negatively charged** particle with the same mass as the **proton**.
Even the shadowy **neutrino** has an antiparticle version called the **antineutrino** — it doesn't do much either.

Particle	Symbol	Relative charge	Rest mass / kg	Lepton no.	Antiparticle	Symbol	Relative charge	Rest mass / kg	Lepton no.
proton	p	+1	1.673×10^{-27}	0	antiproton	$\bar{p}$	−1	1.673×10^{-27}	0
neutron	n	0	1.675×10^{-27}	0	antineutron	$\bar{n}$	0	1.675×10^{-27}	0
electron	e^-	−1	9.11×10^{-31}	1	positron	e^+	+1	9.11×10^{-31}	−1
neutrino	ν	0	0	1	antineutrino	$\bar{\nu}$	0	0	−1

1) In the exam, you'll be **given** the masses of protons, neutrons and electrons. Just remember that the mass of an **antiparticle** is the **same** as the mass of its corresponding particle.

2) The masses in the table are all **rest masses** — the mass of the particle when it's **not moving**. This is because the masses of objects change when they're moving at very high speeds, but you don't need to know about that.

3) You need to **learn the relative charge** on each type of particle (these are all relative to $e = 1.60 \times 10^{-19}$ C).

4) In any particle reaction **charge is conserved** — the total charge before the reaction must be equal to the total charge after the reaction.

5) Neutrinos are **incredibly tiny** — you can assume they have zero mass and zero charge.

6) **Anti-leptons**, like the positron and antineutrino, have a **lepton number of −1**. So whenever a lepton is produced in a particle reaction, an anti-lepton is produced too (to conserve lepton number).

Practice Questions

Q1 Give two differences between a hadron and a lepton.

Q2 What is the only stable hadron? Name another hadron that will decay into it.

Q3 Name two types of lepton. Give their lepton numbers.

Q4 Which antiparticle has zero charge and a rest mass of 1.675×10^{-27} kg?

Q5 What is the symbol for an antineutrino? List the properties of an antineutrino.

Q6 Write down the charge of a positron, given that the charge on an electron is -1.60×10^{-19} C.

Q7 Give one similarity and one difference between a proton and an antiproton.

Exam Questions

Q1 State the decay products of the neutron.
Explain why this decay cannot be due to the strong interaction. [3 marks]

Q2 A particle is detected that has no charge and that does not feel the strong interaction.
Suggest what the particle might be. [1 mark]

Q3 a) Explain why the reaction $\bar{n} \rightarrow \bar{p} + e^+ + \bar{\nu}$ is not possible. [2 marks]

b) Explain why the reaction $\bar{n} \rightarrow \bar{p} + e^- + \bar{\nu}$ is not possible. [2 marks]

Go back to the top of page 160 — do not pass GO, do not collect £200...

There's a frankly silly number of physics words on this page, but it looks worse than it is. Honestly. Give it another read, and don't move on until you're sure you know it all, otherwise the next few pages will sound like nonsense...

Pair Production and Annihilation

Time for one of physics' most famous equations. I know you're on the edge of your seat. I certainly I am...

You can Create *Matter* and *Antimatter* from *Energy*

You've probably heard about the **equivalence** of energy and mass. It all comes out of Einstein's special theory of relativity. **Energy** can turn into **mass** and **mass** can turn into **energy** if you know how — all you need is one fantastic and rather famous formula:

$$E_{rest} = mc^2$$

E_{rest} is the 'rest energy' — the energy equivalent to the mass, m, when it isn't moving. Energy is also approximately equal to mc^2 for masses moving at slow speeds, but things get a bit more complicated when objects are moving near the speed of light (p.167).

As you've probably guessed, there's a bit **more to it** than that:

> When **energy** is converted into **mass** you get **equal amounts** of **matter** and **antimatter**.

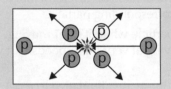

Fire **two protons** at each other at high speed and you'll end up with a lot of **energy** at the point of impact. This energy might be converted into **more particles**.

If an extra **proton** is formed then there will always be an **antiproton** to go with it. It's called **pair production**.

Each *Particle-Antiparticle Pair* is Produced from a *Single Photon*

Pair production only happens if **one gamma ray photon** has enough energy to produce that much mass. It also tends to happen near a **nucleus**, which helps conserve momentum.

You usually get **electron-positron** pairs produced (rather than any other pair) — because they have a relatively **low rest mass**.

You can calculate the **minimum energy** (and therefore the minimum frequency and maximum wavelength) a photon must have for pair production to occur using $E_{rest} = mc^2$.

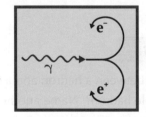

The particle tracks are curved because there's usually a magnetic field present in particle physics experiments (see next page).

> **Example:** An electron and a positron are produced from a single photon. Find the maximum possible wavelength of the photon. (The rest mass of an electron $m_e = 9.11 \times 10^{-31}$ kg.)

1) As **energy before = energy after**, the **minimum energy** the photon can have is equal to the energy needed to produce the particles at rest (i.e. the particles have no kinetic energy).

2) An electron and a positron have the **same rest mass** (m_e), which means that:

$$E_{photon} = E_{rest(electron)} + E_{rest(positron)} = 2m_ec^2$$

This is the minimum energy the photon needs to create the two particles. If the photon has more energy than this, then it could be converted into kinetic energy of the electron and positron, or used to create a more massive particle/antiparticle pair instead.

3) The **energy** of a photon is related to its **wavelength** by the equation: $E_{photon} = \dfrac{hc}{\lambda}$ ⟵ h is the Planck constant (6.63×10^{-34} Js).

4) Just put these two equations for E_{photon} together and **rearrange** to find λ:

$$2m_ec^2 = \frac{hc}{\lambda} \text{ so } \lambda = \frac{hc}{2m_ec^2} = \frac{h}{2m_ec}, \text{ and so: } \lambda = \frac{6.63 \times 10^{-34}}{2 \times (9.11 \times 10^{-31}) \times (3.00 \times 10^8)}$$

$$= 1.212... \times 10^{-12} = \mathbf{1.21 \times 10^{-12} \text{ m (to 3 s.f.)}}$$

This is in the gamma part of the EM spectrum — gamma radiation has a wavelength of approximately 10^{-12} m or less.

Pair Production and Annihilation

The **Opposite** of **Pair Production** is **Annihilation**

1) When a **particle** meets its **antiparticle** the result is **annihilation**.

2) All the **mass** of the particle and antiparticle gets converted to **energy**, in the form of a pair of identical photons.

3) Antiparticles can generally only exist for a **fraction of a second** before they annihilate, so you won't see many of them.

4) Just like with pair production, you can calculate the **minimum energy** of each photon produced (i.e. assuming that the particles have **negligible** kinetic energy).

5) The combined energy of the photons will be equal to the combined energy of the particles, so $2E_{photon} = 2mc^2$ and so: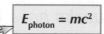

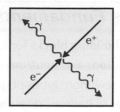

The electron and positron annihilate and their mass is converted into the energy of a pair of identical gamma ray photons.

$$E_{photon} = mc^2$$

You can calculate the minimum frequency and maximum wavelength as before (i.e. by using $E = hf = \frac{hc}{\lambda}$).

You Can Use a **Cloud Chamber** to Observe Pair Production and Annihilation

1) A cloud chamber is basically a large box filled with alcohol (or water) **vapour**.

2) When high energy particles pass through the cloud chamber, they **ionise** alcohol particles along their path.

3) The vapour in the cloud chamber **condenses** around these ions, forming a **trail of alcohol droplets** ('a cloud') along the path of the charged particle.

4) Most cloud chambers include a **magnetic field** at **right-angles** to the direction of particle motion. A moving charge in a magnetic field experiences a force (p.156), so the paths of **charged particles**, like electrons and positrons, will **bend** as they pass through the chamber. Positively and negatively charged particles are deflected in **opposite directions**.

5) As particles travel through a cloud chamber, they **slow down**, as ionising alcohol particles uses energy. This means the paths of charged particles when a magnetic field is present are **spirals**, rather than circles.

6) Gamma ray photons are only **weakly ionising** (p.170) — they pass through the alcohol of the cloud chamber without interacting with it very much. This means they don't produce trails.

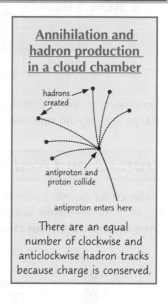

Annihilation and hadron production in a cloud chamber

hadrons created

antiproton and proton collide

antiproton enters here

There are an equal number of clockwise and anticlockwise hadron tracks because charge is conserved.

Practice Questions

Q1 Write down Einstein's famous equation. Define each term used.

Q2 A high energy photon produces a positron. What other particle must be produced?

Q3 Briefly explain how a cloud chamber works.

Q4 What effect does the presence of the vapour in a cloud chamber have on the path of a charged particle if the particle's path is bending due to an applied magnetic field?

Exam Questions

Q1 Explain why the reaction $p + p \rightarrow p + p + n$ is not possible. [1 mark]

Q2 Write down an equation for the reaction between a positron and an electron and state the name of this type of reaction. [2 marks]

Q3 Assuming both particles have negligible kinetic energy, calculate the frequency of the two photons produced when a proton and an antiproton annihilate.
($m_p = 1.673 \times 10^{-27}$ kg, $h = 6.63 \times 10^{-34}$ Js, $c = 3.00 \times 10^8$ ms^{-1}) [3 marks]

Pair production — never seems to happen with my socks...

Learn the key points on these pages and it'll all be plain sailing. And don't forget: a) if energy is converted into a particle, you also get an antiparticle, b) an antiparticle won't last long before it bumps into the right particle and annihilates with it, c) annihilation releases the energy it took to make them to start with...

Quarks

Quarks are the fundamental particles that make up protons and neutrons. If you haven't yet, it's probably best to read p.160–161 before you start — then this will all make a bit more sense...

Quarks are Fundamental Particles

Quarks are the **building blocks** for **hadrons** like **protons** and **neutrons**.

1) To make **protons** and **neutrons** you only need two types of quark — the **up** quark (**u**) and the **down** quark (**d**).

2) There are a few more types of quark, but you don't need to know about them (woohoo!).

The **antiparticles** of hadrons (like antiprotons and antineutrons) are made from **anti-quarks**.

Quarks and Anti-quarks have Opposite Charge

The **anti-quarks** have **opposite charges** to the quarks — as you'd expect.

Quarks:

name	symbol	relative charge
up	u	$+\frac{2}{3}$
down	d	$-\frac{1}{3}$

Anti-quarks:

name	symbol	relative charge
anti-up	$\bar{u}$	$-\frac{2}{3}$
anti-down	$\bar{d}$	$+\frac{1}{3}$

As on p.161, these charges are relative to the elementary charge, *e*.

Remember, if you're thinking about particle reactions in terms of quarks, **charge** and **lepton number** still need to be **conserved**.

Protons and Neutrons are Made from Three Quarks

Evidence for quarks came from **hitting protons** with **high energy electrons**. The way the **electrons scattered** showed that there were **three concentrations of charge** (quarks) **inside** the proton.

The quarks that a particle is made up from is called its 'quark composition'.

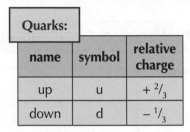
Proton = **uud**

Total relative charge
$= \frac{2}{3} + \frac{2}{3} - \frac{1}{3} = +1$

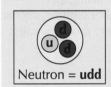
Neutron = **udd**

Total relative charge
$= \frac{2}{3} - \frac{1}{3} - \frac{1}{3} = 0$

Antiprotons are $\bar{u}\bar{u}\bar{d}$ and antineutrons are $\bar{u}\bar{d}\bar{d}$ — so no surprises there then.

Not all hadrons have **three quarks** though. Protons and neutrons are a type of hadron called a **baryon**, which is made up of **three quarks**. There are also hadrons made up of a **quark** and an **anti-quark**, called **mesons** — but you don't really need to know about them.

There's no Such Thing as a Free Quark

What if you **blasted** a **proton** with **enough energy** — could you **separate out** the quarks? Nope. The energy just gets changed into more **quarks and antiquarks** — it's **pair production** again (see p.162) and it makes **mesons**.

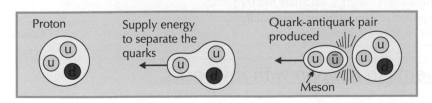

Proton | Supply energy to separate the quarks | Quark-antiquark pair produced

Meson

This is called **quark confinement**.

Quarks

Gluons Provide Force Between Quarks

1) When two particles **interact**, something must **happen** to let one particle know that the other one's there. That's the idea behind **exchange particles**. You can picture them if you think about **balls** and **boomerangs**:

Repulsion — Each time the **ball** is **thrown or caught** the people get **pushed apart**. It happens because the ball carries **momentum**.

Attraction — Each time the **boomerang** is **thrown or caught** the people **get pushed together**. (In real life, you'd probably fall in first.)

The particles don't <u>actually</u> loop round like that, though.

←— REPULSION —→

—→ ATTRACTION ←—

These exchange particles are called **gauge bosons** — they're virtual particles that only last for a very short time.

2) **All forces in nature** are caused by four **fundamental** forces. Each one has its **own gauge boson**: ⟹

3) The exchange particle that causes the **strong force** that 'glues' hadrons like protons and neutrons together is imaginatively called the **gluon**.

4) Because gluons cause a force, you can think of them as **fields** as well as particles. It's just the same as thinking of a **gravitational force** as being caused by a **gravitational field**.

5) As you try to **separate** quarks, you actually **increase** the **energy** of the gluon field, **increasing** the **attraction** between them.

quark — gluon field — quark

Type of Interaction	Gauge Boson	Particles Affected
strong	gluon	hadrons only
electromagnetic	photon	charged particles only
weak	W^+, W^-, Z^0	all types
gravity	graviton?	all types

Particle physicists never bother about gravity because it's so incredibly feeble compared with the other types of interaction. Gravity only really matters when you've got big masses like stars and planets. The graviton may exist but there's no evidence for it.

6) If you keep pulling, eventually the energy in the gluon field will be enough that it produces a **quark-antiquark pair**. This is why you can **never** detect a quark on its own (see p.164).

Gluon field energy increases as you separate the quarks.

Eventually a quark-antiquark pair is produced.

quark   antiquark

+

Practice Questions

Q1 What is a quark?

Q2 What is the relative charge on an anti-down quark?

Q3 Explain why quarks are never observed on their own.

Q4 Name the exchange particle for the strong force felt between two quarks.

Exam Questions

Q1 State the combination of three quarks that make up a neutron. [1 mark]

Q2 Give the quark composition of the proton. Explain how the relative charge of each quark gives rise to its total relative charge. [2 marks]

A quark — not the noise a posh duck makes...

Don't know about you, but I'm getting a wee bit sick of tables of particles to learn. Sadly you need to know all this stuff, so it's time to make yourself a cuppa and give it all another read...

Particle Accelerators

Particle accelerators are devices that (surprisingly) accelerate particles, using electric and magnetic fields. Accelerated particles can be used in scattering experiments to investigate the fundamental particles that make up matter...

Particle Accelerators Cause High-Energy Collisions

There are lots of different types of accelerator out there smashing particles together. One of the main types is the linear accelerator...

1) A **linear accelerator** is a long **straight** tube containing a series of **electrodes**.

2) **Alternating current** is applied to the electrodes so that their **charge** continuously **changes** between + and –.

3) The alternating current is **timed** so that the charged particles are always **attracted** to the **next electrode** in the accelerator and **repelled** from the **previous** one.

4) A particle's **speed** will **increase** each time it **passes** an electrode — so if the accelerator is long enough particles can be made to approach the **speed of light**.

5) The **high-energy particles** leaving a linear accelerator **collide** with a **fixed target** at the end of the tube.

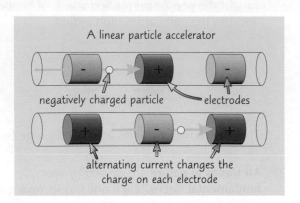

A linear particle accelerator

negatively charged particle — electrodes

alternating current changes the charge on each electrode

A Cyclotron is a Circular Particle Accelerator

1) A cyclotron uses **two semicircular electrodes** to accelerate protons or other charged particles across a gap.

2) An **alternating potential difference** is applied between the electrodes — as the **particles** are **attracted** from one side to the other their **energy increases** (i.e. they are **accelerated**).

3) A **magnetic field** is used to keep the particles moving in a **circular motion** (in the diagram on the right, the magnetic field would be perpendicular to the page).

4) The combination of the **electric** and **magnetic fields** makes the particles **spiral outwards** as their energy increases.

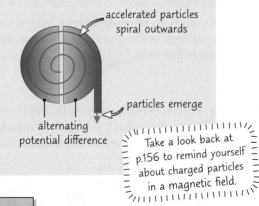

accelerated particles spiral outwards

particles emerge

alternating potential difference

Take a look back at p.156 to remind yourself about charged particles in a magnetic field.

Synchrotrons Produce Very High Energy Beams

1) A **synchrotron** can produce particle collisions with much **higher energies** than either a linear accelerator or a cyclotron.

2) **Electromagnets** keep the particles moving in a **circular path** in **focused beams**.

3) In this way, **synchrotrons** can produce particles with energies reaching from **500 GeV to several TeV**.

4) You can find the **force** experienced by a particle in a synchrotron (or a cyclotron) due to the **magnetic field** using the formula below (see p.156).

$$F = qvB$$

F is the force on the particle (in N), *q* is the charge on the particle (in C), *v* is its velocity in (ms^{-1}), and *B* is the magnetic flux density (in T).

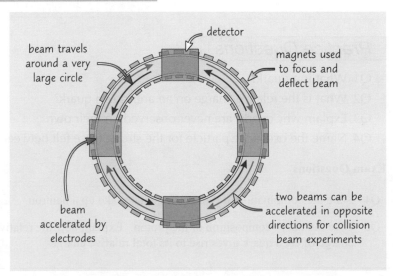

detector

beam travels around a very large circle

magnets used to focus and deflect beam

beam accelerated by electrodes

two beams can be accelerated in opposite directions for collision beam experiments

5) Synchrotrons like the Large Hadron Collider (LHC) at CERN in Switzerland are **really expensive** to build and run, so they need to be funded **internationally**.

Particle Accelerators

Masses **Cannot** Reach the Speed of Light

1) Particles can be accelerated to such high speeds that the effects of **relativity** become noticeable and important.

2) Einstein's theory of **special relativity** only works in **reference frames** that **aren't accelerating** — called **inertial frames**.

3) It's based on two assumptions:

> Physical laws have the same form in all inertial frames.
> The speed of light in free space is invariant.

Invariant means that it always has the same value.

4) One rather interesting consequence of special relativity is that:

> **No particle that has mass** can move at a speed **greater than** or **equal to** the **speed of light, *c*.**

The **Mass** of an Object **Increases** with **Speed**

1) Special relativity is where the idea that **energy is equivalent to mass** comes from. $\Rightarrow$ $\boxed{E_{rest} = mc^2}$

2) It means that the more you **increase** the **kinetic energy** of a mass (like a particle in an accelerator), the **more massive** it gets.

3) This happens to **any** object with kinetic energy, but it's only noticeable at **speeds approaching *c*.**

4) Particle accelerators have to **alter** their magnetic and electric fields to compensate for the relativistic mass of the accelerating particles.

The **Relativistic Factor** — $E_{tot} \div E_{rest}$

The **relativistic factor**, γ, depends on the speed of the particle (see page 129). It's given by:

$$\gamma = \frac{1}{\sqrt{1 - \dfrac{v^2}{c^2}}}$$

It's also equal to the total energy of a particle (i.e. its rest energy plus its kinetic energy) divided by its rest energy, so: $\Longrightarrow$ $\boxed{E_{total} = \gamma E_{rest}}$

For particles travelling at low speeds ($v \ll c$), γ will be very close to 1.

> **Example:** An electron is accelerated to almost the speed of light. It has a rest energy of 5.1×10^5 eV. If $\gamma = 235$, find the total energy of the accelerated electron in MeV.
>
> $E_{total} = \gamma E_{rest} = 235 \times (5.1 \times 10^5) = 1.1985 \times 10^8 \text{ eV} = \textbf{120 MeV (to 2 s.f.)}$

Practice Questions

Q1 Describe the similarities and differences between a linear particle accelerator and a cyclotron.

Q2 Describe how a synchrotron works.

Q3 State what happens to the mass of a particle when it approaches the speed of light.

Q4 Write down an expression for the relativistic factor in terms of the speed of the particle and the speed of light.

Exam Questions

Q1 A proton is accelerated by a synchrotron to a total energy of 500 GeV.
Show that the relativistic factor for a proton of this energy is about 500.
($m_p = 1.673 \times 10^{-27}$ kg, 1 eV $= 1.60 \times 10^{-19}$ J) [3 marks]

Q2 A proton in a cyclotron is travelling at a speed of 6.82×10^5 ms^{-1}. It experiences a force of 4.91×10^{-13} N due to a perpendicular magnetic field. Calculate the strength of the magnetic flux density inside the cyclotron. [2 marks]

Smash high-energy particles together to see what they're made of...

The three types of particle accelerator all have their advantages, but the synchrotron wins hands down for generating very high energy particles. Synchrotrons get pretty big — the LHC is a whopping 27 km loop...

Electron Energy Levels

You'll probably recognise this stuff — you met it in year 1 of A level, back in page 66.
Electrons only exist in set energy levels and leap into higher energy levels when they get excited.

Electrons in Atoms Have Discrete Energy Levels

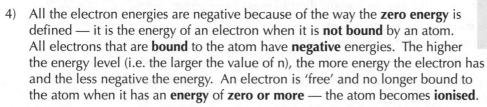

1) **Electrons** in an **atom** can **only exist** in certain **well-defined energy levels**. Each level is given a **number** (called the **principal quantum number** of the electron in that state), with **n = 1** representing the electron's lowest possible energy — its **ground state**.

2) The diagram on the right shows the **energy levels** for **atomic hydrogen**.

3) The **energies involved** are **so tiny** that it makes sense to use a more **appropriate unit** than the joule. The **electronvolt (eV)** is used instead:

> An **electronvolt** is the **kinetic energy gained** by an **electron** when it is **accelerated** through a **potential difference** of 1 volt. 1 eV = 1.60 × 10⁻¹⁹ J.

4) All the electron energies are negative because of the way the **zero energy** is defined — it is the energy of an electron when it is **not bound** by an atom. All electrons that are **bound** to the atom have **negative** energies. The higher the energy level (i.e. the larger the value of n), the more energy the electron has and the less negative the energy. An electron is 'free' and no longer bound to the atom when it has an **energy of zero or more** — the atom becomes **ionised**.

5) Electrons can **move down** an energy level by **emitting** a **photon**. Since these **transitions** are between **definite energy levels**, the **energy** of **each photon** emitted can **only** take **certain values**.

6) The **energy** carried by each **emitted photon** is **equal** to the **difference in energies** between the **two levels** that the electron has moved between. The equation on the right is for a **transition** between levels **n = 2** and **n = 1**:

$$\Delta E = E_2 - E_1 = hf = \frac{hc}{\lambda}$$

h = Planck's constant,
f = frequency of photon,
c = speed of light in a vacuum,
λ = wavelength of photon

7) In the same way, atoms can only **absorb** allowed photon energies. When an atom **absorbs a photon**, an electron **moves up** to another energy level. This **quantisation** of electron energies in atoms produces **line emission** and **absorption spectra** (see below).

> Electrons (as well as protons and neutrons) are **fermions**. That means they obey the **Pauli exclusion principle**. This states that **no two fermions** can be in **exactly** the same **quantum state** at the same time. In the context of energy levels, that means **no more than two** electrons can be in the same **energy level** at the same time.

The Evidence for Energy Levels — Line Spectra

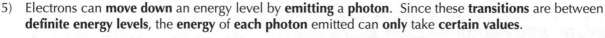

Decreasing wavelength ⟹

1) The **spectrum** of **white light** is **continuous**.

2) If you **split** the **light** up with a **prism**, the **colours** all **merge** into each other — there **aren't** any **gaps** in the spectrum.

3) You get a **line absorption spectrum** when **light** with a **continuous spectrum** passes through a **cool gas**.

4) At **low temperatures**, **most** of the **electrons** in the **gas atoms** will be in their **ground states**.

5) **Photons** of the **correct wavelength** are **absorbed** by the **atoms** to **excite** the **electrons** to **higher energy levels**.

6) These **wavelengths** are then **missing** from the **continuous spectrum** when the light **comes out** the other side of the gas.

7) You see a **continuous spectrum** with **dark lines** in it corresponding to the **absorbed wavelengths**.

8) When an electron falls into a **lower** energy level, it **emits** a photon. **Emission spectra** show the wavelengths of photons emitted. They are made up of a **series** **bright lines** corresponding to the **wavelengths emitted**. If you **compare** the **absorption** and **emission** spectra of a **particular gas**, the **dark lines** in the **absorption spectrum match up** to the **bright lines** in the **emission spectrum**.

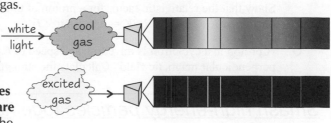

MODULE 6: SECTION 3 — PROBING DEEP INTO MATTER

Electron Energy Levels

More Evidence — *Fluorescent Tubes*

1) Fluorescent tubes use **excited electrons** to produce light. A **high voltage** is applied across mercury vapour, which **accelerates** free electrons that **ionise** some of the mercury atoms, producing even more **free electrons**.

2) When the free electrons **collide** with electrons in other mercury atoms, the electrons in the mercury atoms are **excited** to **higher energy levels**. When they return to their ground states, they **emit UV photons**.

3) A phosphor coating inside the tube **absorbs** these photons, in turn **exciting** its electrons to much higher orbits. These electrons then **cascade** down the energy levels, **emitting photons** in the form of **visible light**.

The *Wave Model* of the *Atom* can Help you Understand *Energy Levels*

1) Since light has both **particle** and **wave** characteristics, de Broglie suggested that **electrons** should have a **wave-like character** (see p.71). Specifically, when they're in orbit **around a nucleus** they ought to behave like the **standing waves** that are formed on a guitar string when it's plucked.

2) Just as standing waves on the guitar string only exist at certain **well-defined frequencies**, only certain standing waves are possible in an atom. The **wavelength** of the electron waves should fit the **circumference** of the orbit a **whole number** of times.

3) The **principal quantum number, n** (corresponding to the number of the energy level), is equal to the number of **complete waves** that fit the circumference.

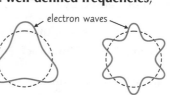

electron waves

Three wavelengths
n = 3

Six wavelengths
n = 6

Not a standing wave.
Forbidden energy.

4) You can think of the electrons as being trapped by a **potential well** made by the nucleus. That way you can think of them as being standing waves between **two fixed walls**.

5) An electron will be able to **escape** the potential well when it has a total energy of **zero or more** (i.e. when KE + PE ≥ 0).

6) You can use the diameter of the atom, d, to find the **de Broglie wavelength**, $\lambda = \frac{h}{p} = \frac{h}{mv}$, of the electron. For n = 1, there is **half a wavelength** contained between the walls, so $\lambda = 2d$. For n = 2, there is **one complete wavelength** contained between the walls, so $\lambda = d$. For n = 3, $\lambda = \frac{2}{3}d$ and so on...

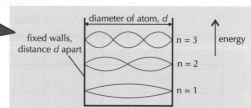

diameter of atom, d

fixed walls, distance d apart

n = 3   energy
n = 2
n = 1

Practice Questions

Q1 Write down the equation you would use to find the difference in energy between two energy levels in an atom.

Q2 Describe how line spectra give evidence for the existence of discrete energy levels in atoms.

Q3 Describe the standing-wave model of electrons in an atom.

Exam Questions

Q1 An electron is created in beta decay and has an energy of 3.9×10^{-14} J.
State and explain whether this electron will remain bound to the nucleus. [2 marks]

Q2 The Balmer series is a series of spectral lines due to photons emitted by excited hydrogen atoms.
One Balmer line is caused by photons with a frequency of 4.57×10^{14} Hz.
a) Find the energy in joules of the photons that make up this line ($h = 6.63 \times 10^{-34}$ Js). [1 mark]
b) Use the diagram of the energy levels in a hydrogen atom on page 168 to identify the energy level transition that causes this spectral line. [2 marks]

Q3 The length of 1 second is defined using the radiation corresponding to a particular quantum transition in a caesium-133 atom. The difference in energy levels is 3.8×10^{-5} eV.
Calculate the frequency of this radiation. [3 marks]

My energy level's about n = 1 after that — I need chocolate...

I always find this stuff the trickiest — I mean, it's not like you can see an electron skipping about inside an atom every day, and the 'electrons are waves as well' plot twist keeps you on your toes. Once you've been through it all a few times though it starts to click, so stick with it and soon it'll be as easy as an electron transition from n = 2 to n = 1.

Radioactive Emissions

Make sure you're happy with the previous section before you start this, or it might not make much sense...

Atomic Structure can be Represented Using Standard Notation

Standard notation summarises all the information you need about an element's **atomic structure**:

The **proton number** or **atomic number** (Z) — there are six protons in a carbon atom.

$^{12}_{6}\text{C}$

The **nucleon number** or **mass number** (A) — there are a total of 12 protons and neutrons in a carbon-12 atom.
The symbol for the element. For carbon, it's C.

Atoms of the **same element** (i.e. that have the same number of protons) that have different numbers of **neutrons** (same Z, different A) are called **isotopes**.

Unstable Isotopes are Radioactive

1) The nucleus is under the **influence** of the **strong nuclear force holding** it **together** and the **electrostatic force pushing** the **protons apart**. It's a very **delicate balance**, and it's easy for a nucleus to become **unstable**.

2) If a nucleus is **unstable**, it **transforms** into a more stable isotope by emitting **radiation**. Its **instability** could be caused by:

- **too many neutrons**
- **too few neutrons**
- **too many nucleons** in total (it's **too massive**)
- **too much energy** in the nucleus

3) The nuclei of some isotopes are unstable and decay — we say these isotopes are **radioactive**.

There are Four Types of Nuclear Radiation

You need to know all about the **four** different types of **nuclear radiation** — here's a handy **table** to get you started.

Radiation	Symbol	Constituent	Relative Charge	Mass (u)
Alpha	α	2 protons and 2 neutrons (a helium nucleus)	+2	4
Beta-minus (Beta)	β or β^-	Electron	−1	Negligible
Beta-plus	β^+	Positron (see p.161)	+1	Negligible
Gamma	γ	Short-wavelength, high-frequency EM wave.	0	0

The masses in this table are given in **atomic mass units** (u).
An atomic mass unit is roughly equal to the mass of a proton or neutron.

The Different Types of Radiation have Different Penetrations

When radiation **hits** an **atom** it can **knock off electrons**, creating an **ion** — so, **radioactive emissions** are also known as **ionising radiation**. The **different types** of radiation have **different ionising powers** as well as different **speeds** and **penetrating powers**.

Radiation	Symbol	Ionising Power	Speed	Penetrating power
Alpha	α	Strong	Slow	Absorbed by paper or a few cm of air
Beta-minus (Beta)	β or β^-	Weak	Fast	Absorbed by ~3 mm of aluminium
Beta-plus	β^+	Annihilated by electron — so virtually zero range		
Gamma	γ	Very weak	Speed of light	Absorbed by many cm of lead, or several m of concrete

α and β particles are also affected by magnetic fields, as they carry a charge. γ radiation isn't affected by a magnetic field. There's more on charged particles in magnetic fields on p.156.

The penetrating power of radiation **decreases** with increasing ionising power. This is because radiation loses energy as it ionises atoms. This means that the **higher** the **ionising power** of a type of radiation, the **more energy** it **loses** in a given distance, so the **shorter** its **range**.

Radioactive Emissions

You can *Investigate* the *Penetration* of Different Kinds of Radiation in the Lab

You can investigate the penetration of different kinds of radiation by using different radioactive sources.
These can be **dangerous** if you don't use them properly:

- Radioactive sources should be kept in a lead-lined box when they're not being used.
- They should only be picked up using long-handled tongs or forceps.
- Take care not to point them at anyone.

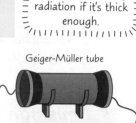
Lead will absorb all types of ionising radiation if it's thick enough.

1) Measure the **background count**. Radioactive decay is **random**, so to get an accurate reading the count needs to be measured over a long enough **time interval** (e.g. 30 s).

2) Divide your count by this time interval to get a **count rate** in s⁻¹. **Repeat** this measurement at least three times and take an average. You should subtract this from all your results.

radiation
radioactive source
absorber
Geiger-Müller tube
Geiger counter

3) Set up the equipment as shown on the right, so that when nothing is placed between the source and tube, the counter records a **high count rate**. You could attach the Geiger-Müller tube to a **data-logger** and a **computer** to reduce **human error**.

4) Insert **different materials** between the source and tube, and record the count rate over a sensible time interval (this will depend on how active your source is).

5) If the count rate remains about **the same**, then the radiation can **penetrate** the material. If the count rate **drops** by a large amount, then the radiation is being **absorbed** and blocked by the material. If the count rate drops to **zero** (after the background count is subtracted), the radiation is being **completely absorbed**.

If you're comparing penetration across different materials, they're unlikely to all have the same thickness. Bear this in mind when you draw your conclusions.

6) You can repeat this experiment with **different sources** to see how different kinds of radiation are blocked by different materials. You'll probably need to change the **distance** between the source and the Geiger-Müller tube for **each source**, as different kinds of radiation have different penetrating powers in **air** (see p.170).

You may investigate penetration of radiation in school using computer simulation software.

7) You could also investigate how the count rate from a particular source is affected by the **thickness** of a given blocking material, e.g. by using **multiple sheets** of **aluminium** for **beta** radiation, or different thicknesses of **lead** for **gamma** radiation.

You Can *Represent Nuclear Decay* Using *Equations*

1) You usually write the particles involved in nuclear decay in **standard notation** (p.170) so you can see what happens to the **protons** and **neutrons**. E.g., the decay of americium-241 to neptunium-237 looks like this:

2) The nucleus you start with is called the **parent nucleus** (here it's americium-241), and the nucleus it decays to is called the **daughter nucleus** (here it's neptunium-237).

$$^{241}_{95}\text{Am} \longrightarrow ^{237}_{93}\text{Np} + ^{4}_{2}\alpha$$

3) Decay equations need to be **balanced** — in every nuclear reaction, including fission and fusion (p.178–179), **charge**, **nucleon number** and **lepton number** (p.160) must be **conserved**.

4) **Beta-minus** particles have a **negative** charge. They're written with a **negative proton number** ($^{0}_{-1}\beta$).

5) **Energy** and **momentum** are also **conserved** in all nuclear reactions. Mass, however, **doesn't** have to be **conserved** — the **mass** of an alpha particle is **less** than the **individual masses** of **two protons** and **two neutrons**. The difference in mass is called the **mass defect**, and the **energy released** when the nucleons **bond together** to form the alpha particle accounts for the missing mass. More on that later (p.176).

α *Emission* Happens in *Heavy Nuclei*

Alpha emission only happens in **very heavy** atoms, like **uranium** and **radium**.
The **nuclei** of these atoms are **too massive** to be stable.

When an alpha particle is emitted, the **proton number decreases** by **two**, and the **nucleon number decreases** by **four**.

Example:

nucleon numbers balance
$$238 = 234 + 4$$
$$^{238}_{92}\text{U} \longrightarrow ^{234}_{90}\text{Th} + ^{4}_{2}\alpha$$
$$92 = 90 + 2$$
proton numbers balance, so charge is conserved

Radioactive Emissions

β⁻ Emission Happens in Neutron-Rich Nuclei

1) **Beta-minus** decay is the emission of an **electron** from the **nucleus** along with an **antineutrino** (p.161). It happens in isotopes that are '**neutron rich**' (have many more **neutrons** than **protons** in their nuclei).

2) One of the **neutrons** in the nucleus **decays** into a **proton** and ejects a beta particle and an antineutrino.

> When a beta-minus particle is emitted, the **proton number increases** by **one**, and the **nucleon number stays the same**.

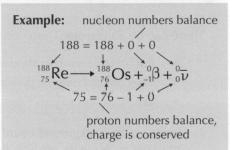

Example: nucleon numbers balance

$$188 = 188 + 0 + 0$$

$$^{188}_{75}\text{Re} \longrightarrow ^{188}_{76}\text{Os} + ^{0}_{-1}\beta + ^{0}_{0}\overline{\nu}$$

$$75 = 76 - 1 + 0$$

proton numbers balance, charge is conserved

β⁺ Emission Happens in Proton-Rich Nuclei

In **beta-plus emission**, a **proton** gets **changed** into a **neutron**, releasing a **positron** and a **neutrino**.

> When a beta-plus particle is emitted, the **proton number decreases** by **one**, and the **nucleon number stays the same**.

Example: $18 = 18 + 0 + 0$ — nucleon numbers balance

$$^{18}_{9}\text{F} \longrightarrow ^{18}_{8}\text{O} + ^{0}_{+1}\overline{\beta} + ^{0}_{0}\nu$$

$$9 = 8 + 1 + 0$$ — proton numbers balance

In both types of beta decay, a lepton and an anti-lepton are produced, so lepton number is conserved (see page 160). In β⁻ decay it's an electron and an antineutrino, and in β⁺ decay, it's a positron and a neutrino.

γ Radiation is Emitted from Nuclei with Too Much Energy

Gamma rays can be emitted from a nucleus with **excess energy** — we say the nucleus is **excited**. This energy is **lost** by emitting a **gamma ray**. This often happens after an **alpha** or **beta** decay has occurred.

> During **gamma emission**, there is **no change** to the nuclear **constituents** — the nucleus just **loses excess energy**.

Practice Questions

Q1 What is an isotope?

Q2 List four factors that could make a nucleus unstable.

Q3 What are the four types of nuclear radiation? What does each one consist of?

Q4 What is one atomic mass unit approximately equal to?

Q5 Which type of radiation has the greatest penetrating power? Which is the most strongly ionising?

Q6 Describe the changes that happen in a nucleus during alpha, beta-minus, beta-plus and gamma decay.

Exam Questions

Q1* A source is known to emit a single type of radiation (alpha, beta-minus or gamma).
   Describe an experiment to identify the type of radiation that the source emits. [6 marks]

Q2 a) Radium-226 (Ra, proton number 88) decays to radon (Rn) by emitting an alpha particle.
      Write a balanced nuclear equation for this reaction. [3 marks]

   b) Potassium-40 (K, proton number 19) decays to calcium (Ca) by emitting an electron.
      Write a balanced nuclear equation for this reaction. [3 marks]

*The quality of your extended response will be assessed in this question.

Radioactive emissions — as easy as α, β, γ...

You need to learn the different types of nuclear radiation and their properties, and how to write equations for all the different types of decay. Just remember that charge and nucleon number are conserved, and you won't go far wrong...

Dangers of Radiation

When you work with nuclear radiation, you need to carefully weigh up the risks and the benefits.

Using Radioactive Materials has **Benefits** and **Risks**

1) **Radioactive materials** can be useful — for example, they're used to **generate power** (p.178-179), in **medicine** for **diagnosis** and **treatment,** and to **kill harmful microorganisms** that might contaminate our **food**.

2) However, they're also dangerous. They can cause **cancerous tumours**, **skin burns**, **sterility**, **radiation sickness**, **hair loss** and even **death**.

3) The result is that radiation is only used when the benefits outweigh the **risks**. There are two parts to the risk: **how likely** it is that the radiation will cause a problem, and **how bad** the problem would be if it did happen.

For example:

1) A **nuclear reactor** melting down would be **catastrophic**, but it's also **very unlikely**, so the risk might be acceptable.

2) Ionising radiation can **cause** cancer, but it can also be used in cancer **treatments** to destroy tumours — see below. The risk of serious damage caused by the treatment is considered **acceptable** if the treatment is likely to **prolong** or **improve** a patient's life.

> You may see this idea expressed as an equation, in the form: risk = probability × consequences.

4) We need to be able to **measure** the dangers radiation poses to humans to make sensible decisions about safety.

Radiation can **Cause** a lot of **Harm** to **Body Tissues**

1) Ionising radiation gets its name because it can knock electrons off atoms, creating ions. When this happens to cells in your body, it can **damage** cells, cause them to **mutate** or even **kill them**.

2) The amount of **energy deposited per kilogram** of tissue is called the **absorbed dose**, and is measured in **grays (Gy)**.

3) To calculate an absorbed dose, you first need the energy of the radiation **absorbed** by a mass of tissue.

$$\text{absorbed dose (Gy)} = \frac{\text{energy deposited (J)}}{\text{mass (kg)}}$$

4) You can find the energy **released** by a source from its activity, the energy of the radiation, and the time interval. If all of the released energy is absorbed by tissue, you can calculate the absorbed dose using the tissue's mass.

Example: A Pu-238 source (half life 88 years) releases alpha particles with an average energy of 8.78×10^{-13} J. Its activity is 1.55×10^4 Bq. Proper safety procedures are not followed in a lab, and a scientist holds the source with his bare hand. Assuming all of the radiation emitted is absorbed by 0.05 g of tissue, calculate the absorbed dose the scientist will receive if he holds the source for ten seconds.

As the half-life of the source is so long, you can assume the activity remains constant during the 10 second period.

1 Bq = 1 decay per second, so multiply the activity by ten to get the number of decays in ten seconds: $(1.55 \times 10^4) \times 10 = 1.55 \times 10^5$

Each decay releases on average 8.78×10^{-13} J. So the energy released in ten seconds is: $(8.78 \times 10^{-13}) \times (1.55 \times 10^5) = 1.3609 \times 10^{-7}$ J

You're told the energy deposited is equal to the energy emitted by the source, so Absorbed dose = energy deposited ÷ mass: $(1.3609 \times 10^{-7}) \div (0.05 \times 10^{-3}) = 2.7218 \times 10^{-3}$
= **2.7×10^{-3} Gy (to 2 s.f.)**

Radiation can be Used to **Treat Cancer**

1) The ability of radiation to damage or kill cells makes it a useful tool to treat **cancer**. However, it's important when treating cancer with radiation to **minimise** the dose absorbed by **healthy tissue** at the same time as **maximising** the dose absorbed by the cancer cells.

2) One way of doing this is to place radioactive sources **inside** the patient, in or next to the tumour.

3) Sources can either be inserted next to the tumour for a **short period** of time, or left within the patient **permanently**.

4) Sources left within a patient permanently are chosen to deliver a **lower dose** per hour than sources inserted for a shorter duration, to **minimise damage** to healthy tissue. They will also have a fairly **short half-life** (p.104) — around 20 or so days. This means they remain active for **long enough** for the cancer cells to be killed (typically a few months) without causing unnecessary damage to surrounding tissue.

Dangers of Radiation

The Quality Factor Affects How Much Damage is Done

1) The amount of **tissue damage** caused by exposure to radiation isn't just due to the amount of energy absorbed — it also depends on the **type of ionising radiation** and the **type of body tissue**.

2) The **effective dose** is a measure that lets you **compare the amount of damage** to body tissues that have been **exposed** to different types of radiation:

> **Effective dose = absorbed dose × quality factor**

The quality factor is sometimes called the radiation quality factor.

3) The **unit** of effective dose is the **sievert (Sv)**.

4) The table on the right shows typical values for the **quality factor**. **For example**, if you exposed a sample of **body tissue** to **1 Gy** of **alpha** radiation, it could do the **same damage** as an exposure of 20 Gy of **gamma** radiation on the same type of body tissue.

Radiation	Typical quality factor	Effective dose of 1 Gy
alpha	20	20 Sv
beta	1	1 Sv
gamma	1	1 Sv

Alpha and Beta Particles have Different Ionising Properties

The higher a radiation's quality factor, the more **ionising** it is. Alpha particles are the most strongly ionising form of radiation, followed by beta particles, then gamma radiation (p.170).

Remember, ionisation happens when electrons are pulled from, or knocked off, an atom.

1) When **beta** or **alpha** particles ionise an atom, they **transfer** some of their **energy** to the atom being ionised.

2) **Alpha** particles are **strongly positive** — so they can **easily pull electrons** off atoms.

3) This means an alpha particle **quickly ionises** many atoms (about 10 000 ionisations per alpha particle) and **loses** all its **energy** — that's why it causes so much **damage** to body tissue.

4) The **beta-minus** particle has **lower mass** and **charge** than the alpha particle, but a **higher speed**. This means it can still **knock electrons** off atoms. Each **beta** particle will ionise about 100 atoms, **losing energy** at each interaction.

5) This **lower** number of **interactions** means that beta radiation causes much **less damage** to body tissue than alpha radiation — explaining the **lower radiation quality factor**.

The Intensity of Gamma Radiation Decreases with Distance

1) Gamma radiation is the most **weakly ionising** form of nuclear radiation, but also the most **penetrating** (see page 170).

2) This means that, although its quality factor is generally **low**, it is more difficult to **shield** yourself from — you'd need many centimetres of lead to block all the radiation coming from a gamma source. This needs to be taken into account when thinking about **lab safety**.

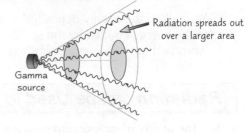

Radiation spreads out over a larger area

Gamma source

3) When gamma radiation travels through an **absorbing material** (e.g. concrete), its **intensity** (the amount of **radiation per unit area**) **decreases exponentially**. So people working near gamma sources with high activity can be protected by the use of thick lead or concrete shielding.

4) A **gamma source** will also **emit** gamma **radiation** in **all directions**. However, this radiation **spreads out** as it gets **further away** from the source, so the **intensity** will **decrease** the further you get from the source. This means you can also protect yourself from gamma sources by simply keeping your **distance**.

It's important to keep your distance from all radioactive sources that you work with, and you should always follow the safety measures given on page 171.

Dangers of Radiation

You Need to Consider the Half-Life when Thinking About Risk

1) The activity of a radioactive source **decreases** over time.

2) As you know from page 103, the **half-life**, $T_{1/2}$, of a radioactive source is the time it takes for the number of **radioactive** nuclei in the source to **halve**. This means it's also the amount of time it takes for the **activity** of the source to halve. You can find the half-life of a radioactive isotope like protactinium-234 experimentally using the method on page 103.

3) The half-life of an isotope is related to its **decay constant**, λ, by the formula:

$$T_{1/2} = \frac{\ln 2}{\lambda}$$

Where ln is the natural log (p.182), λ is the decay constant in s^{-1}, and $T_{1/2}$ is the half-life in seconds.

4) You can calculate a radioactive source's **activity** (the number of decays per second) from its decay constant using the formula:

$$A = \lambda N$$

A is the activity in Bq, and N is the number of undecayed nuclei in the source.

If this stuff seems unfamiliar, flip back to pages 102-104 for a recap.

5) We need to consider $T_{1/2}$ when assessing the **dangers** of a radioactive source and planning how to manage them:

For example:

1) **Radioactive waste** often has a very long half-life, which needs to be considered when deciding whether or not to use nuclear power, and deciding where nuclear waste should be stored.

2) Radioactive isotopes used as **medical tracers** need to have a short half-life to minimise the exposure of patients to radiation, and the chance of environmental contamination when the body excretes them.

Tracers are radioactive sources that are ingested or injected into patients. The radiation they release as they move through the body can then be used to generate images that are useful for medical diagnostics.

Practice Questions

Q1 What factors do we need to take into account when trying to measure the risk posed by radioactive materials?

Q2 What is the difference between 'absorbed dose' and 'effective dose'?

Q3 Describe how the intensity of gamma radiation changes with distance from the source.

Q4 State the equation for calculating the activity of a radioactive source from its decay constant.

Exam Questions

Q1 Radioactive sources need to be handled carefully to prevent harm to users.

    a) State two health risks radioactive sources pose to humans. [2 marks]

    b) Calculate which of the following absorbed doses would cause the greatest damage to a sample of body tissue: 0.6 Gy of alpha radiation with a quality factor of 20, or 9 Gy of beta radiation with a quality factor of 1. [2 marks]

Q2 A patient is being treated for cancer. The treatment involves placing a radioactive source within the tumour, consisting of an isotope with a decay constant of 3.21×10^{-7} s^{-1}. Each decay produces gamma radiation with an average energy of 2.9×10^{-15} J per decay. The source's activity is 5.03×10^8 Bq. The tumour has a mass of 4.2 g.

    a) Calculate the half-life of the isotope. [1 mark]

    b) Assuming that 40% of the radiation emitted by the source is deposited in the tumour, calculate the absorbed dose delivered to the tumour per second, in grays. [2 marks]

    c) Calculate how long it would take for the source to deliver a dose of 0.50 Gy to the tumour. [1 mark]

It's all about risks, benefits, probabilities and consequences...

Radioactive sources can be dangerous, but they can do a lot of good too. We need to weigh up the risks and the benefits carefully when we're using radiation, and (as always) it's important to take safety procedures seriously.

Binding Energy

Turn off the radio and close the door, 'cos you're going to need to concentrate hard on this stuff about binding energy...

The **Mass Defect** is **Equivalent** to the **Binding Energy**

1) The **mass** of a **nucleus** is **less than** the mass of its **constituent parts** — the difference is called the **mass defect**.

2) Mass and energy are **equivalent**, according to Einstein's equation: (there's more on this equation on pages 162-163).

$$E_{rest} = mc^2$$

E_{rest} is the rest energy in J, m is the mass in kg and c is the speed of light in a vacuum in ms^{-1}.

3) As nucleons join together, the total mass **decreases** — this 'lost' mass is **converted** into energy and **released**.

4) If you then **pulled** the nucleus completely **apart** into its separate nucleons, the **energy** you'd have to use to do it would be the **same** as the energy **released** when the nucleus formed. This is called the **binding energy** and is usually measured in MeV. The binding energy is **equivalent** to the **mass defect**.

5) The binding energy and the mass defect are both **negative** quantities. That's because they correspond to mass (and thus energy) **lost** from the nucleus.

You could also find the binding energy of a nucleus by calculating the rest energy of the nucleus and the rest energy of its constituent parts using the equation above and finding the difference.

6) **Calculating** the binding energy from the mass defect is **pretty easy** — it's just $E = mc^2$, where m is the mass defect:

> **Example:** Calculate the binding energy (in MeV) of the nucleus of a lithium atom, ^6_3Li, given that its mass defect is −0.0343 u.
>
> 1) Convert the mass defect into kg:
>   Mass defect = −0.0343 × (1.661 × 10⁻²⁷) = −5.69723 × 10⁻²⁹ kg
>
> 2) Use $E = mc^2$ to calculate the binding energy:
> $E = (−5.69723 × 10^{-29}) × (3.00 × 10^8)^2 = −5.127507 × 10^{-12}$ J
>
> 3) Convert your answer into electron volts:
> $(−5.127507 × 10^{-12}) ÷ (1.60 × 10^{-19}) = −3.204... × 10^7$ eV
>   1 eV = 1.60 × 10⁻¹⁹ J (p.62)   **= −32.0 MeV (to 3 s.f.)**

Atomic mass is usually given in atomic mass units (u), where 1 u = 1.661 × 10⁻²⁷ kg (see page 170).

The **Binding Energy Per Nucleon** is at a **Maximum** around **N = 50**

A useful way of **comparing** the binding energies of different nuclei is to look at the **binding energy per nucleon**.

$$\text{Binding energy per nucleon (in MeV)} = \frac{\text{Binding energy } (B)}{\text{Nucleon number } (A)}$$

So, the binding energy per nucleon for ^6_3Li (in the example above) is −32 ÷ 6 = −5.3 MeV (to 2 s.f.).

1) If you plot a **graph** of **binding energy per nucleon** against **nucleon number**, for all elements, the line of best fit shows a **curve** — sometimes called a **nuclear valley**.

2) The more negative the binding energy per nucleon, the **more energy** is needed to **remove** nucleons from the nucleus — so the more stable the nucleus.

3) The **most stable** nuclei occur around the **minimum point** on the graph — which is at **nucleon number 56** (i.e. **iron**, Fe). Nuclei with a nucleon number close to 56 are bound **most strongly**.

4) Generally, the nuclear reactions that tend to happen are those that make nuclei **more stable** (apart from in extreme conditions such as during a supernova), so nuclei undergoing nuclear reactions will tend to move towards this valley of stability.

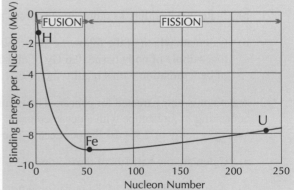

5) **Combining small nuclei** is called nuclear **fusion** (p.179) — this makes the **binding energy per nucleon** much more negative, which means a lot of **energy is released** during nuclear fusion.

6) **Fission** is when **large nuclei** are **split in two** (see p.178) — the **nucleon numbers** of the two **new nuclei** are **smaller** than the original nucleus. This makes the binding energy per nucleon **more negative**. So, energy is also **released** during nuclear fission (but not as much energy per nucleon as in nuclear fusion).

Binding Energy

Use **Binding Energies** to Calculate the **Energy Released** in Nuclear Reactions

1) You can **calculate** the energy released in a **nuclear fission** or **nuclear fusion** reaction (p.178–179) from the **binding energies** of the parent and daughter nuclei — the energy released is equal to the difference between the binding energy of the parent nucleus (or nuclei) and the daughter nucleus (or nuclei).

> **Example:** Uranium-235 (binding energy –1800 MeV) decays to rubidium-92 (binding energy –790 MeV) and caesium-140 (binding energy –1200 MeV) according to the equation:
> $$^{235}_{92}\text{U} \rightarrow {}^{92}_{37}\text{Rb} + {}^{140}_{55}\text{Cs} + 3{}^{1}_{0}\text{n} + \text{energy}.$$ Calculate the energy released in this reaction.

Just find the change in binding energy: –1800 – (–790) – (–1200) = **190 MeV**

> *The neutrons aren't bound to anything, so their binding energies are zero.*

2) You may have to calculate the binding energies of the nuclei involved in a reaction from average **binding energies per nucleon** (as on the graph on page 176).

> **Example:** Deuterium and tritium can fuse to form helium, according to the equation:
> $$^{2}_{1}\text{H} + {}^{3}_{1}\text{H} \rightarrow {}^{4}_{2}\text{He} + {}^{1}_{0}\text{n} + \text{energy}.$$ Calculate how much energy is released in this reaction.

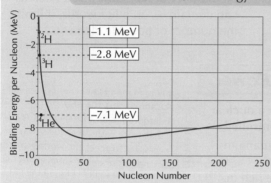

The binding energy per nucleon for deuterium is –1.1 MeV.
The binding energy per nucleon for tritium is –2.8 MeV.
The binding energy per nucleon for helium is –7.1 MeV.

Multiply each of these values by the number of nucleons in each nucleus to find the binding energy of each nucleus:

$$(2 \times -1.1) + (3 \times -2.8) \rightarrow (4 \times -7.1) + 0 + \text{energy}$$
$$(-2.2) + (-8.4) \rightarrow (-28.4) + 0 + \text{energy}$$
$$(-10.6) \rightarrow (-28.4) + 0 + \text{energy}$$

So, energy released = –10.6 – (–28.4) = 17.8 = **18 MeV (to 2 s.f.)**

3) Alternatively, you can calculate the energy released in a nuclear reaction by calculating the **difference in mass** between the parent nucleus (or nuclei) and the daughter nucleus (or nuclei), then using $E = mc^2$ to find the energy that this change in mass is equivalent to.

Practice Questions

Q1 What is the binding energy of a nucleus? How does it relate to the mass defect?

Q2 Sketch a graph of binding energy per nucleon against nucleon number.
Label the regions where fusion and fission occur.

Q3 Which element is the most stable? Explain your answer in terms of the binding energy per nucleon.

Exam Questions

Q1 The mass of a ${}^{14}_{6}\text{C}$ nucleus is 13.99995 u. The mass of a proton is 1.00728 u, and a neutron is 1.00867 u.

a) Calculate the mass defect of a ${}^{14}_{6}\text{C}$ nucleus. Give your answer in atomic mass units.   [2 marks]

b) Calculate the binding energy of the nucleus in MeV.   [3 marks]

Q2 The following equation shows a nuclear reaction between two deuterium (${}^{2}_{1}\text{H}$) nuclei, to form helium-3 (${}^{3}_{2}\text{He}$):
$$^{2}_{1}\text{H} + {}^{2}_{1}\text{H} \rightarrow {}^{3}_{2}\text{He} + {}^{1}_{0}\text{n} + \text{energy}$$

a) What type of nuclear reaction is this?   [1 mark]

b) The binding energy per nucleon is 0 MeV for a neutron, approximately –1.11 MeV for a ${}^{2}_{1}\text{H}$ nucleus, and approximately –2.57 MeV for a ${}^{3}_{2}\text{He}$ nucleus.
Use these values to calculate the energy released by this reaction.   [3 marks]

Don't tie yourself up in knots...

This stuff is a bit of a headache — the idea of a particle having a smaller mass than the particles inside it confuses me no end — but you need to know it. You know the drill by now, back to the top of page 176, and read it all again...

Nuclear Fission and Fusion

What did the nuclear scientist have for her tea? Fission chips... hohoho.

Fission Means Splitting Up into Smaller Parts

1) **Heavy nuclei** (e.g. uranium) are **unstable** and some can randomly **split** into two **smaller** nuclei (and sometimes several neutrons) — this is called **nuclear fission**.

2) This process is called **spontaneous** if it just happens **by itself**, or **induced** if we **encourage** it to happen.

Example:

Fission can be induced by making a neutron enter a ^{235}U nucleus, causing it to become very unstable.

Only low energy neutrons can be captured in this way. A low energy neutron is called a **thermal neutron**.

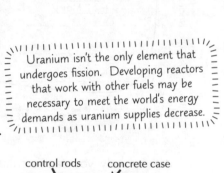

$^{92}_{36}Kr$

$^{1}_{0}n$

$^{1}_{0}n$

$^{1}_{0}n$

fission

$^{1}_{0}n$

$^{235}_{92}U$

Energy

$^{141}_{56}Ba$

3) **Energy is released** during nuclear fission because the new, smaller nuclei have a **higher binding energy per nucleon** (see p.176) and a lower total mass.

4) The **larger** the nucleus, the more **unstable** it will be — so large nuclei are **more likely** to **spontaneously fission**.

5) This means that spontaneous fission **limits** the **number of nucleons** that a nucleus can contain — in other words, it **limits** the number of **possible elements**.

Controlled Nuclear Reactors Produce Useful Power

We can **harness** the **energy** released by nuclear **fission reactions** in a **nuclear reactor**, but it's important that these reactions are very **carefully controlled**.

1) **Uranium** is the main element used as '**fuel**' in nuclear fission (uranium nuclear reactors also release some energy through the fission of plutonium). Nuclear reactors use **fuel rods of uranium** that are rich in ^{235}U. (The rods also contain a lot of ^{238}U, but that doesn't undergo fission.)

2) The **fission** of uranium produces more **neutrons** which then **induce** other nuclei to fission — this is called a **chain reaction**.

3) The **neutrons** will only cause a chain reaction if they are **slowed down** to **thermal neutron** energy levels (see above), so they can be **captured** by the uranium nuclei.

4) To do this, ^{235}U **fuel rods** need to be placed in a **moderator** (for example, **water**). You need to choose a moderator that will slow down some neutrons enough so they can cause **further fission**, keeping the reaction going at a steady rate.

> Uranium isn't the only element that undergoes fission. Developing reactors that work with other fuels may be necessary to meet the world's energy demands as uranium supplies decrease.

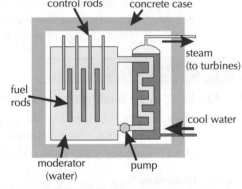

control rods   concrete case

steam (to turbines)

fuel rods

cool water

moderator (water)   pump

5) You want the chain reaction to continue on its own at a **steady rate**, where **one** fission follows another. This means that for each nuclei that fissions, exactly one of the neutrons released triggers another fission. The amount of 'fuel' you need to do this is called the **critical mass** — any less than the critical mass (**sub-critical mass**) and too few neutrons will be captured by other nuclei and the reaction will just peter out. Nuclear reactors use a **supercritical** mass of fuel (where several new fissions normally follow each fission) and **control the rate of fission** using **control rods**.

6) Control rods control the **chain reaction** by **limiting** the number of **neutrons** in the reactor. They **absorb neutrons** so that the **rate of fission** is controlled. **Control rods** are made up of a material that **absorbs neutrons** (e.g. boron), and they can be inserted by varying amounts to control the reaction rate.
In an **emergency**, the reactor will be **shut down** automatically by the **release of the control rods** into the reactor, which will stop the reaction as quickly as possible.

7) **Coolant** is sent around the reactor to **remove heat** produced in the fission — often the coolant is the **same water** that is being used in the reactor as a **moderator**. The **heat** from the reactor can then be used to make **steam** for powering **electricity-generating turbines**.

> If the chain reaction in a nuclear reactor isn't **effectively managed** (such that too few neutrons are absorbed by the control rods), large amounts of **energy** are **released** in a very **short time**.
>
> **Many new fissions will follow each fission**, causing a **runaway reaction** which could lead to an **explosion**. This is what happens in a **fission (atomic) bomb**.

Nuclear Fission and Fusion

There are Costs and Benefits to Nuclear Fission Power Plants

1) Deciding whether or not to build a **nuclear power station** (and if so **where** to build it) is a tricky business.

2) Nuclear fission doesn't produce carbon dioxide, unlike burning **fossil fuels**, so it doesn't contribute to **global warming**. It also provides a **continuous energy supply**, unlike many renewable sources (e.g. wind/solar).

3) However, some of the **waste products** of **nuclear fission** are **highly radioactive** and difficult to handle and store.

4) When waste material is removed from the reactor, it is initially **very hot**, so it is placed in **cooling ponds** until the **temperature falls** to a safe level. The radioactive waste is then **stored** in **sealed containers** in specialist facilities until its **activity has fallen** sufficiently. This can take **many years**, and there's a risk that material could escape from these containers. A leak of radioactive material could be **harmful** to the environment and local human populations both now and in the future, particularly if the material were to contaminate **water supplies**.

5) **Accidents** or **natural disasters** pose a risk to nuclear reactors. In 2011 an earthquake and subsequent tsunami in Japan caused a meltdown at the Fukushima nuclear power plant. Over **100 000 people** were evacuated from the area, and many tonnes of contaminated water leaked into the sea. The **perceived risk** of this kind of disaster leads many people to oppose the construction of nuclear power plants near their homes.

6) Because of all of the safety precautions necessary, **building** and **decommissioning** nuclear power plants is very **time-consuming** and **expensive**.

Fusion Means Joining Nuclei Together

1) **Two light nuclei** can **combine** to create a larger nucleus. This is called **nuclear fusion**.

2) Nuclei can **only fuse** if they have enough energy to overcome the **electrostatic** (Coulomb) **repulsion** between them (p.170), and get close enough for the **strong interaction** to bind them.

3) This means fusion reactions require **much higher temperatures** than fission, as well as high pressures (or high densities). Under such conditions, generally only found inside stars, matter turns into a state called a **plasma**.

4) A lot of **energy** is released during nuclear fusion because the new, heavier nucleus has a **much higher binding energy per nucleon** (and so a lower total mass, see p.176). The energy released helps to **maintain the high temperatures** needed for further fusion reactions.

5) Although the energy released per reaction is generally **lower** in nuclear fusion than fission, the nuclei used in fusion have a **lower mass**, so a mole of the reactants in a fusion reaction weighs less than a mole of the reactants in a fission reaction (p.178). Gram for gram, fusion can release **more energy** than fission.

6) Scientists are trying to develop fusion reactors so that we can generate nuclear **electricity** without the waste you get from fission reactors, but they haven't yet succeeded in creating one that makes more electricity than it uses.

Example: In the Sun, **hydrogen nuclei** fuse to form **helium**:

$${}^2_1H + {}^1_1H \rightarrow {}^3_2He + energy$$

> Nuclear fission and fusion equations need to be balanced, see p.171.

> There's more on moles on p.136.

Practice Questions

Q1 What is meant by the term 'induced fission'?

Q2 Explain what is meant by the expressions 'chain reaction', 'fuel rods' and 'moderator' in terms of nuclear fission.

Q3 What are the similarities and differences between nuclear fusion and fission?

Exam Questions

Q1 Nuclear reactors use carefully controlled chain reactions to produce energy.

a) Describe and explain one feature of a nuclear reactor whose role is to control the rate of fission. Include an example of a suitable material for the feature you have chosen. [3 marks]

b) Explain what happens in a nuclear reactor during an emergency shut-down. [2 marks]

Q2 Discuss two advantages and two disadvantages of using nuclear fission to produce electricity. [4 marks]

If anyone asks, I've gone fission... that joke never gets old...

So, controlled nuclear fission reactions can provide a shedload of energy to generate electricity without producing pesky carbon dioxide, but nuclear energy has costs and risks too... Nothing's ever simple, is it?

Exam Structure and Technique

Good exam technique can make a big difference to your mark, so make sure you read this stuff carefully.

Get Familiar With the **Exam Structure**

For A-level Physics, you'll be sitting **three papers**. You'll need to know the content of **all the modules** in this book for **all three** of your exams.

You'll also do a Practical Endorsement as part of your A-level. It'll involve doing practicals throughout the course, and will be reported separately from your exam results.

Paper 1 — Fundamentals of physics   2 hours 15 minutes
110 marks: 30 for **Section A** (**multiple choice** questions)
   ≈ **20** for **Section B** (**short answer** questions)
   ≈ **60** for **Section C** (**short answer** and **extended response** questions)
	41% of your A-level

Paper 2 — Scientific literacy in physics   2 hours 15 minutes
100 marks: ≈ **30** for **Section A** (**short answer** questions)
   ≈ **45** for **Section B** (**short answer** and **extended response** questions)
   ≈ **25** for **Section C** (**short answer** and **extended response** questions, based on the **Advance Notice article** that you'll be given before the exam)
	37% of your A-level

Paper 3 — Practical skills in physics 1 hour 30 minutes **60 marks**: ≈ **40** for **Section A** (**short answer** and **extended response** questions) ≈ **20** for **Section B** (**short answer** and **extended response** questions, mainly about data analysis).	**22%** of your A-level

If you're taking AS Physics, you'll do different exams altogether.

The **Advance Notice article** for Paper 2 is an article (or articles) on a topic related to something you have **studied** during the course, which you'll need to refer to when answering the questions in **Section C**. It'll be available from the **March** before you sit your A levels, and your teacher should give it to you at least 4 weeks before your exams. **Read it through** carefully **before** the exam — there won't be time to read it in the test. You'll probably go through and discuss it with your **teacher**, and you may want to do some **further research** on the subject it covers. You **can't take any notes** on it into the exam with you — you'll be given a **fresh copy** with your test paper.

Make Sure you Think About **Exam Technique**

1) It's really important you read each question **carefully**, and give an answer that matches what you've been asked.

2) Look for **command words** in the question — they'll give you an idea of the **kind of answer** you should write. Commonly used command words for written questions are **state**, **describe**, **discuss** and **explain**:

- If a question asks you to **state** something, you just need to give a **definition**, **example** or **fact**.
- If you're asked to **describe** what happens in a particular situation, don't waste time explaining why it happens — that's not what the question is after.
- For **discuss** questions, you'll need to include more **detail** — depending on the question you might need to cover what happens, what the effects are, and perhaps include a brief explanation of why it happens.
- If a question asks you to **explain** why something happens you must give **reasons**, not just a description.

3) Look at **how many marks** a question is worth before answering. It'll tell you roughly **how much information** you need to include. See the next page for more about **wordy questions**.

4) The **number of marks** also tells you roughly **how long** to spend on a question — there's just over a minute per mark in the exam. If you get stuck on a question for too long, it may be best to **move on**.

5) The **multiple choice questions** are only worth **one mark each**, so it's not worth stressing over one for ages if you get stuck — you can always come back to it later if there's time at the end.

6) You don't have to work through the paper **in order** — you could leave questions on topics you find harder until last.

You may get some weird questions that seem to have nothing to do with anything you've learnt. DON'T PANIC. Every question will be something you can answer using physics you know, it just may be in a new context.

1) Answering these trickier questions will get you top marks, but make sure you cover the easier marks first.

2) All of the A-level exams could pull together ideas from different parts of physics, so check the question for any keywords that you recognise. For example, if a question talks about acceleration, think about the rules and equations you know, and whether any of them apply to the situation in the question.

Exam Structure and Technique

Be *Prepared* for *Practical Questions...*

1) **Practical skills** are a big part of your course — they're particularly important for **Paper 3**, but could come up in **Paper 1** and **Paper 2** as well, so make sure you're comfortable with everything in **modules 1 and 2** (on practical skills and data analysis) **before your exams** start.

2) You may have to **describe an experiment** to investigate something, or **answer questions** on an experiment you've been given. These could be experiments you've **met before**, or they could be **entirely new** to you.

3) All the questions will be based on physics that you've **covered**, but may include bits from different topics put together in ways you haven't seen before. Don't let this put you off, just **think carefully** about what's going on.

4) Make sure you know the difference between **precision**, **accuracy** and **validity** (p.8). Learn what **uncertainty**, **random errors** and **systematic errors** are (p.12) and make sure you can give some examples of where each might come from.

5) You need to be able to **calculate errors** and **plot** and **interpret graphs** too.

...and *Wordy Ones*

For some questions, you'll need to write a slightly longer answer, where the '**quality** of your **extended response**' will be taken into account. You'll need to make sure you can develop a **clear** and **logical**, **well-structured line of reasoning**, backed up with **relevant information**.

You can avoid losing marks in these questions by making sure you do the following things:

1) Think about your answer before you write it. Your answer needs to be **logically structured** to get the top marks.

2) Make sure your answer is **relevant** to the question being asked and that you **explain** your ideas or argument **clearly**. It's dead easy to go off on a tangent.

3) Back up your points with **evidence** or **explanation**. You'll lose marks if you just make statements without supporting them.

4) Write in **whole sentences** and keep an eye on your **spelling**, **grammar** and **punctuation**. It'll help make sure your answer is clear and easy to read.

> Questions like this will be marked in some way in the exam — e.g. with an asterisk (*). Check the instructions on the front of your paper to find out.

Example: A large group of people walk across a footbridge. When the frequency of the group's footsteps is 1 Hz, the bridge noticeably oscillates.

Describe the phenomenon causing the bridge to oscillate, and suggest what engineers could do to solve this problem. *[6 marks]*

Good Answer

The pedestrians provide a driving force on the bridge, causing it to oscillate. At around 1 Hz, the driving frequency from the pedestrians is roughly equal to the natural frequency of the bridge, causing it to resonate. The amplitude of the bridge's oscillations when resonating at 1 Hz will be greater than at any other driving frequency. The oscillations at this frequency are large enough to be noticed by pedestrians. Engineers could fix this problem by critically damping the bridge to stop any oscillations as quickly as possible. They could also adjust the natural frequency of the bridge so that it was not so close to a known walking frequency of large groups of people.

Bad Answer

resonance
driving frequency = natural frequency
damping

> There's nothing fundamentally wrong with the physics in the bad answer, but you'd miss out on some nice easy marks just for not bothering to link the physics with the context given and not putting your answer into proper sentences.

The penultimate joke in the book better be good... here goes... Oh, I've run out of space...

Make sure you use your exam timetable to plan your revision carefully, and give yourself enough time to revise everything. If you leave it all till the night before, you won't be at your best on the day and might not do as well in the exam...

Maths Skills

At least 40% of the marks up for grabs in A-level Physics will require maths skills, so make sure you know your stuff. As well as being given some tricky calculations, you could be asked to work with exponentials and logarithms and work out values from log graphs. And it's easy when you know how...

Be **Careful** With **Calculations**

1) In calculation questions you should always **show your working** — you may get some marks for your **method** even if you get the answer wrong.

2) Don't **round** your answer until the **very end**. A lot of calculations in A-level Physics are quite **long**, and if you round too early you could introduce errors to your final answer.

3) Be careful with **units**. Lots of formulas require quantities to be in specific units (e.g. time in seconds), so it's best to **convert** any numbers you're given into these before you start. And obviously, if the question **tells** you which units to give your answer in, don't throw away marks by giving it in different ones.

There's more on quantities and their units on p.10.

4) You should give your final answer to the same number of **significant figures** as the data that you use from the question with the **least number** of significant figures (or one more). If you can, write out the **unrounded answer**, then your **rounded** answer with the number of significant figures you've given it to — it shows you know your stuff.

Many Relationships in Physics are **Exponential**

A fair few of the relationships you need to know about in A-level Physics are **exponential** — where the **rate of change** of a quantity is **proportional** to the **amount** of the quantity left. Here are a few that crop up in the A-level course (if they don't ring a bell, go have a quick read about them)...

The equation for finding the Boltzmann factor also includes an exponential function (p.142).

Charge on a capacitor — the decay of charge on a discharging capacitor is proportional to the amount of charge left on the capacitor:
There are also exponential relationships for I and V and for charging capacitors.

$$Q = Q_0 e^{\frac{-t}{CR}}$$ (see p.107)

Radioactive decay — the rate of decay of a radioactive sample is proportional to the **number of undecayed nuclei** in the sample:
The activity of a radioactive sample behaves in the same way.

$$N = N_0 e^{-\lambda t}$$ (see p.104)

You can **Plot** Exponential Relations Using the **Natural Log, ln**

1) Say you've got two variables, x and y, which are related to each other by the formula $y = ke^{-ax}$ (where k and a are constants).

2) The **natural logarithm** of x, **ln** x, is the power to which e (the base) must be raised to to give x.

A logarithm can be to any base you want. Another common one is 'base 10' which is usually written as 'log$_{10}$' or just 'log'.

3) So, by definition, $e^{\ln x} = x$ and $\ln(e^x) = x$.
So far so good... now you need some **log rules**:

$$\ln(AB) = \ln A + \ln B \qquad \ln\left(\frac{A}{B}\right) = \ln A - \ln B \qquad \ln x^n = n \ln x$$

These log rules work for all logs (including the natural logarithm) and you're given them on your formula sheet.

4) So, for $y = ke^{-ax}$, if you take the natural log of both sides of the equation you get:

$$\ln y = \ln(ke^{-ax}) = \ln k + \ln(e^{-ax}) \implies \boxed{\ln y = \ln k - ax}$$

5) Then all you need to do is plot $(\ln y)$ against x, and Eric's your aunty: $\implies$

You get a **straight-line graph** with $(\ln k)$ as the **vertical intercept**, and $-a$ as the **gradient**.

Maths Skills

You Might be Asked to find the *Gradient* of a Log Graph

This log business isn't too bad when you get your head around which bit of the log graph means what.

Example: The graph shows the radioactive decay of isotope X.

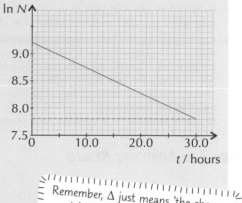

a) Find the initial number of undecayed nuclei, N_0, in the sample.

You know that the number of undecayed nuclei in a sample, N, is related to the initial number of undecayed nuclei, N_0, by the equation $N = N_0 e^{-\lambda t}$.

So: $\ln N = \ln N_0 - \lambda t$

The y-intercept of the graph is $\ln N_0 = 9.2$

$N_0 = e^{9.2} = 9897.129... = $ **9900 nuclei (to 2 s.f.)**

b) Find the decay constant λ of isotope X.

Remember, Δ just means 'the change in'. So Δt is the change in t.

$-\lambda$ is the gradient of the graph, so: $\lambda = \dfrac{\Delta \ln N}{\Delta t} = \dfrac{9.2 - 7.8}{30.0 \times 60 \times 60} = $ **1.3×10^{-5} s^{-1} (to 2 s.f.)**

You can Plot *Any Power Law* as a *Log-Log Graph*

You can use logs to plot a straight-line graph of **any power law** — it doesn't have to be an exponential.

Say the relationship between two variables x and y is:

$$y = kx^n$$

Take the **log** (base 10) of both sides to get:

$$\log y = \log k + n \log x$$

So **log k** will be the **y-intercept** and **n** will be the **gradient** of the graph.

When it came to logs, Geoff always took time to smell the flowers...

Example:

The graph shows how the intensity of radiation from the Sun, I, varies with distance from the Sun, d. I is related to d by the power law $I = kd^n$.
Find n.

$\log I = \log (kd^n) = \log k + \log d^n$
$\qquad = \log k + n \log d$

So n is the gradient of the graph.
Reading from the graph:

$$n = \dfrac{\Delta \log I}{\Delta \log d} = \dfrac{5.4 - 15.4}{10 - 5} = -2$$

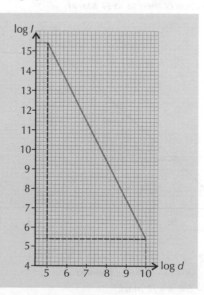

Lumberjacks are great musicians — they have a natural logarhythm...

Well, that's it folks. Crack open the chocolate bar of victory and know you've earned it. Only the tiny detail of the actual exam to go... ahem. Make sure you know which bit means what on a log graph and you'll pick up some nice easy marks. Other than that, stay calm, be as clear as you can and good luck — I've got my fingers, toes and eyes crossed for you.

Answers

Module 1 — Development of Practical Skills in Physics

Page 5 — Planning and Implementing

1 a) Independent variable: light level / distance from the light source, dependent variable: resistance of the LDR *[1 mark]*.

b) Any two of: e.g. the light source used / the angle of the light source to the LDR / the background lighting in the room / the temperature of the room/LDR/wires / the potential difference / the power supply the LDR is connected to / the length of wires in the circuit / the type of wires in the circuit / the multimeter used to measure the resistance.
[2 marks available — 1 mark for each correct answer.]

Page 7 — Analysing Results

1 a)

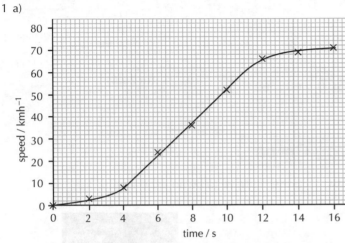

[1 mark for both axes drawn to a sensible scale and 1 mark for labelling both axes correctly, 1 mark for all the points drawn correctly, and 1 mark for a sensible line of best fit.]

b) The graph is linear between 4 and 10 seconds *[1 mark]*.
Accept 11 seconds as the upper limit if the graph in part a) agrees.

c) The maximum acceleration is the value of the steepest gradient, which is the linear portion of the graph *[1 mark]*:

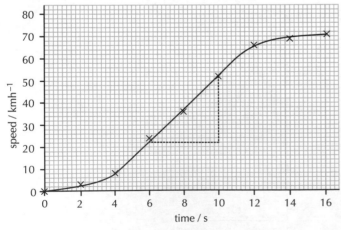

change in speed = 52 − 22 = 30 km h^{-1} = 30 ÷ (60 × 60)
= 0.008333... km s^{-1} *[1 mark]*

change in time = 10 − 6 = 4 s *[1 mark]*

acceleration = 0.008333... ÷ 4 = 0.002083... km s^{-2}
= **0.0021 km s^{-2}** or **27000 km h^{-2} (to 2 s.f.)** *[1 mark]*
Accept an answer in the range 0.0020-0.0022 km s^{-2} or 26000-28000 km h^{-2}.

Page 9 — Evaluating and Concluding

1 50 − (50 × 0.02 / 100) = 49.99 Ω, so the answer is **B**. *[1 mark]*

2 a) t = 0.32 seconds, v = 2.0 ms^{-1} *[1 mark]*

b) E.g. The results do not support this conclusion *[1 mark]*, because the student has only collected data for a small range of times so he cannot draw conclusions about times longer than those he measured *[1 mark]* / because the student has only investigated one object so he cannot draw conclusions about other objects *[1 mark]*.

Module 2 — Fundamental Data Analysis

Page 11 — Quantities, Units and Graphs

1 Work done = force × distance, and force = mass × acceleration. Velocity is distance ÷ time, so has units ms^{-1}. Acceleration is rate of change of velocity, so has units ms^{-1} ÷ s = ms^{-2}.
So the units of work are:
(units of mass) × (units of acceleration) × (units of distance)
[1 mark] = kg × ms^{-2} × m = kg m^2 s^{-2} *[1 mark]*

2 a) You can tell the axes are logarithmic because the increments represent a change by an equal factor *[1 mark]*.
The increments on the horizontal axis increase by a factor of 10 each time, whilst the vertical axis increments increase by a factor of 10^2 each time *[1 mark]*.

b) A sound with a frequency of 100 Hz would need to have an intensity of at least 10^{-8} Wm^{-2} to be heard by a human *[1 mark]*.

Page 13 — Measurements and Uncertainties

1 a) (0.02 ÷ 0.52) × 100 = 3.846... = **3.8 % (to 2 s.f.)** *[1 mark]*

b) (0.02 ÷ 0.94) × 100 = 2.127... = **2.1% (to 2 s.f.)** *[1 mark]*

c) acceleration = change in velocity / time = (0.94 − 0.52) ÷ 2.5
= 0.168 ms^{-2} *[1 mark]*

Absolute error in change of velocity = 0.02 + 0.02 = 0.04 ms^{-1}
Percentage error in change of velocity:
(0.04 ÷ (0.94 − 0.52)) × 100 = 9.523...% *[1 mark]*
Percentage error in time taken = (0.5 ÷ 2.5) × 100 = 20%
Percentage error in acceleration = 9.523...% + 20%
= 29.523...% *[1 mark]*

Absolute error in acceleration = 0.168 × (29.523... ÷ 100)
= 0.0496 ms^{-2}

So the acceleration = **0.17 ± 0.05 ms^{-2} (to 2 s.f.)** *[1 mark]*

Module 3: Section 1 — Imaging and Signalling

Page 15 — The Nature of Waves

1 a) $v = f\lambda$ and $f = 1 / T$
So $v = \lambda / T$, giving $\lambda = vT$ *[1 mark]*
λ = 3.0 × 6.0 = **18 m** *[1 mark]*
The vertical movement of the buoy is irrelevant to this part of the question.

b) The trough to peak distance is twice the amplitude, so the amplitude is 0.60 m *[1 mark]*

2 $I = P ÷ A$ = 10.0 ÷ 0.002 = **5000 Wm^{-2}** *[1 mark]*

Answers

Page 17 — Polarisation

1 a) They are at right angles to one another (90°, 270° etc.) *[1 mark]*.

b) It would be half of the intensity *[1 mark]*.
This is because at 45° the vertical and horizontal contributions are equal, so the intensity is halved between them.

c) E.g. Polaroid sunglasses or 3D film glasses *[1 mark]*.

Page 20 — Forming Images with Lenses

1 a) Rays meeting the lens parallel to the principal axis converge at the focal point. / Waves parallel to the lens axis are given spherical curvature as they pass through the lens. This curvature is centred on the focal point. *[1 mark]*

b) $\frac{1}{v} = \frac{1}{u} + \frac{1}{f}$ so $\frac{1}{v} = -\frac{1}{0.2} + \frac{1}{0.15} = \frac{5}{3}$ *[1 mark]*,
so $v = \frac{3}{5} = $ **0.60 m** *[1 mark]*

2 a) $m = \frac{\text{size of image}}{\text{size of object}} = \frac{47.2}{12.5} = 3.776 = $ **3.78 (to 3 s.f.)** *[1 mark]*

b) $m = \frac{v}{u}$, giving $v = m \times u$ *[1 mark]*
$v = 3.776 \times 4.0 = 15.104 = $ **15 mm (to 2 s.f.)** *[1 mark]*

c) $P = \frac{1}{f} = \frac{1}{v} - \frac{1}{u}$ *[1 mark]*, so $P = \frac{1}{0.015104} - \left(-\frac{1}{0.004}\right) = 316.20...$
$= $ **320 D (to 2 s.f.)** *[1 mark]*

Remember u is negative.

Page 23 — Information in Images

1 a) Number of bits = $\log_2(65\,536) = 16$ *[1 mark]*.
Number of bytes = number of bits ÷ 8 = 16 ÷ 8 = **2 bytes** *[1 mark]*

b) total information = number of pixels × bits per pixel
$= (1920 \times 1080) \times 16 = 3.3177... \times 10^7$
$= $ **3.32 × 10^7 bits (to 3 s.f.)** *[1 mark]*

c) width of square = 1920 × 0.25 = 480 pixels *[1 mark]*
resolution = real size of object ÷ pixels representing object
$= 1.5 \div 480 = 3.125 \times 10^{-3}$
$= $ **3.1 × 10^{-3} m pixel^{-1}** *[1 mark]*

2 a)

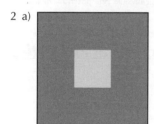

The diagram should show a fairly uniform mid-grey outside, with a lighter square in the centre. *[1 mark]*

b) Noise can be removed by replacing each pixel with the median of itself and the eight pixels surrounding it. *[1 mark]*

c)

100	99	100
97	100	98
101	101	98

[1 mark]

Page 25 — Digital and Analogue Signals

1 a) time period of shortest repeating part = $(1.25 - 0.25) \times 10^{-3}$
$= 1.0 \times 10^{-3}$ s

$f = \frac{1}{T} = \frac{1}{1.0 \times 10^{-3}} = $ **1000 Hz** *[1 mark]*

b)

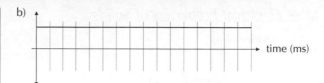

time (ms)

[1 mark for a straight line and 1 mark for the line being above the horizontal axis]
The graph is a straight line because the sample frequency is the same as the fundamental frequency.

Page 27 — Sampling and Transmitting Signals

1 $b = \log_2\left(\frac{V_{total}}{V_{noise}}\right)$ *[1 mark]* $= \log_2\left(\frac{160}{10}\right) = \log_2 16 = $ **4 bits** *[1 mark]*
You don't need to convert the variations from mV to V because the units cancel in the fraction.

2 a) Rate of transmission = samples per second × bits per sample
$= 8000 \times 8$
$= $ **64 000 bits per second** *[1 mark]*

b) 1 byte = 8 bits.
So, 64 000 bits per second = **8000 bytes per second** *[1 mark]*

3 a) rate of transmission = samples per second × bits per sample, so
samples per second = $\frac{\text{rates of transmission}}{\text{bits per sample}} = \frac{128 \times 10^3}{16}$
$= $ **8000 Hz** *[1 mark]*

b) rate of transmission = number of bits to transmit ÷ time taken
number of bits = $(2.0 \times 10^6) \times 8 = 1.6 \times 10^7$ bits *[1 mark]*
rate of transmission = $\frac{1.6 \times 10^7}{110} = 145\,454 = $ **150 kbit s^{-1} (to 2 s.f.)**
[1 mark] 150 > 128, so yes — the connection is sufficient to stream the radio station. *[1 mark]*

Module 3: Section 2 — Sensing

Page 29 — Charge, Current and Potential Difference

1 a) $P = \frac{W}{t} = \frac{75}{6.0} = 12.5 = $ **13 W (to 2 s.f.)** *[1 mark]*

b) $V = \frac{P}{I} = \frac{12.5}{0.18} = 69.44... = $ **69 V (to 2 s.f.)** *[1 mark]*

2 Energy transferred to water = 0.88 × electrical energy input
so the energy input will be 308 / 0.88 = 350 J *[1 mark]*
$V = \frac{W}{Q}$ so $Q = \frac{W}{V}$
$Q = 350 / 230 = 1.52... = $ **1.5 C (to 2 s.f.)** *[1 mark]*
The heat energy that the kettle transfers to the water is less than the electrical energy input because less than 100% of the electrical energy is transferred to the water.

Page 31 — Resistance and Conductance

1 a) $R = \frac{V}{I} = \frac{1.5}{2.8} = 0.5357... = $ **0.54 Ω (to 2 s.f.)** *[1 mark]*

b) $G = \frac{I}{V} = \frac{0.15}{1.5} = $ **0.10 S (or 0.10 Ω^{-1})** *[1 mark]*

c) The wires have a resistance that causes power dissipation *[1 mark]*. The power that is dissipated is transferred to heat, making the wires warm *[1 mark]*.

Answers

Page 33 — Electrical Properties of Solids

1 a) E.g.

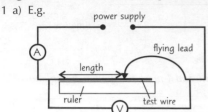

[1 mark for sensible circuit diagram]

Measure the diameter of the wire using a micrometer (to calculate the cross-sectional area) *[1 mark]*. Connect the wire in a circuit as shown above. Use the flying lead to vary the length of wire connected to the circuit *[1 mark]*. Take a measurement from the voltmeter and the ammeter for each length of wire used, and use these to calculate the wire's resistance at each length using the formula $R = \frac{V}{I}$ *[1 mark]*. Plot a graph of resistance against length, then calculate the gradient of the line of best fit *[1 mark]*. Multiply the gradient of the graph by the cross-sectional area to get ρ (as $\rho = \frac{RA}{L}$). *[1 mark]*

b) E.g.

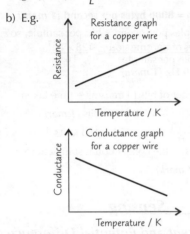

[1 mark for each correct graph]

The graphs of resistance and conductance against temperature for a copper wire are straight lines, the graphs for an NTC thermistor are curves in the opposite direction *[1 mark]*. This is because copper is a metal and has a high number of mobile charge carriers. As temperature increases, the electrons become less free to move so resistance increases and conductance decreases *[1 mark]*. An NTC thermistor is a semiconductor so has fewer free electrons to begin with, but as temperature increases more electrons are freed so conductance rapidly increases and resistance rapidly decreases. *[1 mark]*

Page 35 — E.m.f. and Internal Resistance

1 a) $\varepsilon = I(R + r)$ so $I = \varepsilon/(R + r) = 24/(4.0 + 0.80)$ *[1 mark]*
= **5.0 A (to 2 s.f.)** *[1 mark]*

b) $v = Ir = 5.0 \times 0.80 = $ **4.0 V (to 2 s.f.)** *[1 mark]*
You could have used $\varepsilon = V + v$ and calculated V using $V = IR_{drill}$

2 **C** *[1 mark]*
$\varepsilon = I(R + r)$, but since there are two cells in series replace r with $2r$, and ε with 2ε, then rearrange to find I.

Page 37 — Conservation of Energy & Charge in Circuits

1 a) Resistance of parallel resistors:
$1/R_{parallel} = 1/6.0 + 1/3.0 = 1/2 \Rightarrow R_{parallel} = 2.0\,\Omega$ *[1 mark]*

Total resistance:
$R_{total} = 4.0 + R_{parallel} = 4.0 + 2.0 = $ **6.0 Ω** *[1 mark]*

b) $V = I_3 R_{total} \Rightarrow I_3 = V / R_{total} = 12 / 6.0 = $ **2.0 A** *[1 mark]*

c) $V = IR = 2.0 \times 4.0 = $ **8.0 V** *[1 mark]*

d) E.m.f. = sum of p.d.s in circuit, so $12 = 8.0 + V_{parallel}$
$V_{parallel} = 12 - 8.0 = $ **4.0 V** *[1 mark]*

e) $I = V/R$, so $I_1 = 4.0 / 3.0 = $ **1.3 A (to 2 s.f.)** *[1 mark]*
$I_2 = 4.0 / 6.0 = $ **0.67 A (to 2 s.f.)** *[1 mark]*
You can check your answers by making sure that $I_3 = I_2 + I_1$.

Page 39 — The Potential Divider

1 a) $V_A / V_B = R_A / R_B$ so $V_A = V_B \times (R_A / R_B)$
$= 6.75 \times (35 \div 45) = $ **5.25 V** *[1 mark]*

b) Input p.d. $= V_A + V_B = 5.25 + 6.75 = $ **12 V** *[1 mark]*

c) $V_B = \frac{R_B}{R_A + R_B} V_{in} = \frac{45}{75 + 45} \times 12 = $ **4.5 V** *[1 mark]*

2 a) $V_{AB} = \frac{R_2}{R_1 + R_2} V_{in} = (50 / (30 + 50)) \times 12 = 7.5\,V$ *[1 mark]*
Ignore the 10 Ω — no current flows that way.

b) Total resistance R_T of the parallel circuit:
$1/R_T = 1 / 50 + 1 / (10 + 40) = 1 / 25$
$R_T = 25\,\Omega$ *[1 mark]*

Use $V_{out} = (R_2 / (R_1 + R_2)) V_{in}$ to find the p.d. over the whole parallel arrangement: $(25 / (30 + 25)) \times 12 = 5.454...\,V$ *[1 mark]*

Use $V_{out} = (R_2 / R_1 + R_2) V_{in}$ again to find the p.d. across AB:
$V_{AB} = 40 / (40 + 10) \times 5.454... = 4.363...$
= **4.4 V (to 2 s.f.)** *[1 mark]*

current through 40 Ω resistor $= V/R$
$= 4.363... / 40 = $ **0.11 A (to 2 s.f.)** *[1 mark]*
This question might look tricky, but it's basically just one potential divider on top of another.

Module 3: Section 3 — Mechanical Properties of Materials

Page 41 — Hooke's Law

1 a) First find the force constant:
$F = kx$ and so $k = F \div x$
$k = 10 \div (4.0 \times 10^{-3}) = $ **2500 Nm^{-1}** *[1 mark]*
Now find the extension when the 15 N force is applied:
$x = F \div k = 15 \div 2500 = $ **6.0 × 10^{-3} m** or **6.0 mm** *[1 mark]*
You could also find the new extension by using the fact that force is proportional to extension. The new force is 1.5 times the original force, so the new extension will be 1.5 times the original extension: 1.5 × 4.0 mm = 6.0 mm.

b) Any one from e.g. the string now stretches much further for small increases in force *[1 mark]*. / When the string is loosened it is longer than at the start *[1 mark]*.

2 If the rubber band obeys Hooke's law, then force will be proportional to extension ($F = kx$). 5.0 N is double 2.5 N, so increasing the load should mean the extension is doubled too. The extension under the 2.5 N load is 10.4 – 6.0 = 4.4 cm. The extension under the 5.0 N load is 16.2 – 6.0 = 10.2 cm. 10.2 is not double 4.4 *[1 mark]*, so the rubber band does not obey Hooke's law *[1 mark]*.
Or you could show that k is different for 2.5 N and 5.0 N.

Answers

Page 43 — Stress, Strain and Elastic Energy

1 a) strain = extension ÷ original length
$$= 4.0 \times 10^{-3} \div 2.00 = \mathbf{2.0 \times 10^{-3}} \textbf{ (to 2 s.f.)} \textit{ [1 mark]}$$

  b) stress = tension ÷ cross-sectional area
$$A = \pi r^2 \text{ or } \pi (d^2 \div 4) = \pi \times ((1.0 \times 10^{-3})^2 \div 4)$$
$$= 7.8539... \times 10^{-7} \text{ m}^2 \textit{ [1 mark]}$$
    stress $= 300 \div (7.8539... \times 10^{-7})$
$$= \mathbf{3.8 \times 10^8 \text{ Nm}^{-2}} \textbf{ (to 2 s.f.)} \textit{ [1 mark]}$$

2 a) $F = kx$ so $k = F \div x = 50 \div (3.0 \times 10^{-3})$
$$= \mathbf{1.7 \times 10^4 \text{ Nm}^{-1}} \textbf{ (to 2 s.f.)} \textit{ [1 mark]}$$

  b) $E = \frac{1}{2}Fx = \frac{1}{2} \times 50 \times 3.0 \times 10^{-3} = \mathbf{7.5 \times 10^{-2} \text{ J}} \textit{ [1 mark]}$
You could also find E using $E = \frac{1}{2}kx^2$ with your value of k from part a).

3 $E = \frac{1}{2}kx^2 = \frac{1}{2} \times 40.8 \times 0.05^2 = 0.051 \text{ J} \textit{ [1 mark]}$
To find maximum speed, assume all this energy is converted to kinetic energy in the ball. $E_{kinetic} = E$
$E = \frac{1}{2}mv^2$, so $v^2 = 2E \div m$ *[1 mark]*
$v^2 = (2 \times 0.051) \div 0.012 = 8.5$
So $v = \mathbf{2.92 \text{ ms}^{-1}} \textbf{ (to 3 s.f.)} \textit{ [1 mark]}$

Page 45 — The Young Modulus

1 a) $E = $ stress ÷ strain, so strain = stress ÷ E
$$= 2.6 \times 10^8 \div 1.3 \times 10^{11} \textit{ [1 mark]}$$
$$= \mathbf{2.0 \times 10^{-3}} \textit{ [1 mark]}$$

  b) stress = tension ÷ cross-sectional area, so:
cross-sectional area = tension ÷ stress $= 100 \div (2.6 \times 10^8)$
$$= \mathbf{3.8 \times 10^{-7} \text{ m}^2} \textbf{ (to 2 s.f.)} \textit{ [1 mark]}$$

2 Cross-sectional area $= \pi r^2$ or $\pi (d^2 \div 4)$.
So the cross-sectional area $= \pi \times ((0.6 \times 10^{-3})^2 \div 4)$
$$= 2.827... \times 10^{-7} \textit{ [1 mark]}$$
stress = tension ÷ cross-sectional area
$$= 80 \div (2.827... \times 10^{-7}) = 2.829... \times 10^8 \textit{ [1 mark]}$$
strain = extension ÷ original length $= (3.6 \times 10^{-3}) \div 2.50$
$$= 1.44 \times 10^{-3} \textit{ [1 mark]}$$
$E = $ stress ÷ strain $= (2.829... \times 10^8) \div (1.44 \times 10^{-3}) \textit{ [1 mark]}$
$$= 1.964... \times 10^{11} = \mathbf{2.0 \times 10^{11} \text{ Nm}^{-2}} \textbf{ (to 2 s.f.)} \textit{ [1 mark]}$$

3 The Young modulus is the gradient of a stress-strain graph, so
$$E = \frac{10 \times 10^8}{15 \times 10^{-3}} = 6.66... \times 10^{10}$$
$$= \mathbf{6.7 \times 10^{10} \text{ Nm}^{-2}} \textbf{ (to 2 s.f.)} \textit{ [1 mark]}$$

Page 47 — Mechanical Properties of Solids

1 Material C would be the best choice as it has a strength of 2000 MPa *[1 mark]*. Support beams for bridges need to be strong enough to support heavy loads without deforming *[1 mark]*. This is more important than toughness, so whilst other materials are tougher, they would be less suitable as their strength is much smaller than material C's *[1 mark]*.

2 *5-6 marks:*
The answer clearly explains three properties of materials and why they would be useful when creating riding helmets.
The answer is structured in a logical way, with relevant information supporting it throughout.

3-4 marks:
The answer either: describes two properties of materials and fully explains why they would be useful when creating riding helmets or correctly identifies three useful material properties with minimal explanation for why they would be useful when creating riding helmets. The answer has some logical structure, with mostly relevant information supporting it.

1-2 marks:
The answer describes two properties without explanation, or correctly describes one property with a brief explanation as to why it is useful when creating riding helmets.
The answer is basic, poorly structured and unsupported by relevant information.

0 marks:
No relevant information is given.

Here are some points your answer may include:
- The material would need to be stiff so that it would keep its shape and not crush the rider's head when a force was applied to it.
- It would also need to be tough so that it could absorb the energy of an impact without breaking.
- The material should be strong so that the helmet withstands the force of the impact without deforming or breaking.

Answers

Page 49 — Structures of Materials

1 a) Instead of increasing the space between the ions in the metal, the applied force causes planes of ions to slip across each other. This slipping is what causes the plastic deformation *[1 mark]*. Dislocations or imperfections lower the stress needed to cause slipping, meaning that a lower stress is needed in order to cause plastic deformation *[1 mark]*.

b) Alloying a metal is the process of adding ions from a second material into the crystal lattice *[1 mark]*. These ions are placed inside dislocations to 'pin' them down *[1 mark]*. This means a greater stress is needed to cause slipping, and so the chance of slipping is reduced *[1 mark]*. Alloying the sample will make it harder and less ductile *[1 mark]*.

2 C *[1 mark]*

3 **5-6 marks:**

The answer thoroughly describes two methods and how they measure the size and/or spacings of atoms. References may be made to other additional methods. The time frame has been referenced, showing an appreciation that increased knowledge has lead to the creation of new methods which can directly observe atomic size.
The answer is structured in a logical way, with relevant information supporting it throughout.

3-4 marks:

The answer correctly identifies two methods for calculating atomic size and/or spacing. Brief explanations of these methods are given. No reference to how changing methods over time have lead to direct measurements of atomic sizes/spacing. The answer has some logical structure, with mostly relevant information supporting it.

1-2 marks:

The answer attempts to identify experiments to measure atomic size and spacing, but doesn't describe them.

The answer is basic, poorly structured and unsupported by relevant information.

0 marks:

No relevant information is given.

Here are some points your answer may include:

- Rayleigh's oil drop method was used to estimate atomic sizes.
- This involved comparing the volume of an oil drop to the area and thickness of a thin sheet of oil floating on water.
- From this, the height of an oil molecule could be found.
- The size of an atom is roughly equal to the size of an oil molecule divided by the number of atoms in an oil molecule, so Rayleigh's measurements could be used to find an upper limit for the size of individual atoms.
- Modern day methods include X-ray crystallography, where X-rays are diffracted by a sample.
- The diffraction patterns are then analysed, in order to investigate atomic spacing.
- Scanning Tunnelling Microscopes are used to probe a surface of a sample.
- A voltage is applied to the microscope's fine tip. Electrons then tunnel from the sample to the tip, creating a current.
- The height of the tip is adjusted to keep this current constant, so the surface of the sample can be mapped to find atomic size and spacing.
- Scanning Electron Microscopes and Atomic Force Microscopes create a digital image of the surface, with 'blobs' representing each atom.

- By knowing the magnification of the image, atomic size and spacing can be calculated from the image.
- Modern day techniques are able to investigate the spacing of atoms as well as their size.
- The accuracy with which atomic size can be found has increased over time, as Rayleigh's oil drop experiment could only roughly calculate molecular not atomic sizes.

Module 4: Section 1 — Waves and Quantum Behaviour

Page 51 — Superposition and Coherence

1 a) $10.2 \div 0.6 = 17$. As the path difference is a whole number of wavelengths, constructive interference occurs *[1 mark]*.

b)

[1 mark for correct direction] The magnitude of the phasor is the same size as for the first sound wave *[1 mark]*.

Page 53 — Standing Waves

1 a)

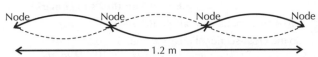

[1 mark for the correct shape, 1 mark for labelling the length]

b) For a string vibrating at three times the fundamental frequency, length = $3\lambda / 2$
1.2 m $= 3\lambda / 2$
$\lambda = $ **0.8 m** *[1 mark]*

c) When the string forms a standing wave, its amplitude varies from a maximum at the antinodes to zero at the nodes *[1 mark]*. In a progressive wave all the points have the same amplitude *[1 mark]*.

d) $T = 4 \times 2 \times 10^{-3} = 8 \times 10^{-3}$ s *[1 mark]*
$f = 1 / (8 \times 10^{-3}) = 125 = $ **130 Hz (to 2 s.f.)** *[1 mark]*

Page 55 — Refraction and Refractive Index

1 a) $n_{diamond} = c / c_{diamond} = (3.00 \times 10^8) / (1.24 \times 10^8) = 2.419...$
= **2.42 (to 3 s.f.)** *[1 mark]*

b) $n_{diamond} = \sin i / \sin r$ *[1 mark]*
$\sin r = \sin 50 / 2.419... = 0.316...$
$r = \sin^{-1}(0.316...) = 18.459... = $ **18° (to 2 s.f.)** *[1 mark]*
Don't forget to write the degree sign in your answer.

2 a) $\dfrac{\sin i}{\sin r} = \dfrac{c_{1st\,medium}}{c_{2nd\,medium}} = \dfrac{c}{c_A}$

$c_A = \dfrac{c \sin r}{\sin i} = \dfrac{3.00 \times 10^8 \times \sin(27)}{\sin(40)} = 2.118... \times 10^8$ *[1 mark]*
$c_A = $ **2.1 × 10⁸ ms⁻¹ (to 2 s.f.)** *[1 mark]*
Remember, the speed of light in air is approximately c.

b) $n = \dfrac{c}{c_{medium}} = \dfrac{3.00 \times 10^8}{1.7 \times 10^8} = 1.764... = $ **1.8 (to 2 s.f.)** *[1 mark]*

c) $n_1 \sin i = n_2 \sin r$
$1.4\sin(27) = 1.76...\sin r$ so $\sin r = \dfrac{1.4 \sin(27)}{1.76...} = 0.3601...$ *[1 mark]*
$\sin^{-1}(0.3601...) = 21.1... = $ **21° (to 2 s.f.)** *[1 mark]*
The angle of incidence for B is the same as the angle of refraction for A.

Answers

Page 57 — Diffraction

1 When a wavefront meets an obstacle, the waves will diffract round the corners of the obstacle. When the obstacle is much bigger than the wavelength, little diffraction occurs. In this case, the mountain is much bigger than the wavelength of short-wave radio. So the "shadow" where you cannot pick up short wave is very long *[1 mark]*.

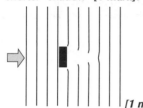

[1 mark]

When the obstacle is comparable in size to the wavelength, as it is for the long-wave radio waves, more diffraction occurs. The wavefront re-forms after a shorter distance, leaving a shorter "shadow" *[1 mark]*.

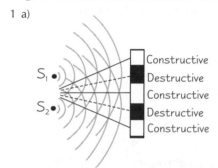

[1 mark]

Page 59 — Two-Source Interference

1 a)

[1 mark for correct placement of constructive interference patterns, 1 mark for correct placement of destructive interference patterns]

b) The light sources must be coherent *[1 mark]*.

2 a) $\lambda = v / f = 330 / 1320 = $ **0.25 m** *[1 mark]*.

b) Separation $= X = D\lambda / d$

$= 7 \times 0.25 / 1.5$ m *[1 mark]* $= 1.166... = $ **1.2 m (to 2 s.f.)** *[1 mark]*.

Page 61 — Diffraction Gratings

1 a) Use $\sin \theta = n\lambda / d$

For the first order, $n = 1$

So, $\sin \theta = \lambda / d$ *[1 mark]*

No need to actually work out d. The number of lines per metre is $1 / d$. So you can simply multiply the wavelength by that.

$\sin \theta = 6.00 \times 10^{-7} \times 4.0 \times 10^5 = 0.24$

$\theta = \sin^{-1}(0.24) = 13.8865... = $ **14° (to 2 s.f.)** *[1 mark]*

For the second order, $n = 2$ and $\sin \theta = 2\lambda / d$. *[1 mark]*

You already have a value for λ / d. Just double it to get $\sin \theta$ for the second order.

$\sin \theta = 0.48$

$\theta = \sin^{-1}(0.48) = 28.685... = $ **29° (to 2 s.f.)** *[1 mark]*

b) No. Putting $n = 5$ into the equation gives a value of $\sin \theta$ of 1.2, which is impossible *[1 mark]*.

2 $\sin \theta = n\lambda / d$, so for the 1st order maximum, $\sin \theta = \lambda / d$

$\sin 14.2° = \lambda \times 3.70 \times 10^5$ *[1 mark]*

$\lambda = 6.629... \times 10^{-7}$

$= $ **663 nm (or 6.63×10^{-7} m) (to 3 s.f.)** *[1 mark]*.

Page 63 — Light — Wave or Particle?

1 a) At threshold voltage:

$E_{photon} = e \times V = 1.60 \times 10^{-19} \times 1.74 = 2.784 \times 10^{-19}$

$= $ **2.78×10^{-19} J (to 3 s.f.)** *[1 mark]*

b) $E = \dfrac{hc}{\lambda}$ so $h = \dfrac{E\lambda}{c}$

$\lambda = 7.00 \times 10^{-7}, c = 3.00 \times 10^8$

So, $h = \dfrac{2.784 \times 10^{-19} \times 7.00 \times 10^{-7}}{3.00 \times 10^8}$ *[1 mark]*

$= 6.496.... \times 10^{-34}$

$= $ **6.50×10^{-34} Js (to 3 s.f.)** *[1 mark]*

c) $V = 1.74 - 0.0400 = 1.70$ V

$E_{photon} = e \times V = 1.60 \times 10^{-19} \times 1.70 = 2.72 \times 10^{-19}$ J *[1 mark]*

$E = \dfrac{hc}{\lambda}$ so $h = \dfrac{E\lambda}{c}$

So, $h = \dfrac{2.72 \times 10^{-19} \times 7.00 \times 10^{-7}}{3.00 \times 10^8}$

$= 6.346.... \times 10^{-34}$

$= $ **6.35×10^{-34} Js (to 3 s.f.)** *[1 mark]*

Page 65 — The Photoelectric Effect

1 $\phi = 2.9$ eV $= 2.9 \times (1.60 \times 10^{-19})$ J $= 4.64 \times 10^{-19}$ J *[1 mark]*

$f = \dfrac{\phi}{h} = \dfrac{4.64 \times 10^{-19}}{6.63 \times 10^{-34}} = 6.99... \times 10^{14}$

$= $ **7.0×10^{14} Hz (to 2 s.f.)** *[1 mark]*

2 a) The work function is the minimum energy needed to break an electron free from the surface of a metal *[1 mark]*.

b) Energy is conserved so $E_{before} = E_{after}$

$E_{before} = \phi + E_{kin}$ so $\phi = 9.0$ eV $- 3.6$ eV $= 5.4$ eV *[1 mark]*

$5.4 \times 1.60 \times 10^{-19} = 8.64 \times 10^{-19}$ J *[1 mark]*

$f = \dfrac{\phi}{h} = \dfrac{8.64 \times 10^{-19}}{6.63 \times 10^{-34}} = 1.303... \times 10^{15}$

$= $ **1.3×10^{15} Hz (to 2 s.f.)** *[1 mark]*

3 An electron needs to gain a certain amount of energy (the work function energy) before it can leave the surface of the metal *[1 mark]* and the electron can only absorb one photon *[1 mark]*.

The energy of a photon is given by $E = hf$ so the energy an electron can absorb depends only on the frequency of the photon *[1 mark]*.

Page 67 — Energy Levels and Photon Emission

1 a) The movement of an electron from a lower energy level to a higher energy level by absorbing energy *[1 mark]*.

b) $-2.18 \times 10^{-18} - -2.04 \times 10^{-18} = -1.4 \times 10^{-19}$ which corresponds to the $n = 4$ level *[1 mark]*.

c)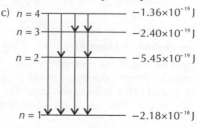

[1 mark per 2 correct transitions]

Answers

d) There would be 6 lines on the emission spectra *[1 mark]*
The transitions from $n = 4$ to $n = 3$ and $n = 2$ to $n = 1$ are in two transition paths, but would only produce one line on the emission spectra (as they will always emit a photon of the same energy).

e) $\Delta E = E_3 - E_1 = hf$
$\Delta E = -2.40 \times 10^{-19} - -2.18 \times 10^{-18} = 1.94 \times 10^{-18}$ J *[1 mark]*
$f = \Delta E \div h = (1.94 \times 10^{-18}) \div (6.63 \times 10^{-34}) = 2.926... \times 10^{15}$
$= \mathbf{2.93 \times 10^{15}}$ **Hz (to 3 s.f.)** *[1 mark]*

Page 70 — The "Sum Over Paths" Theory

1 Probability $\propto$ (resultant phasor amplitude)^2
Probability of electron reaching point A $\propto (6.3)^2 = 39.69$ *[1 mark]*
Probability of electron reaching point B $\propto (4.5)^2 = 20.25$ *[1 mark]*
$39.69 \div 20.25 = 1.96$, so an electron is **1.96 times** as likely to reach point A as point B *[1 mark]*.

2 The frequency of phasor rotation $= 6.0 \times 10^{14}$ rotations per second.
Use time (s) = distance (m) ÷ speed (ms^{-1}) to find the time taken for the photon to reach the detector.
$t = 0.12 \div c = 0.12 \div 3.0 \times 10^8 = 4.0 \times 10^{-10}$ s *[1 mark]*
So the number of phasor rotations along this path is:
$f \times t = 6.0 \times 10^{14} \times 4.0 \times 10^{-10} = \mathbf{2.4 \times 10^5}$ **rotations** *[1 mark]*

3 Photons take every possible path. To find out the probability of a photon taking a particular path, the resultant phasors describing each individual path are summed *[1 mark]*. Usually, these cancel each other out, with the quickest path (a straight line) having the largest resultant amplitude. The probability of a photon arriving at a certain point is proportional to the resultant phasor amplitude squared *[1 mark]*. This means that light is most likely to take the quickest path, a straight line, as that is the path with the largest contribution to the resultant vector. As the detector is around the corner from the source, instead of in a straight line view of the source, the photons have a very low probability of reaching the detector *[1 mark]*.

4 All of the phasors are pointing in the same direction, so the focal point is described by point B *[1 mark]*.
The lens will focus the photons by ensuring the paths take the same time to reach the focal point.

Page 73 — Quantum Behaviour of Electrons

1 a) $E = hf$ so $f = (5.22 \times 10^{-19}) / (6.63 \times 10^{-34}) = 7.873... \times 10^{14}$
$= \mathbf{7.87 \times 10^{14}}$ **Hz (to 3 s.f.)** *[1 mark]*

b) $E_{kinetic} = \frac{1}{2}mv^2$ so $v = \sqrt{\dfrac{2E}{m}} = \sqrt{\dfrac{2 \times 5.22 \times 10^{-19}}{9.11 \times 10^{-31}}}$
$v = 1.07... \times 10^6$ *[1 mark]*

$\lambda = \dfrac{h}{mv} = \dfrac{6.63 \times 10^{-34}}{9.11 \times 10^{-31} \times 1.07... \times 10^6} = 6.798... \times 10^{-10}$

So you need a spacing of $\mathbf{6.80 \times 10^{-10}}$ **m (to 3 s.f.)** to cause diffraction *[1 mark]*

c) $v = \dfrac{h}{m\lambda} = \dfrac{6.63 \times 10^{-34}}{9.11 \times 10^{-31} \times 2.3 \times 10^{-10}}$
$= 3.164... \times 10^6$ *[1 mark]*
From part b) you know the original velocity was $1.07... \times 10^6$.
$(3.16... \times 10^6) - (1.07... \times 10^6) = 2.09... \times 10^6$
$= \mathbf{2.1 \times 10^6}$ **ms^{-1} (to 2 s.f.)** *[1 mark]*

2 a) The accelerating voltage was increased *[1 mark]*.

b) As the accelerating voltage is increased, the only thing which changes is the electron's velocity (kinetic energy) *[1 mark]*.
As wavelength is inversely related to the velocity, the larger the velocity, the smaller the wavelength. This means the spread of the lines is smaller *[1 mark]*.

Module 4: Section 2 — Space, Time and Motion

Page 75 — Scalars and Vectors

1
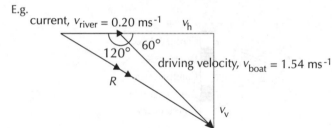

$F^2 = 20^2 + 75^2 = 6025$
So $F = \sqrt{6025} = 77.62... = 78$ N (to 2 s.f.)
$\tan \theta = 20 / 75 = 0.266...$
So $\theta = \tan^{-1} 0.266... = 14.93... = 15°$ (to 2 s.f.)
The resultant force on the rock is **78 N (to 2 s.f.)** *[1 mark]*
at an angle of **15° (to 2 s.f.)** *[1 mark]* to the vertical.
Make sure you know which angle you're finding — and label it on your diagram.

2 horizontal component, v_h
velocity 20.0 ms^{-1}, 15°, vertical component, v_v
horizontal component $v_h = 20.0 \times \cos 15.0° = 19.318...$
$= \mathbf{19.3}$ **ms^{-1} (to 3 s.f.)** *[1 mark]*
vertical component $v_v = 20 \times \sin 15.0° = 5.1763...$
$= \mathbf{5.18}$ **ms^{-1} (to 3 s.f.)** *[1 mark]*

3 E.g.
current, $v_{river} = 0.20$ ms^{-1} v_h
120°   60°
driving velocity, $v_{boat} = 1.54$ ms^{-1}
R v_v

horizontal component $v_{river} = 0.20$ ms^{-1}
vertical component $v_{river} = 0$ ms^{-1}
horizontal component $v_{boat} = 1.54 \times \cos 60 = 0.77$ ms^{-1}
vertical component $v_{boat} = 1.54 \times \sin 60 = 1.333...$ ms^{-1}
So, horizontal $v_{resultant} = 0.20 + 0.77 = 0.97$ ms^{-1} *[1 mark]*
vertical $v_{resultant} = 0 + 1.333... = 1.333...$ ms^{-1} *[1 mark]*
Combine the vertical and horizontal components of R.

$v_h = 0.97$ ms^{-1}
θ
R $v_v = 1.333...$ ms^{-1}

$v_{resultant} = \sqrt{0.97^2 + 1.333...^2} = 1.649...$ ms^{-1}
$= \mathbf{1.6}$ **ms^{-1} (to 2 s.f)** *[1 mark]*
$\tan \theta = 1.333... \div 0.97$ so $\theta = \tan^{-1} 1.374... = 53.97...$
$= \mathbf{54°}$ **(to 2 s.f)** *[1 mark]*
So the resultant velocity of the boat is 1.6 ms^{-1} at an angle of 54° to the current.

Answers

Page 77 — Motion with Constant Acceleration

1 a) Take upwards as positive.

$a = -9.81$ ms^{-2}, $t = 5$ s, $u = 0$ ms^{-1}, $v = ?$

use : $v = u + at$

$v = 0 + -9.81 \times 5$ *[1 mark]*

$v = -49.05 = -49$ ms^{-1} (to 2 s.f.) *[1 mark]*.

NB: It's negative because she's falling downwards and upwards was taken as the positive direction.

b) Use: $s = \left(\frac{u+v}{2}\right)t$ or $s = ut + \frac{1}{2}at^2$

$s = \frac{-49.05}{2} \times 5$ $s = 0 + \frac{1}{2} \times -9.81 \times 5^2$ *[1 mark]*

$s = -122.625$ m $s = -122.625$ m

So she falls **120 m (to 2 s.f.)** *[1 mark]*

2 a) $v = 0$ ms^{-1}, $t = 3.2$ s, $s = 40$ m, $u = ?$

use: $s = \left(\frac{u+v}{2}\right)t$

$40 = 3.2u \div 2$ *[1 mark]*

$u = 80 \div 3.2 = $ **25 ms^{-1}** *[1 mark]*

b) Use: $v^2 = u^2 + 2as$

$0 = 25^2 + 80a$ *[1 mark]*

$-80a = 625$

$a = -7.81... = $ **-7.8 ms^{-2} (to 2 s.f.)** *[1 mark]*

You could also have solved this using $v = u + at$.

3 a) Take upstream as negative: $v = 5$ ms^{-1}, $a = 6$ ms^{-2}, $s = 1.2$ m,

$u = ?$

use: $v^2 = u^2 + 2as$

$5^2 = u^2 + 2 \times 6 \times 1.2$ *[1 mark]*

$u^2 = 25 - 14.4 = 10.6$

$u = -3.255... = $ **-3.3 ms^{-1} (to 2 s.f.)** *[1 mark]*

The negative root is taken because the boat is moving upstream at the start, which was taken as the negative direction.

b) From furthest point: $u = 0$ ms^{-1}, $a = 6$ ms^{-2}, $v = 5$ ms^{-1}, $s = ?$

use: $v^2 = u^2 + 2as$

$5^2 = 0 + 2 \times 6 \times s$ *[1 mark]*

$s = 25 \div 12 = 2.083... = $ **2.1 m (to 2 s.f.)** *[1 mark]*

4 a) Use $v = u + at$ with $t = 0$ as the starting time.

In the first second, $u = 3$, $v = 3 + a$

In the second second, $u = 3 + a$, $v = (3 + a) + a = 3 + 2a$

In the third second, $u = 3 + 2a$, $v = (3 + 2a) + a = 3 + 3a$

[1 mark]

For the third second, use: $s = \left(\frac{u+v}{2}\right)t$

$6 = \left(\frac{3 + 2a + 3 + 3a}{2}\right) \times 1 = \left(\frac{6 + 5a}{2}\right)$ *[1 mark]*

$12 = 6 + 5a$

$6 = 5a$

$a = $ **1.2 ms^{-2}** *[1 mark]*

There's another way to work out acceleration — the cyclist travelled 6 m in the third second, so for the period 2-3 s his average velocity must have been 6 ms^{-1}. So at $t = 2.5$ seconds his speed must have been 6 ms^{-1}. You can use acceleration = change in speed ÷ time taken and get $a = 3 \div 2.5 = 1.2$ ms^{-2}.

b) In the fourth second, $u = 3 + 3a$, $v = (3 + 3a) + a = 3 + 4a$

Use $s = \left(\frac{u+v}{2}\right)t$ for the fourth second:

$s = \frac{1}{2}(3 + 3a + 3 + 4a) \times 1 = \frac{1}{2}(6 + 7 \times 1.2) \times 1$ *[1 mark]*

$= $ **7.2 m** *[1 mark]*

Page 79 — Acceleration of Free Fall

1 a) The air resistance on a falling small steel ball will be less than that on a beach ball. The air resistance on the ball used in this experiment needs to be negligible in order to be able to calculate the value of g *[1 mark]*.

b) E.g. the experiment might be affected by random error caused by the wind *[1 mark]*. To remove this error, conduct the experiment indoors and close all windows *[1 mark]*. The experiment might be affected by systematic error if the ruler is not aligned properly so would give slightly incorrect vertical height measurements *[1 mark]*. To remove this, use a clamp to ensure the rule is straight and unmoving *[1 mark]*.

c) Use: $s = ut + \frac{1}{2}at^2$ *[1 mark]*

$u = 0$ and $a = g$, so $s = \frac{1}{2}gt^2$ or $\frac{1}{2}g = \frac{s}{t^2}$ *[1 mark]*

So the gradient of a graph of s against t^2, $\frac{\Delta s}{\Delta t^2}$, is equal to half the acceleration, i.e. $\frac{1}{2}g$ *[1 mark]*.

2 Change of height $\Delta h = 15.03 - 11.04 = 3.99$ m *[1 mark]*

Frequency of 4 Hz means there are 4 frames per second, so each frame takes 1 s $\div 4 = 0.25$ s *[1 mark]*

$v = \Delta h \div \Delta t = 3.99 \div 0.25 = 15.96$ ms^{-1}

So $\Delta v = 15.96 - 13.51 = 2.45$ ms^{-1} *[1 mark]*

$a = \Delta v \div \Delta t = 2.45 \div 0.25 = $ **9.8 ms^{-2}** *[1 mark]*

Page 81 — Projectile Motion

1 a) You only need to worry about the vertical motion of the stone.

$u = 0$ ms^{-1}, $s = -230$ m, $a = -g = -9.81$ ms^{-2}, $t = ?$

You need to find t, so use: $s = ut + \frac{1}{2}at^2$

$-230 = 0 + \frac{1}{2} \times -9.81 \times t^2$ *[1 mark]*

$t = \sqrt{\frac{2 \times (-230)}{-9.81}} = 6.847... = $ **6.8 s (to 2 s.f.)** *[1 mark]*

b) You know that in the horizontal direction:

$u = v = 8.0$ ms^{-1}, $t = 6.847...$ s, $a = 0$, $s = ?$

So use velocity = $\frac{\text{distance}}{\text{time}}$, $v = \frac{s}{t}$

$s = v \times t = 8.0 \times 6.847...$ *[1 mark]* $= 54.781...$

$= $ **55 m (to 2 s.f.)** *[1 mark]*

2 You know that for the arrow's vertical motion (taking upwards as the positive direction):

$a = -9.81$ ms^{-2}, $u = 30$ ms^{-1} and the arrow will be at its highest point just before it starts falling back towards the ground, so $v = 0$ ms^{-1}.

$s = $ the vertical distance travelled from the arrow's firing point.

So use $v^2 = u^2 + 2as$

$0 = 30^2 + 2 \times -9.81 \times s$ *[1 mark]*

$900 = 2 \times 9.81s$

$s = \frac{900}{2 \times 9.81} = 45.87...$ *[1 mark]*

So the maximum distance reached from the ground

$= 45.87... + 1 = $ **47 m (to 2 s.f.)** *[1 mark]*

Page 83 — Displacement-Time Graphs

1 Split graph into four sections:

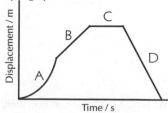

A: acceleration *[1 mark]*

B: constant velocity *[1 mark]*

C: stationary *[1 mark]*

D: constant velocity in opposite direction to A and B *[1 mark]*

Answers

2 a)

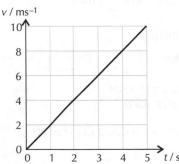

[4 marks — 1 mark for each section correctly drawn]

b) A: $v = s \div t = 5 \div 8 = 0.625 = $ **0.63 ms^{-1} (to 2 s.f)**

B: $v = $ **0 ms^{-1}**

C: $v = 3 \div 5 = $ **0.6 ms^{-1}**

D: $v = -8 \div 10 = $ **−0.8 ms^{-1}**

[2 marks for all correct or just 1 mark for 2 or 3 correct]

Page 85 — Velocity-Time Graphs

1 a)

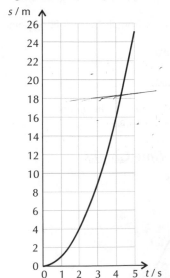

[1 mark for correct axes, 1 mark for correct line]

b) Use $s = ut + \frac{1}{2}at^2$

$t = 1$, $s = $ **1 m**

$t = 2$, $s = $ **4 m**

$t = 3$, $s = $ **9 m**

$t = 4$, $s = $ **16 m**

$t = 5$, $s = $ **25 m**

[2 marks for all correct or 1 mark for at least 3 pairs of values right]

[1 mark for correctly labelled axes, 1 mark for correct curve]

c) E.g. another way to calculate displacement is to find the area under the velocity-time graph *[1 mark]*.

E.g. displacement after 5 seconds $= \frac{1}{2} \times 5 \times 10 = $ **25 m** *[1 mark]*

Page 87 — Motion Experiments and Models

1 a) If it takes 1 frame to pass the reference point,

$t = 1 \times \frac{1}{26} = 0.03846...$ s *[1 mark]*

$v = L \div t = 0.15 \div 0.03846...$ *[1 mark]* $= $ **3.9 ms^{-1}** *[1 mark]*

b) E.g. any one of: Use a camera with a higher frame rate *[1 mark]* so the time can be measured more precisely, which decreases the overall uncertainty of the velocity *[1 mark]* / Use longer trollies marked with distances *[1 mark]* to make sure the trolley takes at least one frame to pass the reference point so more accurate time assumptions can be made *[1 mark]*.

2 Acceleration is 10 ms^{-2} so $\Delta v = 10$ ms^{-1} every second.

E.g.:

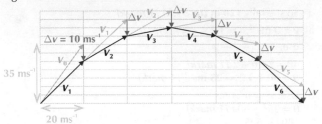

[1 mark correctly drawing vector v_0 and Δv nose-to-tail and correctly drawing resultant vector v_1, 1 mark for correctly using v_1 as the starting velocity for the second internal, 1 mark for correctly drawing full symmetrical parabola.]

Page 89 — Forces

1

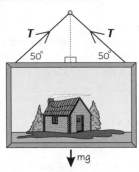

The picture is in equilibrium, so the forces are balanced.

Resolving vertically:

Weight = vertical component of tension × 2

$8 \times 9.81 = 2T \sin 50°$ *[1 mark]*

$78.48 = 0.7660... \times 2T$

$102.448... = 2T$

$T = 51.224... = $ **50 N (to 1 s.f.)** *[1 mark]*

2

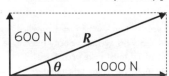

By Pythagoras:

$R = \sqrt{1000^2 + 600^2} = 1166.19... = $ **1170 N (to 3 s.f.)** *[1 mark]*

$\tan \theta = (600 \div 1000)$

so $\theta = \tan^{-1} 0.6 = 30.96...° = $ **31.0° (to 3 s.f.)** *[1 mark]*

Page 91 — Newton's Laws of Motion

1 a) When the parachutist first jumps out of the plane, the only vertical force acting on her is due to gravity, so there is a net downward force *[1 mark]*. Newton's 2nd law states that, for a body of constant mass, the acceleration is proportional to the net force, so she will accelerate downwards *[1 mark]*.

b) $F = ma = 78 \times 9.81 = 765.18 = $ **765 N (to 3 s.f.)** *[1 mark]*

Answers

2 Force perpendicular to river flow = 500 – 100 = 400 N *[1 mark]*
Force parallel to river flow = 300 N
Resultant force = $\sqrt{400^2 + 300^2}$ = 500 N *[1 mark]*
$a = F \div m = 500 \div 250 =$ **2 ms^{-2}** *[1 mark]*

Page 93 — Momentum and Impulse

1 a) total momentum before collision = total momentum after
$(0.145 \times 1.94) + 0 = (0.145 \times -0.005) + 0.148v$ *[1 mark]*
$0.2813 + 0.000725 = 0.148v$, so $v = 1.90557...$
= **1.9 ms^{-1} (to 2 s.f.)** *[1 mark]*

b) Kinetic energy before the collision =
$(\frac{1}{2} \times 0.145 \times 1.94^2) + (\frac{1}{2} \times 0.148 \times 0^2) = 0.272861$ J
Kinetic energy after the collision =
$(\frac{1}{2} \times 0.145 \times 0.005^2) + (\frac{1}{2} \times 0.148 \times 1.90557...^2) = 0.26871...$ J
[1 mark]

The collision is not perfectly elastic / is inelastic *[1 mark]*, as the kinetic energy is greater before the collision than after it *[1 mark]*.

c) $F\Delta t = \Delta mv = (0.145 \times 0.005) - (0.145 \times 0) = 0.000725$
so $F = \Delta mv \div \Delta t = 0.000725 \div 0.15$ *[1 mark]*
= $0.00483... =$ **4.8 ×10^{-3} N (to 2 s.f.)** *[1 mark]*

Page 96 — Terminal Velocity

1 a) The velocity increases at a steady rate, which means the acceleration is constant *[1 mark]*. Constant acceleration means there must be no atmospheric resistance (atmospheric resistance would increase with velocity, leading to a decrease in acceleration). So there must be no atmosphere *[1 mark]*.

b) velocity

[1 mark for a smooth curve that levels out, 1 mark for correct position relative to existing line]
Your graph must be a smooth curve which levels out. It must NOT go down at the end.

c) (The graph becomes less steep)
because the acceleration is decreasing *[1 mark]*
because air resistance increases with speed *[1 mark]*
(The graph levels out)
because air resistance has become equal to weight *[1 mark]*
If the question says 'explain', you won't get marks for just describing what the graph shows — you have to say why it is that shape.

2 a) The 15 cm cone will have the lowest terminal velocity *[1 mark]* because it has the largest surface area and therefore the largest drag *[1 mark]*.

b) velocity

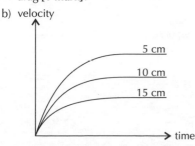

[3 marks, 1 mark for each correct line.]

c) E.g. The shape/slant/height of the cone because it would affect the amount of air resistance *[1 mark]*.

d) The curve for the largest cone would reach a higher terminal velocity *[1 mark]* because the shape is more streamlined *[1 mark]* so the air resistance would be lower at a given speed *[1 mark]*.

Page 99 — Work and Power

1 $\Delta E = F \times \Delta s$ so $F = \Delta E \div \Delta s = 7.5 \div 3.6$ *[1 mark]*
= $2.083... =$ **2.1 N (to 2 s.f.)** *[1 mark]*

2 a)

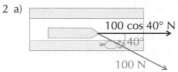

Force in direction of travel = 100 cos 40° = 76.60... *[1 mark]*
$\Delta E = F\Delta s = 76.60... \times 1500 = 114\,906.6...$ J
= **110 000 J (to 2 s.f.)** *[1 mark]*

b) Use $P = Fv$
= 100 cos 40° × 0.80 = $61.28... =$ **61 W (to 2 s.f.)** *[1 mark]*

3 a) Use $\Delta E = F\Delta s = 20.0 \times 9.81 \times 3.00 =$ **588.6 J** *[1 mark]*
Remember that 20.0 kg is not the force — it's the mass.
So you need to multiply it by 9.81 Nkg^{-1} to get the weight.

b) Use $P = Fv$
= (20.0 × 9.81) × 0.25 = $49.05 =$ **49 W (to 2 s.f.)** *[1 mark]*

Page 101 — Conservation of Energy

1 a) Use kinetic energy = $\frac{1}{2}mv^2$ and g.p.e. = mgh
$\frac{1}{2}mv^2 = mgh$ *[1 mark]*
$\frac{1}{2}v^2 = gh$
$v^2 = 2gh = 2 \times 9.81 \times 2.0 = 39.24$ *[1 mark]*
$v = 6.264... = $ **6.3 ms^{-1} (to 2 s.f.)** *[1 mark]*
'No friction' allows you to say that the changes in kinetic and potential energy will be the same.

2 a) If there's no air resistance, k.e. = g.p.e. = mgh
So kinetic energy = 0.020 × 9.81 × 8.0
= $1.5696 =$ **1.6 J (to 2 s.f.)** *[1 mark]*

b) If the ball rebounds to 6.5 m, it has gravitational potential energy:
g.p.e. = mgh = 0.020 × 9.81 × 6.5 = 1.2753 J *[1 mark]*
So 1.5696 – 1.2753 = 0.2943 = **0.29 J (to 2 s.f.)** is transferred to heat and sound *[1 mark]*

3 At half of the maximum height, half of the elastic potential energy of the trampoline has been converted into gravitational potential energy and half into kinetic energy.
So kinetic energy = 2750 ÷ 2 = 1375 J *[1 mark]*
$\frac{1}{2}mv^2 = 1375$ so $v^2 = (2 \times 1375) \div 70.0 = 39.28...$ *[1 mark]*
$v = \sqrt{39.28...} = 6.2678... =$ **6.27 ms^{-1} (to 3 s.f.)** *[1 mark]*

Module 5: Section 1 — Creating Models

Page 104 — Radioactivity and Exponential Decay

1 a) $A = \lambda N = 0.014 \times 51\,000 = 714 =$ **710 Bq (to 2 s.f.)** *[1 mark]*

b) $T_{1/2} = \ln 2 \div \lambda = \ln 2 \div 0.014 = 49.51... =$ **50 s (to 2 s.f.)** *[1 mark]*

c) $N = N_0 e^{-\lambda t} = 51\,000 \times e^{-(0.014 \times 300)} = 764.77...$
= **760 (to 2 s.f.)** *[1 mark]*

d) E.g. Models allow you to make predictions in situations where there would otherwise be too many factors to consider *[1 mark]*.

Page 105 — Capacitors

1 a) $E = \frac{1}{2}CV^2 = 0.5 \times 0.50 \times 12^2 = 36$ J, so the answer is **A** *[1 mark]*

b) $C = \frac{Q}{V}$ so $Q = CV = 0.50 \times 12 =$ **6.0 C** *[1 mark]*

Answers

Page 108 — Charging and Discharging

1 a) $RC = (1.0 \times 10^3) \times (250 \times 10^{-6}) = 0.25$ s *[1 mark]*

$V = V_0(1 - e^{\frac{-t}{RC}}) = 6.0 \times (1 - e^{\frac{-0.25}{0.25}}) = 3.792...$
$= \textbf{3.8 V (to 2 s.f.)}$ *[1 mark]*

b) $Q = Q_0 e^{\frac{-t}{RC}}$ so after 0.7 seconds: $Q = Q_0 e^{\frac{-0.7}{0.25}}$
$= Q_0 \times 0.06$ (to 1 s.f.) *[1 mark]*

So there is **6% (to 1 s.f.)** of the initial charge left on the capacitor after 0.7 seconds *[1 mark]*.

2 a) The charge falls to 37% after RC seconds *[1 mark]*,
so $t = (1.6 \times 10^3) \times (320 \times 10^{-6}) = \textbf{0.512 seconds}$ *[1 mark]*

b) $\frac{dQ}{dt} = -\frac{Q}{RC} = -\frac{5.5 \times 10^{-3}}{0.512}$
$= -0.0107... = \textbf{−0.011 Cs}^{-1}$ **(to 2 s.f.)** *[1 mark]*

Page 111 — Modelling Decay

1 a)

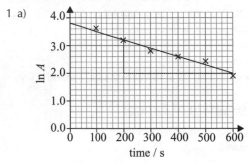

λ = gradient = $(3.2 - 2.0) \div (600 - 200) = \textbf{3.0} \times \textbf{10}^{-3}$ s^{-1} *[1 mark]*

b) At $t = 0$, $\ln A_0 = 3.8$, so $A_0 = e^{3.8} = 44.70...$
$= \textbf{45 Bq (to 2 s.f.)}$ *[1 mark]*

2 $RC = 520 \times 10^{-6} \times 144 \times 10^3 = 74.88$ s *[1 mark]*
$\lambda = 1 \div 74.88 = 0.0133... = \textbf{0.013 s}^{-1}$ **to 2 s.f.** *[1 mark]*

3 $RC = (0.20 \times 10^6) \times (10.0 \times 10^{-6}) = 2.0$ s

t / s	ΔQ / C	Q / C
0		0.050
0.50	$= -(0.05 \div 2.0) \times 0.50$ $= -0.0125$	$= 0.050 + (-0.0125)$ $= 0.0375$
1.0	$= -(0.0375 \div 2.0) \times 0.50$ $= -9.375 \times 10^{-3}$	$= 0.0375 + (-9.375 \times 10^{-3})$ $= 0.028125$

So the answer is **0.028 C (to 2 s.f.)**

[1 mark for each correct iteration]

Page 113 — Simple Harmonic Motion

1 a) Simple harmonic motion is an oscillation in which the restoring force is always directly proportional to the object's displacement *[1 mark]* and always acts towards the midpoint *[1 mark]*.

b) The acceleration of a falling bouncy ball is due to gravity. This acceleration is constant, so the motion is not SHM. *[1 mark]*.

2 a) Maximum velocity $= \omega A = 2\pi f A = 2\pi \times 1.5 \times 0.050 = 0.47$ ms^{-1}
so the answer is **D** *[1 mark]*

b) Clock started when object released, so $x = A\cos(2\pi ft)$ *[1 mark]*
$x = 0.050 \times \cos(2\pi \times 1.5 \times 0.10) = 0.02938...$
$= \textbf{0.029 m (to 2 s.f.)}$ *[1 mark]*

Page 115 — Investigating Simple Harmonic Motion

1 a) Extension of spring $= 0.200 - 0.100 = 0.100$ m *[1 mark]*.
$F = kx$ and $F = mg$ so $k = mg/x = 0.10 \times 9.81 / 0.100 = 9.81$
$= \textbf{9.8 Nm}^{-1}$ **(to 2 s.f.)** *[1 mark]*

b) i) maximum extension $= 0.10 + 0.020 = 0.12$ m
$E = \frac{1}{2}kx^2 = \frac{1}{2} \times 9.81 \times 0.12^2 = 0.070632$
$= \textbf{0.071 J (to 2 s.f.)}$ *[1 mark]*

ii) $T = 2\pi\sqrt{\frac{m}{k}}$ so $T \propto \sqrt{m}$ and $m \propto T^2$ *[1 mark]*

So the mass needed is $2^2 \times 0.10 = \textbf{0.40 kg}$ *[1 mark]*

Alternatively, you could calculate the new period of the oscillations (2 × 0.63), then rearrange the equation $T = 2\pi\sqrt{\frac{m}{k}}$ to find m.

2 $5T_{\text{short pendulum}} = 3T_{\text{long pendulum}}$
$T = 2\pi\sqrt{\frac{L}{g}}$ so: $5 \times 2\pi\sqrt{\frac{0.20}{g}} = 3 \times 2\pi\sqrt{\frac{L}{g}}$ *[1 mark]*
multiplying both sides by $\frac{\sqrt{g}}{2\pi}$ gives: $5 \times \sqrt{0.20} = 3 \times \sqrt{L}$
Squaring both sides gives: $25 \times 0.20 = 9L$ *[1 mark]*
so $L = 25 \times 0.20 \div 9 = 0.555... = \textbf{0.56 m (to 2 s.f.)}$ *[1 mark]*

Page 117 — Modelling Simple Harmonic Motion

1 a) $k \div m = 0.82 \div 0.025 = 32.8$ Nm^{-1}kg

t / s	Δv / ms^{-1}	v ms^{-1}
0		0
0.05	$= -32.8 \times 0.024 \times 0.05$ $= -0.03936$	$= 0 + (-0.03936)$ $= -0.03936$
0.10	$= -0.0361...$	$= -0.0754...$
0.15	$= -0.0299...$	$= -0.105...$

Δx / m	x / m
	0.024
$= -0.03936 \times 0.05$ $= -0.001968$	$= 0.024 + (-0.001968)$ $= 0.022032$
$= -0.00377...$	$= 0.0182...$
$= -0.00527...$	$= 0.0129...$

So at $t = 0.15$, $x = \textbf{0.013 m (to 2 s.f.)}$ *[1 mark for each correct stage of iteration, to a total of 3 marks. Otherwise 1 mark for an attempt at an iterative method.]*

b) $d^2x/dt^2 = -\frac{k}{m}x$
d^2x/dt^2 is at its maximum when $x = A$ *[1 mark]*

The bob was pulled 0.024 m from its equilibrium position, so $A = 0.024$ m
so $d^2x/dt^2 = -\frac{0.82}{0.025} \times 0.024 = -0.7872$
$= \textbf{−0.79 ms}^{-2}$ **(to 2 s.f.)** *[1 mark]*

You'd also get the mark if you left out the negative sign — a positive value of d^2x/dt^2 just means the pendulum is on the other side of its swing.

Page 119 — Free and Forced Vibrations

1 a) E.g.

[1 mark for showing a peak at the natural frequency, 1 mark for a sharp peak.]

Answers

b) *[See graph in part a). 1 mark for a smaller peak at the natural frequency.]*
The peak will actually be slightly to the left of the natural frequency due to the damping, but you'll get the mark if the peak is at the same frequency in the diagram.

2 A system is critically damped if it returns to rest in the shortest time possible when it's displaced from equilibrium and released *[1 mark]*. It is used in e.g. the suspension in a car *[1 mark]*.

Module 5: Section 2 — Out Into Space

Page 121 — Circular Motion

1 a) $v = r\omega = (1.5 \times 10^{11}) \times (2.0 \times 10^{-7})$ *[1 mark]*
$= 30\,000\ \text{ms}^{-1} = \textbf{30 kms}^{-1}$ *[1 mark]*

b) i) $F = m\omega^2 r = (6.0 \times 10^{24}) \times (2.0 \times 10^{-7})^2 \times (1.5 \times 10^{11})$ *[1 mark]*
$= \textbf{3.6} \times \textbf{10}^{22}$ **N** *[1 mark]*

   ii) The gravitational force between the Sun and the Earth *[1 mark]*.

2 a) $a = v^2 \div r = 15^2 \div 12 = 18.75 = \textbf{19 ms}^{-2}$ **(to 2 s.f.)** *[1 mark]*

b) Since $a = \omega^2 r$, $\omega^2 = \dfrac{a}{r} = \dfrac{18.75}{12}$, so $\omega = 1.25\ \text{rad s}^{-1}$ *[1 mark]*

$\omega = 2\pi \div T$, so $T = 2\pi \div \omega = 5.026... = \textbf{5.0 s}$ **(to 2 s.f.)** *[1 mark]*

Page 123 — Gravitational Fields

1 a) $F_{grav} = -\dfrac{GmM}{r^2} = -\dfrac{(6.67 \times 10^{-11}) \times 25 \times (7.35 \times 10^{22})}{(1740 \times 10^3)^2}$ *[1 mark]*

$= -40.48... = \textbf{-40 N}$ **(to 2 s.f.)** *[1 mark]*

b) i) $\frac{1}{2}mv^2 = mgh$ *[1 mark]*,

so $v = \sqrt{2gh} = \sqrt{2 \times 1.62 \times 4.5}$
$= 3.818... = \textbf{3.8 ms}^{-1}$ **(to 2 s.f.)** *[1 mark]*

   ii) As the rock rises in the gravitational field, its kinetic energy is transferred into gravitational potential energy and it slows down *[1 mark]*. It stops gaining height once all of its initial kinetic energy has been transferred into gravitational potential energy ($\frac{1}{2}mv^2 = mgh$) *[1 mark]*. It then changes direction and begins to fall, losing gravitational potential energy and gaining kinetic energy until it collides with the surface of the Moon *[1 mark]*.

Page 125 — Gravitational Potential and Orbits

1 a) $r = 6400 + 200 = 6600$ km
$g = -\dfrac{GM}{r^2} = -\dfrac{(6.67 \times 10^{-11}) \times (5.98 \times 10^{24})}{(6600 \times 10^3)^2}$ *[1 mark]*

$= -9.156... = \textbf{-9.2 Nkg}^{-1}$ **(to 2 s.f.)** *[1 mark]*

b) $V_{grav} = -\dfrac{GM}{r} = g \times r$
$= -9.156... \times 6600 \times 10^3$ *[1 mark]* $= -6.04... \times 10^7$
$= \textbf{-6.0} \times \textbf{10}^7$ **Jkg**$^{-1}$ **(to 2 s.f.)** *[1 mark]*

c) $E_{grav} = -\dfrac{GmM}{r} = V_{grav} \times m$
$= -6.04... \times 10^7 \times 3015 = -1.822... \times 10^{11}$
$= \textbf{-1.8} \times \textbf{10}^{11}$ **J (to 2 s.f.)** *[1 mark]*

d) $v = \sqrt{\dfrac{GM}{r}} = \sqrt{\dfrac{6.67 \times 10^{-11} \times 5.98 \times 10^{24}}{6600 \times 10^3}}$ *[1 mark]*
$= 7773.9... = \textbf{7800 ms}^{-1}$ **(to 2 s.f.)** *[1 mark]*

Module 5: Section 3 — Our Place in the Universe

Page 127 — Using Astronomical Scales

1 a) $m = -2.5 \log_{10} I + \text{constant}$, so $\log_{10} I = \dfrac{m - \text{constant}}{-2.5}$

So $I = 10^{\frac{m - \text{constant}}{-2.5}}$ *[1 mark]*

So $\dfrac{I_1}{I_2} = \dfrac{10^{\frac{m_1 - \text{constant}}{-2.5}}}{10^{\frac{m_2 - \text{constant}}{-2.5}}}$ *[1 mark]*

$= 10^{\left(\frac{m_1 - \text{constant}}{-2.5} - \frac{m_2 - \text{constant}}{-2.5}\right)}$

$= 10^{-\frac{1}{2.5}(m_1 - \text{constant} - m_2 + \text{constant})}$

$= 10^{-\frac{1}{2.5}(m_1 - m_2)}$

$= 10^{\frac{1}{2.5}(m_2 - m_1)} = 10^{\frac{1}{2.5}(2 - 1)} = 10^{\frac{1}{2.5}} = \textbf{10}^{\frac{2}{5}}$ *[1 mark]*

Remember your power laws: $x^a \div x^b = x^{a-b}$.

b) From part a) $\dfrac{I_1}{I_2} = 10^{\frac{1}{2.5}(m_2 - m_1)}$

$m_1 = 1$, $m_2 = 6$, so $\dfrac{I_1}{I_2} = 10^{\frac{1}{2.5}(6-1)} = 10^2$
$= \textbf{100 times greater intensity}$ *[1 mark]*

2 a) A light-year is the distance travelled by electromagnetic waves through a vacuum in one year *[1 mark]*.

b) Average number of seconds in a year $= 365.25 \times 24 \times 60 \times 60$
$= 3.15... \times 10^7$ s

Distance $= $ speed $\times$ time $= 3.00 \times 10^8 \times 3.15... \times 10^7$ *[1 mark]*
$= 9.467... \times 10^{15}$
$= \textbf{9.47} \times \textbf{10}^{15}$ **m (to 3 s.f.)** *[1 mark]*

You'd also get the marks if you used 3.16×10^7 s for the number of seconds in a year, it's given in your data and formulae booklet.

c) To see something, light from the object must reach us. Light travels at a finite speed, so it takes time for that to happen *[1 mark]*. The universe has a finite age, so we can only see so far *[1 mark]*.

Page 129 — Astronomical Distances and Velocities

1 a) $2d = ct$ *[1 mark]*, so $d = [(3.00 \times 10^8) \times (4.6 \times 60)] \div 2$ *[1 mark]*
$d = (8.28 \times 10^{10}) \div 2 = \textbf{4.14} \times \textbf{10}^{10}$ **m (to 3 s.f.)** *[1 mark]*

b) Any two of: The speed of the radio waves (the speed of light) is constant *[1 mark]*. / The time taken for the radio waves to reach Venus is the same as the time taken for them to return to Earth *[1 mark]*. / The speed of Venus relative to the Earth is much less than the speed of light *[1 mark]*.

2 a) First pulse: $d = ct \div 2 = (3.00 \times 10^8 \times 2.8) \div 2$
$= 4.2 \times 10^8$ m *[1 mark]*

Second pulse: $d = ct \div 2 = (3.00 \times 10^8 \times 3.8) \div 2$
$= 5.7 \times 10^8$ m *[1 mark]*

Change in distance $= (5.7 \times 10^8) - (4.2 \times 10^8) = 1.5 \times 10^8$ m
So relative velocity $v = d \div t = (1.5 \times 10^8) \div 1$
$= \textbf{1.5} \times \textbf{10}^8$ **ms**$^{-1}$ *[1 mark]*

b) $t = \dfrac{t_0}{\sqrt{1 - \frac{v^2}{c^2}}} = \dfrac{1}{\sqrt{1 - \frac{(1.5 \times 10^8)^2}{(3.00 \times 10^8)^2}}}$ *[1 mark]*

$= 1.154... = \textbf{1.2 s}$ **(to 2 s.f.)** *[1 mark]*

Page 131 — The Hot Big Bang Theory

1 a) Hubble's law suggests that the universe originated with the hot big bang *[1 mark]* and has been expanding ever since *[1 mark]*.

Answers

b) i) $H_0 = v / d = 75$ kms^{-1} / 1 Mpc
75 kms^{-1} = 75 × 10^3 ms^{-1} and 1 Mpc = 3.09 × 10^{22} m
So H_0 = (75 × 10^3 ms^{-1}) ÷ (3.09 × 10^{22} m)
  = 2.427... × 10^{-18} s^{-1}
  = **2.43 × 10^{-18} s^{-1} (to 3 s.f.)**
[1 mark for the correct value, 1 mark for the correct unit]

ii) $t = 1/H_0$ so t = 1 ÷ (2.427... × 10^{-18}) = 4.12 × 10^{17} s *[1 mark]*
(4.12 × 10^{17}) ÷ (3.16 × 10^7) = 1.303... × 10^{10}
  = **13 billion years (to 2 s.f.)** *[1 mark]*
So the observable universe has a radius of
13 billion light-years (to 2 s.f.) *[1 mark]*.

2 a) $\frac{\Delta\lambda}{\lambda} = \frac{v}{c}$ so $v = c\frac{\Delta\lambda}{\lambda}$ = 3.00 × 10^8 × $\frac{(890 \times 10^{-9}) - (650 \times 10^{-9})}{650 \times 10^{-9}}$
  = 1.107... × 10^8
  = **1.1 × 10^8 ms^{-1} (to 2 s.f.)** *[1 mark]*
away from us *[1 mark]*
You can tell the galaxy is moving away from us as the wavelength
of the spectral line has increased (it has been red shifted).

b) $v = H_0 d$ so $d = v / H_0$ = (1.107... × 10^8) ÷ (2.4 × 10^{-18})
  = 4.615... × 10^{25} m *[1 mark]*
(4.615... × 10^{25}) ÷ (9.5 × 10^{15})
  = 4.858... ×10^9
  = **4.9 × 10^9 ly (to 2 s.f.)** *[1 mark]*

c) $\frac{\Delta\lambda}{\lambda} = \frac{v}{c}$ is only valid if $v \ll c$ — it isn't in this case *[1 mark]*.

3 It suggests that the very early universe was very hot, producing
lots of electromagnetic radiation *[1 mark]* and that the universe's
expansion has stretched the radiation into the microwave region
[1 mark].

Module 5: Section 4 — Matter: Very Simple

Page 133 — Temperature and Specific Thermal Capacity

1 a) There is a net transfer of thermal energy from the water to the
stone, as the stone is colder than the water. The water loses
energy, so its temperature decreases. *[1 mark]*.

b) $\Delta E = mc\Delta\theta$ = 0.025 × 4180 × (12 − 15)
  = −313.5 = **−310 J (to 2 s.f.)** *[1 mark]*

2 a) Energy needed = $\Delta E = mc\Delta\theta$ = 0.93 × 210 × (34.2 − 18.5)
  = 3066.21 J *[1 mark]*

$E = W = VIt$ so $t = E ÷ VI$
  = 3066.21 ÷ (32 × 5.0)
  = 19.163... = **19 s (to 2 s.f.)** *[1 mark]*

b) The actual time taken will be longer *[1 mark]* because energy is
lost heating the insulating container *[1 mark]* / because energy is
lost due to resistance in the circuit *[1 mark]*.

Page 136 — Ideal Gases

1 At constant volume, the pressure of a gas is directly proportional
to its absolute temperature *[1 mark]*.
The graph plotted will be a straight line *[1 mark]*. It will cross the
temperature axis at absolute zero (−273.15 °C or 0 K) *[1 mark]*.

2 a) number of moles, n = mass ÷ molar mass = 0.014 ÷ 0.028
  = 0.50 *[1 mark]*

number of particles, $N = nA_v$ = 0.50 × 6.02 × 10^{23} = 3.01 × 10^{23}
  = **3.0 × 10^{23} (to 2 s.f.)** *[1 mark]*

b) T = 27°C = 27 + 273 = 300 K *[1 mark]*
$pV = NkT$ so $p = NkT ÷ V$
  = ((3.01 × 10^{23}) × (1.38 × 10^{-23}) × 300) ÷ 0.010
  = 124 614
  = **120 000 Pa (to 2 s.f.)** *[1 mark]*

c) The pressure would also halve because it is proportional to the
number of molecules — $pV = NkT$ *[1 mark]*.

3 $pV = NkT$ so $pV ÷ T = Nk$ = constant *[1 mark]*
$(pV ÷ T)_{ground} = (pV ÷ T)_{raised}$
$\frac{(1.0 \times 10^5) \times 10.0}{293} = \frac{p_{raised} \times 25}{260}$
$p_{raised} = \frac{(1.0 \times 10^5) \times 10.0 \times 260}{293 \times 25}$ = 35 494.88...
  = **35 000 Pa (to 2 s.f.)** *[1 mark]*

Page 139 — Kinetic Theory and Internal Energy

1 a) $pV = \frac{1}{3}Nm\overline{c^2}$ so $\overline{c^2} = \frac{3pV}{Nm} = \frac{3 \times 1.0 \times 10^5 \times 7.0 \times 10^{-5}}{2.0 \times 10^{22} \times 6.6 \times 10^{-27}}$
  = 159 090.90... *[1 mark]*
$\sqrt{\overline{c^2}} = \sqrt{159\,090.90...}$ = 398.86... = **400 ms^{-1} (to 2 s.f.)** *[1 mark]*

b) The increase in temperature will increase the average speed and
therefore momentum of the gas particles *[1 mark]*. This means
that as the particles hit the walls of the flask there will be a greater
change in momentum, meaning the impulse of the collisions is
greater, and thus exerting a greater force on the walls of the flask
[1 mark]. As the particles are travelling faster they will also hit the
walls (and exert a force) more frequently *[1 mark]*. This leads to
an increase in pressure (as pressure = force ÷ area) *[1 mark]*.

2 a) speed = distance / time so time = distance / speed = 8.0 ÷ 410
  = 0.0195...
  = **0.020 s (to 2 s.f.)** *[1 mark]*

b) Although the particles are moving at an average of 410 ms^{-1}, they
are frequently colliding with air molecules/other air freshener
particles *[1 mark]*. This means their motion follows a random
walk, so their movement in any one direction is limited and they
only slowly move from one end of the room to the other *[1 mark]*.

c) average energy per particle = $\frac{3}{2}kT$
  = $\frac{3}{2}$ × (1.38 × 10^{-23}) × (273 + 22)
  = 6.1065 × 10^{-21}
  = **6.1 × 10^{-21} J (to 2 s.f.)** *[1 mark]*
Remember, you need the temperature in kelvins, not degrees Celsius.

Module 5: Section 5 — Matter: Hot or Cold

Page 141 — Activation Energy

1 a) Average thermal energy is approximately kT.

i) kT = 1.38 × 10^{-23} × 290
  = 4.002 × 10^{-21} = **4.0 × 10^{-21} J (to 2 s.f.)** *[1 mark]*

ii) kT = 1.38 × 10^{-23} × 360
  = 4.968 × 10^{-21} = **5.0 × 10^{-21} J (to 2 s.f.)** *[1 mark]*

b) An activation energy is needed to break the strong attractive
forces between the particles in the oil *[1 mark]*.
The higher average thermal energy of the particles at 360 K
means they are more likely to have an energy greater than the
activation energy *[1 mark]*, so more particles will be able to break
the attractive forces and so the oil will be less viscous *[1 mark]*.

Page 143 — The Boltzmann Factor

1 a) kT = 1.38 × 10^{-23} × 298 = 4.1124 × 10^{-21}
  = **4.11 × 10^{-21} J (to 3 s.f.)** *[1 mark]*

b) Proportion of molecules with energy of at least E_A is
approximately given by the Boltzmann factor, $e^{-\frac{E_A}{kT}}$:
At 298 K: $\frac{E_A}{kT}$ = (9.4 × 10^{-20}) ÷ (4.1124 × 10^{-21})
  = 22.857... *[1 mark]*
So $e^{-\frac{E_A}{kT}}$ = $e^{-22.857...}$
  = 1.183... × 10^{-10} = **1.2 × 10^{-10} (to 2 s.f.)** *[1 mark]*

Answers

c) Rate of reaction is approximately proportional to the Boltzmann factor, $e^{-\frac{E_A}{kT}}$:

From b), at 298 K, $e^{-\frac{E_A}{kT}} = 1.183... \times 10^{-10}$

At 313 K: $\frac{E_A}{kT} = (9.4 \times 10^{-20}) \div (1.38 \times 10^{-23} \times 313)$
$= (9.4 \times 10^{-20}) \div (4.3194 \times 10^{-21})$
$= 21.762...$ **[1 mark]**

So at 313 K, $e^{-\frac{E_A}{kT}} = e^{-21.762...} = 3.538... \times 10^{-10}$ **[1 mark]**

So the rate of reaction increases by a factor =
(rate of reaction at 313 K) ÷ (rate of reaction at 298 K)
$= (3.538... \times 10^{-10}) \div (1.183... \times 10^{-10})$
$= 2.990... = $ **3.0 (to 2 s.f.) [1 mark]**

Module 6: Section 1 — Electromagnetism

Page 145 — Magnetic Fields

1 a) A current-carrying wire at right angles to an external uniform magnetic field feels a force because the field around the wire and the external field are added together. This can change the shape of the resultant flux lines **[1 mark]**. Flux lines have a tendency to contract (get shorter) and straighten, which causes an electromagnetic force that pushes on the wire **[1 mark]**.

b) The force acts horizontally towards the observer **[1 mark]**

2 a) $F = ILB = 3.0 \times 0.040 \times 2.0 \times 10^{-5}$ **[1 mark]**
$= 2.4 \times 10^{-6}$ N **[1 mark]**

b) The force is zero **[1 mark]** because there is no component of the current that is perpendicular to the magnetic field **[1 mark]**.

Page 147 — Electromagnetic Induction

1 a) $\phi = BA = (2.0 \times 10^{-3}) \times 0.23$
$= 4.6 \times 10^{-4}$ Wb **[1 mark]**

flux linkage $= \phi N = (4.6 \times 10^{-4}) \times 150$
$= 0.069$ Wb **[1 mark]**

b) Change in flux linkage $= (3.5 \times 10^{-4} \times 150) - 0.069$
$= -0.0165$ Wb

$\varepsilon = -\frac{d(\phi N)}{dt} = -\frac{-0.0165}{2.5}$ **[1 mark]**
$= 6.6 \times 10^{-3}$ V **[1 mark]**

The e.m.f. is positive to oppose the reduction in magnetic flux that caused it **[1 mark]**.
The positive e.m.f. induces a magnetic field around the coil that tries to 'top up' the falling magnetic field back to its initial value — it opposes the reduction in the uniform magnetic field.

Page 149 — Transformers and Dynamos

1 a) An ideal transformer is one that is 100% efficient. **[1 mark]**

b) $\frac{V_1}{V_2} = \frac{N_1}{N_2}$ so, $N_2 = \frac{V_2}{V_1} \times N_1 = \frac{45}{9.0} \times 150$ **[1 mark]**
$= 750$ turns **[1 mark]**

c) $\frac{I_2}{I_1} = \frac{N_1}{N_2}$ so, $I_2 = \frac{N_1}{N_2} \times I_1 = \frac{150}{750} \times 1.5$ **[1 mark]** $= 0.30$ A **[1 mark]**

Module 6: Section 2 — Charge and Field

Page 151 — Electric Fields

1 a) $E_{electric} = \frac{kQ}{r^2} = \frac{Q}{4\pi\varepsilon_0 r^2}$

$= \frac{1.60 \times 10^{-19}}{4\pi \times (8.85 \times 10^{-12}) \times (1.00 \times 10^{-10})^2}$ **[1 mark]**

$= 1.4386... \times 10^{11}$
$= $ **1.44×10^{11} NC^{-1} (or Vm^{-1}) (to 3 s.f.) [1 mark]**

b) electric potential energy $= \frac{kQq}{r} = \frac{Qq}{4\pi\varepsilon_0 r}$

$= \frac{(1.60 \times 10^{-19}) \times (6.4 \times 10^{-19})}{4\pi \times (8.85 \times 10^{-12}) \times (3.25 \times 10^{-9})}$ **[1 mark]**

$= 2.833... \times 10^{-19} = $ **2.8×10^{-19} J (to 2 s.f.) [1 mark]**

c)
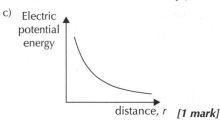

Electric potential energy vs distance, r **[1 mark]**

d) The electric force $F_{electric}$ due to the electric field at that point **[1 mark]**.

Page 153 — Electric Potential

1 $V_{electric} = \frac{kQ}{r} = \frac{Q}{4\pi\varepsilon_0 r}$

$= \frac{-1.60 \times 10^{-19}}{4\pi \times (8.85 \times 10^{-12}) \times 0.00100}$ **[1 mark]**

$= -1.438... \times 10^{-6} = $ **-1.44×10^{-6} V (to 3 s.f.) [1 mark]**

2 $V_{electric} = \frac{kQ}{r} = \frac{Q}{4\pi\varepsilon_0 r}$, so $Q = V_{electric} \times 4\pi\varepsilon_0 r$
$= 500.0 \times 4 \times \pi \times (8.85 \times 10^{-12}) \times (3.5 \times 10^{-3})$ **[1 mark]**
$= 1.94... \times 10^{-10} = $ **1.95×10^{-10} C (to 3 s.f.) [1 mark]**

3 a) $E_{electric} = V_{electric}$: $d = 1500 \div (4.5 \times 10^{-3}) = 3.33... \times 10^5$ Vm^{-1}
$= $ **3.3×10^5 Vm^{-1} (to 2 s.f.) [1 mark]**

The field is perpendicular to the plates going from positive to negative. **[1 mark]**

b) From the equation $E = \frac{V}{d}$, if the distance is doubled and the electric field strength remains constant, then the voltage must also double, so $V = $ **3000 V [1 mark]**

4 Similarities — Any two from: Both gravitational and electric field strengths are forces per unit — gravitational field strength, g, is force per unit mass and electric field strength, $E_{electric}$, is force per unit positive charge. / Both gravitational and electric potentials are potential energy per unit — gravitational potential, V_{grav}, is potential energy per unit mass and electric potential, $V_{electric}$, is potential energy per unit positive charge. / Both are zero at infinity. / The force between two point masses is an inverse square law, and so is the force between two point charges. / The field lines for a point mass and the field lines for a negative point charge are the same. **[2 marks — 1 mark for each correct similarity]**
Differences — Any one from: Gravitational forces are always attractive, whereas electric forces can be attractive or repulsive. / The size of an electric force depends on the medium between the charges, e.g. plastic or air. For gravitational forces, this makes no difference. / Objects can be shielded from electric fields, but not from gravitational fields. **[1 mark for one correct difference]**

Page 155 — Millikan's Oil-Drop Experiment

1 a) The forces acting on the drop are its weight, acting downwards **[1 mark]** and the equally sized force due to the electric field, acting upwards **[1 mark]**.

b) Electric force = weight, so $\frac{qV}{d} = mg$ and $q = \frac{mgd}{V}$ **[1 mark]**

$q = \frac{1.63 \times 10^{-14} \times 9.81 \times 3.00 \times 10^{-2}}{5000} = 9.59... \times 10^{-19}$ C **[1 mark]**

Divide by the magnitude of the charge on an electron:
$(9.59... \times 10^{-19}) \div (1.60 \times 10^{-19}) = 5.99... = 6$ (to 1 s.f.)
$\Rightarrow q = $ **6e [1 mark]**

Answers

c) The forces on the oil drop as it falls are its weight and the viscous force from the air *[1 mark]*. As the oil drop accelerates, the viscous force increases until it equals the oil drop's weight *[1 mark]*. At this point, there is no resultant force on the oil drop, so it stops accelerating, but continues to fall at terminal velocity *[1 mark]*.

d) At terminal velocity, $mg = 6\pi\eta rv$.

Rearranging, $v = \dfrac{mg}{6\pi\eta r}$ *[1 mark]*
Find the radius of the oil drop, using mass = volume × density:

$m = \frac{4}{3}\pi r^3\rho$. So, $r^3 = \dfrac{3m}{4\pi\rho} = \dfrac{3\times1.63\times10^{-14}}{4\pi\times880} = 4.42...\times10^{-18}$
and $r = 1.64...\times10^{-6}$ m *[1 mark]*.

So, $v = \dfrac{1.63\times10^{-14}\times9.81}{6\pi\times1.84\times10^{-5}\times1.64...\times10^{-6}} = 2.808...\times10^{-4}$

$= \mathbf{2.8\times10^{-4}}$ **ms^{-1} (to 2 s.f.)** *[1 mark]*

Page 157 — Charged Particles in Magnetic Fields

1 a) $F = qvB = 1.60\times10^{-19}\times5.00\times10^6\times0.770$ *[1 mark]*
$= \mathbf{6.16\times10^{-13}}$ **N** *[1 mark]*

b) The force on the particle due to the electric field is $F = Eq$

If the particle travels in a straight line, the force due to the electric field must balance the force due to the magnetic field.
So equating, $Eq = qvB = 6.16\times10^{-13}$ N,

so $E = \dfrac{6.16\times10^{-13}}{1.60\times10^{-19}}$ *[1 mark]*
$= \mathbf{3.85\times10^6}$ **NC^{-1} (to 3 s.f.)** *[1 mark]*

2 a) The electron is moving in a circular path, so electromagnetic force = centripetal force
$qvB = \dfrac{mv^2}{r}$ *[1 mark]*
Cancelling v from both sides gives: $qB = \dfrac{mv}{r}$ *[1 mark]*

b) $r = \dfrac{mv}{qB} = \dfrac{(9.11\times10^{-31})\times(2.3\times10^7)}{(1.60\times10^{-19})\times(0.6\times10^{-3})} = 0.218...$
$= \mathbf{0.22}$ **m** *[1 mark]*

Module 6: Section 3 — Probing Deep into Matter

Page 159 — Scattering to Determine Structure

1 a) Alpha particles and atomic nuclei are both positively charged *[1 mark]*. If an alpha particle travels close to a nucleus, there will be a significant electrostatic force of repulsion between them *[1 mark]*. This force deflects the alpha particle from its original path *[1 mark]*.

b) The majority of the alpha particles are not scattered because the nucleus is a very small part of the whole atom and so most alpha particles don't get close enough to the nucleus to be scattered *[1 mark]*.

2 Initial particle energy = 4.0 MeV
$4.0\times10^6\times1.60\times10^{-19} = 6.40\times10^{-13}$ J *[1 mark]*

Electric potential energy $= \dfrac{kq_{proton}Q_{nucleus}}{r} = \dfrac{q_{proton}Q_{nucleus}}{4\pi\varepsilon_0 r}$

$= 6.40\times10^{-13}$ J at distance of closest approach *[1 mark]*

$r = \dfrac{q_{proton}Q_{nucleus}}{4\pi\varepsilon_0\times6.40\times10^{-13}}$ *[1 mark]*

$= \dfrac{(1\times1.60\times10^{-19})\times(13\times1.60\times10^{-19})}{4\pi\times(8.85\times10^{-12})\times(6.40\times10^{-13})}$

$= 4.675...\times10^{-15} = \mathbf{4.7\times10^{-15}}$ **(to 2 s.f.)** *[1 mark]*

Page 161 — Particles and Antiparticles

1 A proton, an electron and an antineutrino *[1 mark]*.
The electron and the antineutrino are leptons *[1 mark]*. Leptons are not affected by the strong nuclear interaction, so the decay can't be due to the strong nuclear interaction *[1 mark]*.

2 A neutrino / an antineutrino *[1 mark]*

3 a) Antineutrons and antiprotons have a lepton number of 0, and positrons and antineutrinos both have a lepton number of –1 *[1 mark]*.
$0 \neq 0 - 1 - 1$, so lepton number is not conserved *[1 mark]*.

b) Antineutrons and antineutrinos both have a relative charge of 0, and antiprotons and electrons both have a relative charge of –1 *[1 mark]*. $0 \neq -1 - 1 + 0$, so charge is not conserved *[1 mark]*.

Page 163 — Pair Production and Annihilation

1 The creation of a particle of matter requires the creation of its antiparticle. In this case no antineutron has been produced *[1 mark]*.

2 $e^+ + e^- \rightarrow \gamma + \gamma$ *[1 mark]*. This is called annihilation *[1 mark]*.

3 The energy of each particle is equal to $E_{rest} = m_p c^2$ (since kinetic energy is negligible).
When the proton and the antiproton annihilate, two identical photons are produced. So $2E_{photon} = 2m_p c^2$ and so $E_{photon} = m_p c^2$.
$E_{photon} = hf$, so $m_p c^2 = hf$,
$f = \dfrac{m_p c^2}{h}$ *[1 mark]*
$= \dfrac{(1.673\times10^{-27})\times(3.00\times10^8)^2}{(6.63\times10^{-34})}$ *[1 mark]*
$= 2.271...\times10^{23} = \mathbf{2.27\times10^{23}}$ **Hz (to 3 s.f.)** *[1 mark]*

Page 165 — Quarks

1 udd *[1 mark]*

2 proton = uud *[1 mark]*
Relative charge of down quark = –1/3
Relative charge of up quark = 2/3
Total relative charge = 2/3 + 2/3 – 1/3 = +1 *[1 mark]*

Page 167 — Particle Accelerators

1 $E_{rest} = m_p c^2 = 1.673\times10^{-27}\times(3.00\times10^8)^2$
$= 1.5057\times10^{-10}$ J *[1 mark]*
$(1.5057\times10^{-10}) \div (1.60\times10^{-19}) = 9.410...\times10^8$ eV *[1 mark]*
$E_{total} = \gamma E_{rest}$ so $\gamma = E_{total}/E_{rest} = 500\times10^9 \div 9.410...\times10^8$
$= 531.31... = \mathbf{500}$ **(to 1 s.f.)** *[1 mark]*

2 $F = qvB$ so $B = F/qv$
$= (4.91\times10^{-13}) \div ((1.60\times10^{-19})\times(6.82\times10^5))$
$= 4.499... = \mathbf{4.50}$ **T (to 3 s.f.)** *[1 mark]*

Page 169 — Electron Energy Levels

1 The electron will escape the nucleus / not remain bound *[1 mark]* because its energy is greater than zero *[1 mark]*.

2 a) $E = hf = 6.63\times10^{-34}\times4.57\times10^{14} = 3.02991\times10^{-19}$
$= \mathbf{3.02\times10^{-19}}$ **J (to 3 s.f.)** *[1 mark]*

b) $3.02991\times10^{-19} \div 1.60\times10^{-19} = 1.893...$ eV *[1 mark]*
The difference between energy levels n = 3 and n = 2 is 3.4 – 1.5 = 1.9 eV. This is the closest figure to the energy of the photon, so the electron must have fallen between these energy levels *[1 mark]*.

3 3.8×10^{-5} eV $= 3.8\times10^{-5}\times1.60\times10^{-19}$
$= 6.08\times10^{-24}$ J *[1 mark]*
$\Delta E = hf$ so $f = \Delta E \div h = (6.08\times10^{-24}) \div (6.63\times10^{-34})$ *[1 mark]*
$= 9.170...\times10^9 = \mathbf{9.2\times10^9}$ **Hz (to 2 s.f.)** *[1 mark]*

Answers

Module 6: Section 4 — Ionising Radiation and Risk

Page 172 — Radioactive Emissions

1 **5-6 marks:**

The answer gives a full description of an experiment to identify the type of radiation emitted by the source, including the results expected for alpha, beta and gamma emitters. The answer includes a discussion of correcting for background radiation. The answer has a clear and logical structure.

3-4 marks:

The answer describes an experiment to identify the type of radiation emitted by the source, including the results expected for alpha, beta and gamma emitters, but may omit some details. The answer has some structure.

1-2 marks:

There is some description of an experiment to identify the type of radiation emitted by the source, but the answer lacks detail. The answer has no clear structure.

0 marks:

No relevant information is given.

Here are some points your answer may include:

- Measure the background count over a sensible interval (e.g. 30 seconds) and divide by the time to get the count rate.
- Take at least three measurements and calculate an average background count rate.
- The background count rate should be subtracted from all of the results.
- Place the source in front of a Geiger-Müller tube attached to a Geiger counter, so that the counter records a high count rate when there is nothing between the source and tube.
- Insert different materials between the source and the tube, and record the count rate by measuring the count over a fixed time interval (selected depending on how active the source is) and dividing by this time.
- If the count rate drops significantly, then some of the radiation is being absorbed by the material. If it drops to zero after the background count rate has been subtracted, then all of the radiation is being absorbed.
- If the radiation is blocked by a piece of paper, the source is emitting alpha radiation.
- If the radiation is blocked by a thin (3 mm) sheet of aluminium, the source is a beta emitter.
- If a thick sheet of lead is needed to block the radiation, then the source is a gamma emitter.
- The radioactive source should only be handled using long-handled tongs and should not be pointed at anyone.
- The radioactive source should be kept in a lead-lined box when not in use.

2 a) $^{226}_{88}Ra \rightarrow \, ^{222}_{86}Rn + \, ^{4}_{2}\alpha$

[3 marks available — 1 mark for alpha particle, 1 mark each for proton and nucleon number of radon]

b) $^{40}_{19}K \rightarrow \, ^{40}_{20}Ca + \, ^{0}_{-1}\beta + \, ^{0}_{0}\bar{\nu}$

[3 marks available — 1 mark for beta particle and neutrino, 1 mark each for proton and nucleon number of calcium]

Page 175 — Dangers of Radiation

1 a) Any two of e.g.: They can cause cancerous tumours. / They can cause skin burns. / They can cause infertility. / They can cause hair loss. / They can cause radiation sickness. / They can cause death.
   [1 mark per correct answer, maximum 2 marks]

b) Effective dose = absorbed dose × quality factor
   For 0.6 Gy of alpha radiation, the effective dose is
   0.6 × 20 = 12 Sv
   For 9 Gy of beta radiation, the effective dose is
   9 × 1 = 9 Sv **[1 mark for both calculations]**
   So, exposure to 0.6 Gy of alpha radiation would cause more damage to a sample of body tissue than 9 Gy of beta radiation **[1 mark]**.

2 a) $T_{1/2} = \dfrac{\ln 2}{\lambda} = \dfrac{\ln 2}{3.21 \times 10^{-7}} = 2.159... \times 10^6$
   $= \mathbf{2.16 \times 10^6}$ **s (to 3 s.f.) [1 mark]**

b) energy deposited = activity × energy per decay × fraction of radiation absorbed
   = $(5.03 \times 10^8) \times (2.9 \times 10^{-15}) \times 0.4$
   = 5.8348×10^{-7} J **[1 mark]**

   absorbed dose = energy deposited ÷ mass
   = $(5.8348 \times 10^{-7}) \div (4.2 \times 10^{-3})$
   = $1.38... \times 10^{-4} = \mathbf{1.4 \times 10^{-4}}$ **Gy (to 2 s.f.) [1 mark]**
   Remember to convert the mass to kg.

c) $0.50 \div (1.38... \times 10^{-4}) = 3599.09... = \mathbf{3600}$ **s (= 1 hour) [1 mark]**

Page 177 — Binding Energy

1 a) There are 6 protons and 8 neutrons, so the mass of individual parts = (6 × 1.00728) + (8 × 1.00867) = 14.11304 u **[1 mark]**
   Mass of $^{14}_{6}C$ nucleus = 13.99995 u
   Mass defect = 13.99995 − 14.11304 = **−0.11309 u** **[1 mark]**

b) mass in kg = −0.11309 × (1.661×10^{-27})
   = $-1.8784... \times 10^{-28}$ kg **[1 mark]**

   binding energy, $E = mc^2 = (-1.8784... \times 10^{-28}) \times (3.00 \times 10^8)^2$
   = $-1.69058... \times 10^{-11}$ J **[1 mark]**

   1 eV = 1.60×10^{-19} J,
   so energy = $(-1.69058... \times 10^{-11}) \div (1.60 \times 10^{-19})$
   = $-1.056... \times 10^8$ eV = **−106 MeV (to 3 s.f.) [1 mark]**

2 a) Fusion **[1 mark]**

b) There are two deuterium atoms before the reaction, each containing two nucleons, so:
   binding energy before reaction = 2 × 2 × −1.11 = −4.44 MeV
   [1 mark]
   There is one helium atom after the reaction, containing three nucleons, and a free neutron with a binding energy of zero, so:
   binding energy after reaction = (−2.57 × 3) + 0 = −7.71 MeV
   [1 mark]
   Energy released = difference in binding energy = −4.44 − (−7.71)
   = **3.27 MeV [1 mark]**

Page 179 — Nuclear Fission and Fusion

1 a) E.g. control rods limit the rate of fission by absorbing neutrons **[1 mark]**. The number of neutrons absorbed by the rods is controlled by varying the amount they are inserted into the reactor **[1 mark]**. A suitable material for the control rods is boron **[1 mark]**.

b) In an emergency shut-down, the control rods are released into the reactor **[1 mark]**. The control rods absorb the neutrons, and stop the reaction as quickly as possible **[1 mark]**.

2 Advantages: e.g. the reaction in a nuclear reactor doesn't produce carbon dioxide **[1 mark]**, it can produce a continuous supply of electricity, unlike some renewable sources **[1 mark]**.
   [1 mark for each advantage, maximum 2 marks]
   Disadvantages — any two of: e.g. it could be dangerous if the reactor gets out of control, as a runaway reaction could cause an explosion **[1 mark]** / nuclear fission produces radioactive waste which is dangerous if it escapes into the environment **[1 mark]** / nuclear power-plants are expensive to build and decommission **[1 mark]** / nuclear waste has a long half-life, so has to be managed for a long time **[1 mark]**.
   [1 mark for each disadvantage, maximum 2 marks]

Index

Index

Index

Index

Index

PRBR72